Mechanics of Materials

Professor of Engineering
University of California, Los Angeles

F. R. Shanley

McGRAW-HILL BOOK COMPANY   *New York*   *San Francisco*

MECHANICS of MATERIALS

St. Louis   Toronto   London   Sydney

Mechanics of Materials

Library of Congress catalog card number: 65-25922

2 3 4 5 6 7 8 9 – MP – 10 9 8 7

56393

Preface

This book was originally intended to be a revision of the author's *Strength of Materials* (1957), but the revisions became so extensive that the book is being published as an entirely separate work.* The organization of subjects in *Strength of Materials* was based on the level of abstraction involved. Although this viewpoint has not been abandoned in the present text, the order of introduction of the subjects has been changed to improve the efficiency of the book from the pedagogical point of view.

It is hoped that the new book will meet the requirements of educators who wish to introduce mechanics of materials at an early stage in the engineering curriculum. For short courses, much of the material in small print may be omitted. The book can also be used as a supplementary text for courses on structural design.

During the five years involved in the preparation of the manuscript, there has been a growing realization of the importance of *design* (or synthesis).† There has also been increasing emphasis on the scientific aspects of engineering. The enormous capability of electronic computers has been utilized in analysis and has now begun to play an important role in design. Rapid progress in astronautics has been accompanied by the appearance of new materials, new forms of construction, severe environmental conditions, increased emphasis on weight reduction, and so on. The interdisciplinary nature of engineering projects has received much attention.

---

* *Strength of Materials* will continue to be available.

† In this text the word *design* is always used in the scientific sense, that is, an engineering design will be based, to some extent at least, on the laws of nature. Such usage excludes the treatment of design from the purely intuitive or aesthetic point of view.

These changes are reflected to some extent in the present text.

An elementary course in *statics* is a prerequisite for the use of the present text. (A few examples of the use of matrix algebra in statics are included as optional material for those who have had some training in this subject.) After defining elements, components, and systems from the point of view of *force transmission*, the text takes up the behavior of structural components under various states of loading, emphasizing the concept of force transmission as the function to be performed.

The component itself may be considered as a subclass of a structural *system*. The transition between component and system appears to be a logical basis on which to limit the scope of a textbook of the present type. However, in order that this transition be accomplished smoothly, Chapter 15 has been included to cover the principles and philosophy of the design of structural systems.

From the educational viewpoint, it would seem to be important that the curriculum provide, relatively early, some opportunity for the student to actually "design" something, in the process of which he would utilize his knowledge of mathematics and physical laws. Such opportunities provide a strong motivation for the engineering student, who has usually selected engineering (rather than pure science) because he has a strong desire to create something on the physical level.* Almost all engineering systems contain components which perform a structural function (even though this function may be secondary). It therefore appears logical to introduce some examples of structural design in the engineering curriculum.

Modern textbooks on properties of materials are based largely on the *element* level. In this book we apply such knowledge to components under various states of loading. A special objective of this text is to provide the engineer with methods by which he can utilize the tensile stress-strain diagram in the analysis of states of loading both within and beyond the elastic range.

In treating the analysis of a state of stress, the classical framework of the theory of elasticity has been adopted. The *tensors* of stress and strain are treated from the physical point of view (the student is not required to have any previous knowledge of tensor analysis). It is important to reveal that certain quantities obey similar laws of transformation; therefore a special point is made of showing that stress, line force, strain, and moment of inertia, all classified as tensor quantities, are analyzed by the same procedures of matrix algebra.

Although the treatment of shear and bending moment diagrams is

---

*The author has found that elementary design problems requiring individual solutions, which can be compared as to efficiency, provide a competitive atmosphere which stimulates student interest. Some typical problems are outlined in Ref. 76, and similar problems are included in the text.

usually covered in statics, a brief review of these matters is included in Chapter 6. Emphasis is placed on the fundamental differential relationships involved. The use of *singularity functions* makes it possible to treat local and discontinuous loading functions by simple integration methods. The analysis of deflections of beams due to bending moments is also simplified by the use of singularity functions.

The subject of *buckling* occupies a long chapter. The student is introduced to the fundamental concept of structural instability by analyzing a simple column, including inelastic behavior. Although the necessary mathematical tools for developing the theory of *local buckling* will not be available to the student, local buckling is a very important phenomenon in the design of efficient structures. Without some knowledge of this subject, it is impossible to develop structural optimization methods for compressive loadings. (See Sec. 15.10.)

The insidious combination of *stress concentration* and *fatigue* has been given special attention. An elementary treatment of brittle fracture has been included, in view of the increased use of refractory materials for operation at high temperatures (as in re-entry space vehicles).

Multiordinal problems have been extensively used. This idea permits the instructor to assign certain important problems with considerable flexibility as to physical proportions, properties, and size.

The appendixes include typical properties and actual stress-strain diagrams for various materials. Information on temperature effects and statistical effects is also included.

The author wishes to express his thanks and appreciation for the assistance that he has been given from various sources during the preparation of this new book. A fellowship from the Simon Guggenheim Memorial Foundation provided an opportunity to spend many months studying the whole subject of structural design philosophy, with particular emphasis on safety and optimization. A grant from the UCLA Engineering Development Program, sponsored by the Ford Foundation, assisted the author in publication of the *Design Notebook* (Ref. 77). Another grant, from the same source, permitted members of the faculty of the Structures Division to make an intensive study of the engineering curriculum with respect to structures and related subjects.

Credit must be given for many helpful suggestions from the instructors who used the earlier book. Important contributions were made by various experts who carefully reviewed earlier versions of the new manuscript. Among these were Dr. Vincent Anderson San Fernando Valley, Professor of Engineering, State College, and Professors James Gere of Stanford University, Lawrence E. Malvern of Michigan State University, and D. K. Wright, Jr., of Case Institute of Technology.

Dr. Lewis P. Felton of the Structures Division provided valuable technical assistance in preparing the problems and appendixes and in critically reviewing the manuscript and proofs. Mr. Iraj Farhoomand assisted in the solution of problems. Mrs. Edith Corsario deserves special thanks for her secretarial services during the final stages of the preparation of the manuscript.

F. R. Shanley

Contents

Symbols

A	area (of material cross section)
$\textcircled{A}$	area (enclosed by median line)
a	acceleration; subscript "axial"
B	base of rectangular cross section
b	base of rectangular cross section; width over which force is distributed; subscript "bending"
C	constant; compliance
c	maximum distance from neutral axis (in bending); coefficient of fixity (columns)
D	depth of rectangular cross section; diameter
E	modulus of elasticity for axial loading (Young's modulus); subscript "Euler"; subscript "elastic"
E_s	secant modulus
E_t	tangent modulus
e	eccentricity; subscript "effective"
F	force
f	subscript "flange"
G	modulus of elasticity for plane shear loading (modulus of rigidity)
g	acceleration of gravity ($= 32.2$ ft/sec^2)
h	height (of rectangular cross section; free drop, etc.); mean depth of two-flange beam
I	moment of inertia (second moment of area)
I_p	polar moment of inertia
I_x	I about x axis
i	subscript indicating an individual element; subscript "inside"
J	section property for torsion of round sections
j	subscript indicating an individual element or station
K	factor or constant; spring constant; stiffness

K_t	theoretical (elastic) stress-concentration factor
k	constant; influence coefficient
kip	kilopound = 1,000 lb
ksi	kips per square inch = 1,000 psi
L	length
L_e	effective length (for columns)
ln	hyperbolic (natural) logarithm = $\log_e$
M	moment (general)
M_b	bending moment
M_t	torsional moment
m	mass (in slugs)
N	number; number of cycles to failure in fatigue
n	number; subscript "normal"
o	subscript "outside"; "original"; "base"
P	force; probability; subscript "plastic"
p	pressure; pitch of riveted joint; subscript "polar"
psi	pounds per square inch
Q	static moment (first moment of area); fictitious (virtual) load
q	line force (load per unit length, running load, shear flow); notch-sensitivity factor (fatigue)
R	radius; reaction (beams); ratio (for interaction curves)
$r\cdot$	distance normal to neutral axis (torsion)
r_c	core radius
s	distance along curved line; subscripts "shear"; "secant"
T	torque (usually replaced by M_t); temperature
t	thickness (of sheet or tube); time; subscripts "torsion," "tangent"
U	energy
u	energy per unit volume; subscript "ultimate"
V	shear; volume (of material); velocity
$\textcircled{V}$	enclosed volume
W	weight
w	density
y	distance normal to neutral plane (bending); deflection of beam; subscript "yield"
Z	section modulus (bending)
α	coefficient of thermal expansion (linear); effective-length coefficient (columns)
β	volumetric modulus of elasticity
γ	shear strain
Δ	symbol for "finite element of . . ."; "finite change of . . ."
δ	deflection
ϵ	normal strain

η	efficiency; inelastic reduction factor (buckling); length (dimensionless)
θ	angle
ν	Poisson's ratio
ρ	radius of gyration of cross section
Σ	operator "summation"
σ	stress (normal)
τ	stress (shear)
ϕ	angle
ω	angular acceleration

Conversion of units

$$1 \text{ in.} = 2.540 \text{ cm}$$
$$1 \text{ in.}^2 = 6.452 \text{ cm}^2$$
$$1 \text{ in.}^3 = 16.39 \text{ cm}^3$$
$$1 \text{ lb} = 0.4536 \text{ kg}$$
$$1 \text{ psi} = 7.03 \times 10^{-4} \text{ kg/mm}^2$$
$$1 \text{ in.-lb} = 1.152 \text{ kg-cm}$$
$$1 \text{ knot} = 1.15155 \text{ mph}$$
$$60 \text{ mph} = 88 \text{ fps}$$

Mechanics of Materials

Chapter 1

Uniaxial Loading

1.1 Introduction

*Mechanics of Materials** deals with the behavior of solid bodies under the action of forces. Such behavior includes deformation, failure by actual separation, failure by buckling, the effects of time, repeated loading, and other phenomena. Some principles of design of elementary force transmitting structures are included in Chap. 15.

For convenience we divide force-transmitting members roughly into three classes: *elements, components, systems,* which are defined as follows.

The word *element* usually refers to a small body of material or a small section through a component. However, the word element is often used synonomously with component in the literature. A *component* of a structural system is a single member of finite dimensions. A *structural system* consists of an assembly of components, suitably joined together by *joints* or *fittings.*

The primary function of a structural component or system is the transmission of force.

The engineer may be required to predict the behavior of a component or system for which the material properties, dimensions, loading, and environmental conditions are known. This type of engineering may be properly called *analysis.* On the other hand, the engineer may be asked to create a structural system which will perform certain force-transmission functions within certain limitations on behavior. This type of engineering is called *design.* In

---

* Other names: *Strength of Materials, Resistance of Materials, Mechanics of Deformable Bodies.*

1

general, some degree of optimization is inherent in design. For example, the civil engineer is usually concerned with doing the job at minimum cost. On the other hand, the importance of weight in aerospace applications may frequently override the cost.

The laws of behavior of bodies under the action of forces and different environments constitute a part of the science of Mechanics. Although many simple objects are designed purely on an empirical or esthetic basis, the type of design for which engineers are trained goes beyond this and makes the best possible use of the laws of Mechanics, together with empirical data and past experience.

1.2 Classification of states of loading

For slender members a general state of loading can be resolved into the following simple states:

Axial	(tension or compression)
Transverse	(shear)
Bending	(flexure)
Torsion	(twist)

It is convenient to work with these states separately in analyzing the behavior of components. Figure 1.1 shows the components of a general

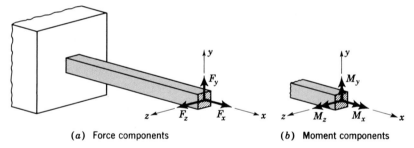

(a) Force components   **(b)** Moment components

Figure 1.1. Loads at a "cut" section.

system of forces at a particular cross section of a slender structural member. The section is "cut" normal to the longitudinal axis. For clarity, force and moment vectors are shown separately in (a) and (b), but they all act simultaneously on the same cross section. *A double-headed arrow is used for moments, and the right-hand rule* gives the sense of the moment. The subscript indicates the direction of the force or moment vector.*

In Fig. 1.1 the force F_x represents *axial loading*. When such loading (tension or compression) acts along one axis only, it is called *uniaxial*. The x axis in Fig. 1.1 may be regarded as the axis of force transmission.

---

* In Chap. 2 a double subscript is used, in which the first letter refers to the surface orientation. This notation is not necessary when all vectors act on the same surface.

Forces F_y and F_z act normal to the longitudinal axis. Such loading is called *transverse*, or *shear*. These two forces are obviously components of a single transverse resultant force.*

Moment M_x produces *torsion*. Moments M_y and M_z produce *bending;* they are components of a single resultant bending moment.

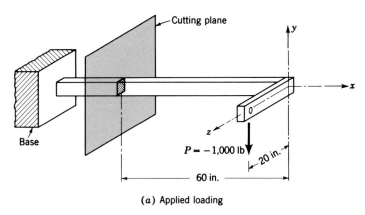

(a) Applied loading

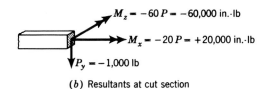

(b) Resultants at cut section

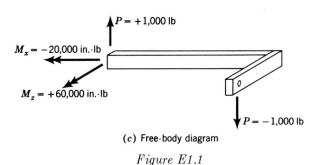

(c) Free-body diagram

Figure E1.1

When a member in static equilibrium is "cut," each portion becomes a "free body." The forces acting on one of the cut surfaces can be represented by a summation of all forces and moments that were acting on

---

* In statics, forces are usually denoted by the symbol F. In structural analysis the symbol P is more commonly used for a concentrated force. Both are used in this book.

the free body that was "removed." These forces and moments are usually stated in terms of their components, as described above.

The following examples illustrate some of the standard procedures used in determining the state of loading. The use of vector algebra and matrix algebra is illustrated, but the latter is not essential for what follows.

EXAMPLE 1.1. Figure E1.1 shows a situation in which a "cut" has been made at a certain station. In sketch *b* the internal resultant forces and moments are shown acting on the left portion of the cut body. (The weight of the beam is excluded, in this model.)

In this simple example the values of the internal resultant forces and moments at the cut section (*a*) can be computed by inspection. In sketches *b* and *c* the *sense* of a vector component is indicated by a plus or minus sign. In accordance with Newton's third law, the vectors in sketches *b* and *c* are of opposite sign. Sketch *c* represents a *free body*. If such a portion of the structure were actually to be isolated from its surroundings by cutting, all forces and moments shown must respectively add up to zero (vectorially); otherwise there would be acceleration.

The resultant loading at the cut section may be concisely described by stating the components of forces and moments in the order of the reference axes (x, y, z). Thus $\mathbf{P} = (0, -1{,}000, 0)$ lb; $\mathbf{M} = (20{,}000, 0, -60{,}000)$ in.-lb.

EXAMPLE 1.2 Calculation of moments. This example illustrates the use of the cross product (or vector product) of vector algebra for calculating moments.

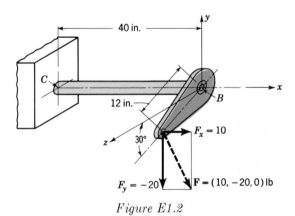

Figure E1.2

The resultant state of loading is to be found at two points, B and C (Fig. E1.2). The force vector is designated by the triplet $(10, -20, 0)$ lb. The moment-arm vector $\mathbf{r}$ is also designated by a triplet. Then*

$$\mathbf{M} = \mathbf{r} \times \mathbf{F}$$

---

* Boldface type will not be used for components of vectors.

AT STATION B

$$r_y = -12 \sin 30° = -6 \text{ in.}, \qquad r_z = 12 \cos 30° = 10.4 \text{ in.}, \qquad (r_x = 0)$$
$$\mathbf{r} = (0, -6, 10.4) \text{ in.} \qquad \mathbf{F} = (10, -20, 0) \text{ lb}$$

$$\mathbf{M}_{(B)} = \begin{vmatrix} \mathbf{i} & \mathbf{j} & \mathbf{k} \\ r_x & r_y & r_z \\ F_x & F_y & F_z \end{vmatrix} = \begin{vmatrix} \mathbf{i} & \mathbf{j} & \mathbf{k} \\ 0 & -6 & 10.4 \\ 10 & -20 & 0 \end{vmatrix}$$

$$= \mathbf{i} \begin{vmatrix} -6 & 10.4 \\ -20 & 0 \end{vmatrix} - \mathbf{j} \begin{vmatrix} 0 & 10.4 \\ 10 & 0 \end{vmatrix} + \mathbf{k} \begin{vmatrix} 0 & -6 \\ 10 & -20 \end{vmatrix}$$

$$= 208\mathbf{i} + 104\mathbf{j} + 60\mathbf{k}$$

AT STATION C

$$\mathbf{r} = (40, -6, 10.4) \text{ in.} \qquad \mathbf{F} = (10, -20, 0) \text{ lb}$$

$$\mathbf{M}_{(C)} = \begin{vmatrix} \mathbf{i} & \mathbf{j} & \mathbf{k} \\ r_x & r_y & r_z \\ F_x & F_y & F_z \end{vmatrix} = \begin{vmatrix} \mathbf{i} & \mathbf{j} & \mathbf{k} \\ 40 & -6 & 10.4 \\ 10 & -20 & 0 \end{vmatrix}$$

$$= 208\mathbf{i} + 104\mathbf{j} - 740\mathbf{k}$$

Answers:

AT STATION B

$$M_x = 208 \text{ in.-lb} \qquad M_y = 104 \text{ in.-lb} \qquad M_z = 60 \text{ in.-lb}$$

AT STATION C

$$M_x = 208 \text{ in.-lb} \qquad M_y = 104 \text{ in.-lb} \qquad M_z = -740 \text{ in.-lb}$$

EXAMPLE 1.3 Rotation of axes. This two-dimensional example illustrates the operation of rotating the base axis system. The forces and moments are first transmitted to point B on the structural axis (Fig. E1.3), in terms of components in the x, y, z system; then the components in the x', y', z' system are found.* The z and z' axes are identical, normal to the paper, and directed toward the reader.

For rotation of axes,

$$F'_x = F_x \cos \theta + F_y \sin \theta$$
$$F'_y = -F_x \sin \theta + F_y \cos \theta$$

Then
$$F'_x = 800 \times 0.5 + 400 \times 0.866 = 400 + 347 = 747 \text{ lb}$$
$$F'_y = -800 \times 0.866 + 400 \times 0.5 = 692 + 200 = -492 \text{ lb}$$
$$M'_z = M_z = 800 \times 70 + 400 \times 60 = 80,000 \text{ in.-lb}$$

Check:
$$|F| = \sqrt{800^2 + 400^2} = \sqrt{800,000} = 895 \text{ lb}$$
$$|F'| = \sqrt{747^2 + 492^2} = \sqrt{800,000} = 895 \text{ lb}$$

* The primes identify the second axis system. Primes are attached to symbols for forces and moments (instead of to axis symbols) for printing convenience.

To illustrate the use of matrix algebra,* we use the rotation matrix

$$[R] = \begin{bmatrix} \cos\theta & \sin\theta \\ -\sin\theta & \cos\theta \end{bmatrix}$$

The rotated vector† is given by

$$\{F'\} = [R]\{F\}$$

Expanding the matrices gives

$$\begin{Bmatrix} F'_x \\ F'_y \end{Bmatrix} = \begin{bmatrix} \cos\theta & \sin\theta \\ -\sin\theta & \cos\theta \end{bmatrix} \begin{Bmatrix} F_x \\ F_y \end{Bmatrix} = \begin{bmatrix} 0.500 & 0.866 \\ -0.866 & 0.500 \end{bmatrix} \begin{Bmatrix} 800 \\ 400 \end{Bmatrix}$$

Performing the matrix multiplication gives the same equations as before.

* May be omitted if students have no knowledge of elementary matrix algebra.
† Braces are often used instead of square brackets, in expressing a vector in matrix form.

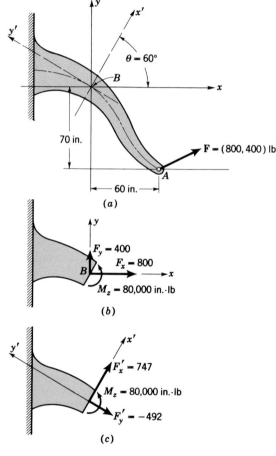

Figure E1.3

The equations of rotational transformation in three dimensions are obtained by adding, algebraically, the components of each force along the respective axes, giving

$$F'_x = l_{x'x}F_x + l_{x'y}F_y + l_{x'z}F_z$$
$$F'_y = l_{y'x}F_x + l_{y'y}F_y + l_{y'z}F_z$$
$$F'_z = l_{z'x}F_x + l_{z'y}F_y + l_{z'z}F_z$$

where $l_{x'x}$ is the direction cosine of the angle between x' and x axes, and so on. In matrix algebra the transformation is

$$\begin{Bmatrix} F'_x \\ F'_y \\ F'_z \end{Bmatrix} = \begin{bmatrix} l_{x'x} & l_{x'y} & l_{x'z} \\ l_{y'x} & l_{y'y} & l_{y'z} \\ l_{z'x} & l_{z'y} & l_{z'z} \end{bmatrix} \begin{Bmatrix} F_x \\ F_y \\ F_z \end{Bmatrix}$$

1.3 Force-deflection relationships

Figure 1.2 shows a member transmitting a tension force P. The force is applied to the member through a joint or fitting. Joints may be pinned, riveted, welded, or otherwise fastened. The distribution of internal forces in the vicinity of a joint is usually rather complicated. We therefore ignore it in the conceptual model of Fig. 1.2b.

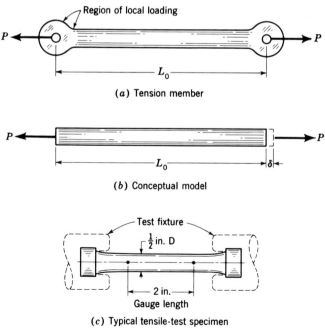

(a) Tension member

(b) Conceptual model

(c) Typical tensile-test specimen

Figure 1.2. Axially loaded member.

The above simplification is an application of Saint-Venant's principle, which states in effect that

The internal force distribution in a member, at some distance from a point of local force application, depends only on the magnitude and location of the resultant force (see Ref. 1, p. 139; also Sec. 7.2).

To predict the behavior of a member subjected to pure tensile loading, it is necessary to have certain information on the mechanical properties of the material. Such information is usually obtained by means of a

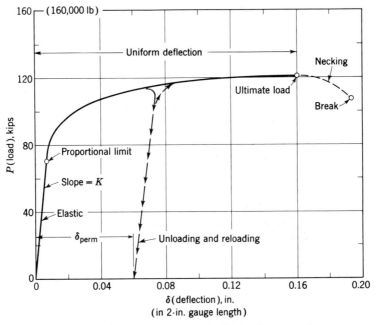

Figure 1.3. Load-deflection curve obtained in tensile test.

tensile test. Although other types of tests are employed to obtain additional information, the tensile test is the most widely used.

A typical coupon used for a routine tensile test is shown in Fig. 1.2c. The gauge length* L_0 is commonly 2 in. Changes in this length are measured by a sensitive instrument, while the loading is continuously increased at some known rate. (Alternatively, the rate of change of length may be controlled.) In such a test the specimen becomes longer and slimmer. These changes in dimensions are called *deformations*. Care must be taken to ensure that displacements of the body as a whole are excluded.

---

* The "standard" gauge length, in some countries, is a certain multiple of the diameter.

The word *deflection* is used in this text to describe a deformation measured in a particular direction or with respect to a particular axis. A deformation may be linear (e.g., extension) or angular (e.g., twist).

When the measured load P is plotted against change of length δ (called axial deflection), a *force-deflection* curve is obtained, as illustrated by Fig. 1.3.

The linear portion of the curve is called the *elastic range*. If the loading is stopped within the elastic range and is then allowed to decrease to zero, the deflection will also decrease to zero. *Elastic behavior is character-ized by absence of permanent deformation after loading.* A more restricted definition is: *elastic behavior is characterized by a linear relationship be-tween load and deformation.* This definition constitutes Hooke's law, which can be stated as follows:

Deformation is proportional to load.

Because the behavior of many materials follows this law quite closely, Hooke's law is of great importance. It is the basis of the *theory of elasticity.* Hooke's law is not restricted to axial loading; any form of loading, such as the application of moments, is included.

Hooke's law can be expressed, for axial loading, in either of two ways:

$$\delta = \frac{P}{K} \qquad (1.1)$$

where K is the *stiffness* (or *spring constant*)

$$\delta = CP \qquad (1.2)$$

where C is the *compliance* (or *flexibility*). Obviously $C = 1/K$.

For some materials (like rubber) the force-deflection curve is not linear; nevertheless, the deflection returns virtually to zero after loading and unloading. In this sense the material is elastic, but it does not obey Hooke's law. Unless otherwise noted, the word elastic is used in the *Hookean* sense.

The work done on the specimen, up to a load P_1 or deflection δ_1 is given by

$$U = \int_0^{\delta_1} P \, d\delta \qquad (1.3)$$

where U is a symbol for work. (In general this symbol is used for other forms of energy.)

In Fig. 1.3 the work is represented by the area under the $P–\delta$ curve. *Elastic energy,* which is equal to the work done during loading, is therefore given by

$$\boxed{U_E = \tfrac{1}{2}P\delta} \qquad\qquad (1.4a)$$

Elastic energy is recoverable.

Equation (1.4a) can be expressed in terms of either P or δ by substituting from Eqs. (1.1) or (1.2). For example:

$$U_E = \frac{1}{2}\frac{P^2}{K} \qquad\qquad (1.4b)$$

$$U_E = \tfrac{1}{2}K\delta^2 \qquad\qquad (1.4c)$$

EXAMPLE 1.4.   A spring is tested in a testing machine and two of the readings are as follows:

$$\text{at } P_1 = 400 \text{ lb} \qquad \delta_1 = 0.21 \text{ in.}$$
$$\text{at } P_2 = 1{,}000 \text{ lb} \qquad \delta_2 = 0.50 \text{ in.}$$

Find the spring constant and the compliance. Also calculate the energy absorbed at $P = 1{,}000$ lb.

SOLUTION: Taking each test point separately we would have

$$K_1 = \frac{400}{0.21} = 1{,}910 \text{ lb/in.}$$

$$K_2 = \frac{1{,}000}{0.50} = 2{,}000 \text{ lb/in.}$$

Since this indicates a "zero error" in the measuring equipment, the most reliable way to calculate K is to use the formula

$$K = \frac{\Delta P}{\Delta \delta} = \frac{1{,}000 - 400}{0.5 - 0.21} = 2{,}070 \text{ lb/in.}$$

Then
$$C = \frac{1}{K} = 4.83 \times 10^{-4} \text{ in./lb}$$

If several readings are taken, the slope of the $P\text{-}\delta$ curve can be obtained by curve fitting.

The energy absorbed is (assuming the plotted straight line goes through the origin)

$$U = \tfrac{1}{2}P\delta = \tfrac{1}{2} \times 1{,}000 \times 0.5 = 250 \text{ in.-lb}$$

For greater accuracy,

$$U = \tfrac{1}{2}P\delta = \tfrac{1}{2}CP^2$$
$$= \tfrac{1}{2} \times 4.83 \times 10^{-4} \times 1{,}000^2$$
$$= 242 \text{ in.-lb}$$

1.4 The stress-strain diagram

The force-deflection diagram of Fig. 1.3 tells us how a particular member will behave under tensile load. How can we use this information to predict the behavior of a member made from similar material but having a different length and different cross-sectional area? Common sense suggests that a member twice as long, having the same cross-sectional area, will have twice as much axial deflection, provided that the deformation is uniformly distributed over the length. Experiments show that for metals and many other materials deformation is uniformly distributed over the length, up to the maximum load. Beyond that point the additional deflection (shown by the broken line in Fig. 1.3) occurs by localized *necking* over a relatively short length. Some materials will break (rupture) while the load is still increasing and before necking begins.

The deflection per unit length is called strain. Engineering strain is defined as deflection per unit of original length. For uniaxial loading (δ and L_0 coaxial) the strain is called *normal*. For uniform distribution of δ over L_0 the following equation applies

$$\epsilon = \frac{\delta}{L_0} \tag{1.5}$$

where δ is the increase in length, measured with respect to the original length L_0. Normal strain is arbitrarily called positive for an increase in length.

The following general definition of engineering normal strain applies when the deflection is not uniformly distributed over the length:

$$\epsilon = \lim_{\Delta x \to 0} \frac{\Delta \delta}{\Delta x}$$

This equation is usually written as

$$\boxed{\epsilon = \frac{d\delta}{dx}} \tag{1.6}$$

where dx is measured along L_0. In routine testing, L_0 is called the "gauge length."

All "strain gauges" and similar instruments measure deformation (change of length), which must be divided by another measured length to obtain strain. In this sense "strain" is an abstraction, or derived quantity.

If we were to test two "identical" specimens side by side (in parallel), common sense tells us that the total force required to produce the same change in length would be doubled. This suggests that the behavior is controlled by the force per unit of cross-sectional area, which is called *stress. Engineering stress* is defined as force per unit of original (unloaded) cross-sectional area.* For pure uniaxial loading, the following equation applies:

$$\sigma = \frac{P}{A_0} \qquad (1.7)$$

where P is the axial force, and A_0 is the original area of a cross section normal to the line of action of the force.

Because the force acts normal to the cross-sectional area, the stress is further classified as *normal stress*. The symbol σ always represents normal stress, in this text. (Other symbols are frequently employed.)

A more general definition of normal stress is needed in situations where the stress is nonuniformly distributed over the cross-sectional area. The following equation then applies

$$\sigma = \lim_{\Delta A_0 \to 0} \frac{\Delta P}{\Delta A_0}$$

This equation is usually written as

$$\boxed{\sigma = \frac{dP}{dA_0}} \qquad (1.8)$$

Under tensile loading the cross-sectional area will become smaller. If we divide the force P by the actual cross-sectional area (A) existing at that value of force, we obtain the so-called "true stress":

$$\sigma_{\text{true}} = \frac{P}{A_{\text{actual}}} \qquad (1.9)$$

True stress is of scientific interest, but for most engineering purposes "engineering" stress and "engineering" strain are used.† *We therefore omit the subscripts for A_0 and L_0 hereafter, with the understanding that A and L refer to the unloaded member, unless otherwise noted.*

Stress cannot be measured directly. We can measure force and can also calculate the cross-sectional area from measurements of length. In this sense stress, like strain, is an abstraction, or derived quantity.

The force-deflection diagram may be reduced to a *stress-strain diagram* by dividing all values of P by A and all values of δ by L. Figure 1.3 is thereby linearly transformed into Fig. 1.4. This is a typical tensile stress-strain diagram for a structural material. For the engineer it is the most important source of information on mechanical behavior of materials.

---

* In defining stress a distinction must be made between "stress" and "state of stress." The latter is taken up in Chap. 2. See Ref. 1, p. 108, for historical discussion.

† For example, in design calculations the designer wishes to find the required *unloaded* cross-sectional area A_0.

Figure 1.5 shows the initial portion of Fig. 1.4 replotted to a magnified strain scale. (Note that in such a diagram the strains shown may represent only a very small fraction of the total strain available.) In determining certain material properties (E and σ_y, Sec. 1.5) it is necessary to plot the diagram in this manner.

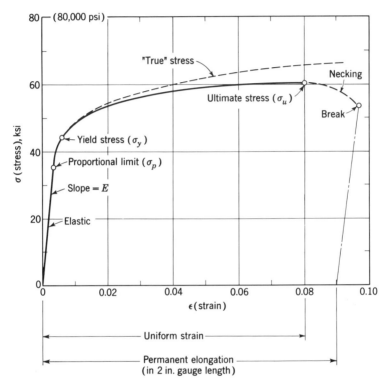

Figure 1.4. Stress-strain diagram obtained from tensile test.

Partial stress-strain diagrams for several materials are plotted in Fig. 1.6. The great advantage of the stress-strain diagram (over the force-deflection curve) is that it is almost entirely independent of the size of the member and therefore represents only the properties of the material.*

The compressive branch of the stress-strain diagram (not shown in figures) tends to be quite similar to the tensile branch, up to stresses somewhat beyond the yield stress. In making compression tests of slender specimens it is necessary to provide lateral support against buckling

* Very fine filaments, single crystals, and large components are likely to show considerable variations from the stress-strain diagrams obtained for specimens of normal size. Other important effects, such as temperature and rate of loading, are discussed later.

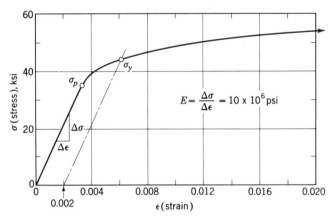

Figure 1.5. Tensile stress-strain diagram (enlarged strain scale).

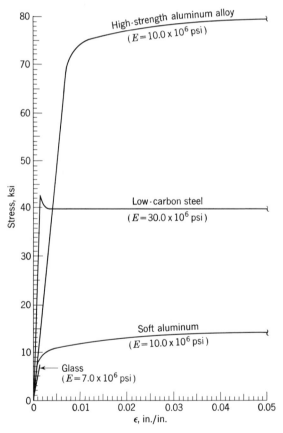

Figure 1.6. Partial stress-strain diagrams. (See also Appendix A.)

(rollers may be used). Some materials (concrete for example) exhibit considerably different behavior in tension and compression.

1.5 *Material properties*

Some of the material properties obtained from the tensile test are defined below. (See Figs. 1.4, 1.5, and 1.6 for graphical interpretations.)

ULTIMATE TENSILE STRESS $(\sigma_u)_t$ (*often abbreviated UTS*). *The stress corresponding to the maximum load reached in the tensile test* (equals maximum load divided by the original cross-sectional area). This is generally regarded as a measure of a material's *strength*.

PROPORTIONAL LIMIT (σ_p). *The stress at which strain ceases to be proportional to stress* (the limit of the straight part of the diagram). This quantity indicates the range of stress in which the assumption of elastic action will be valid.*

YIELD STRESS (σ_y). *The stress determined by some arbitrary permanent strain.* The most commonly used yield stress is the one determined by a line passing through a strain of 0.002, parallel with the elastic line, as shown in Fig. 1.5. The yield stress represents a practical upper limit for the actual stress developed in a structure.

ELONGATION. *The total normal strain that has occurred at failure* (usually measured as the total permanent strain *after* failure). Elongation is generally specified in percent and is regarded as a measure of the *ductility* of a material.

MODULUS OF ELASTICITY OR YOUNG'S MODULUS (E). *The ratio of stress to strain, in the elastic range.* The quantity E may be regarded as the slope of the *straight* portion of the stress-strain diagram. As shown in Fig. 1.5,

$$E = \frac{\Delta\sigma}{\Delta\epsilon}$$

A more common definition of E is given by

$$E = \frac{\sigma}{\epsilon} \qquad (1.10)$$

This is satisfactory if there is no question about the accuracy of the measurements in the region of zero stress and strain. The modulus of elasticity is a measure of the *stiffness* of a material, that is, its resistance to axial deflection in tension or compression.

---

* For many materials there is no sharp transition between elastic and inelastic behavior. The value assigned to σ_p will then depend on the accuracy of the measuring equipment.

ENERGY PER UNIT VOLUME (u).   *The area under the stress-strain diagram.*
The total energy per unit volume, up to the point of failure, is given by
the entire area under the stress-strain diagram. This definition follows
directly from the fact that, in converting the force-deflection curve into
a stress-strain diagram, all vertical measurements (forces) were divided
by the cross-sectional area and all horizontal measurements (deflection)
were divided by length. Therefore the area under the original curve was
divided by the product of length and cross-sectional area, which represents
volume.

The total energy per unit volume is a measure of *toughness*, that is, a
measure of the ability to absorb energy without failure.

POISSON'S RATIO.   *The absolute value of the ratio of transverse strain to
longitudinal strain in pure tension.* During a tensile test the width (or
thickness) of a test specimen will decrease. When this change in width is
divided by the original width, the *transverse strain* is obtained.

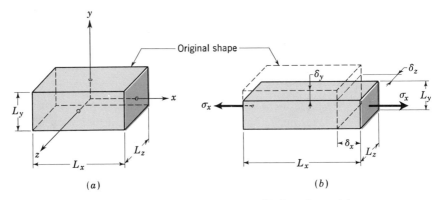

Figure 1.7. Lateral contraction (Poisson's ratio).

Figure 1.7 shows a rectangular element of material under zero stress,
sketch a, and under a tensile stress σ_x, sketch b. The deflections (greatly
exaggerated in the sketch) are denoted by δ_x, δ_y, and δ_z. It will be observed that δ_x is positive, whereas δ_y and δ_z are negative. The corresponding strains are found by dividing the deflections by the corresponding
initial lengths:

$$\epsilon_x = \frac{\delta_x}{L_x} \qquad \epsilon_y = -\frac{\delta_y}{L_y} \qquad \epsilon_z = -\frac{\delta_z}{L_z}$$

If the strain ratios $-\epsilon_y/\epsilon_x$ and $-\epsilon_z/\epsilon_x$ are calculated from the observed
data, they will be found to lie in the range 0.28 to 0.33 for most structural
metals,[*] provided that the elastic range is not exceeded.

---

[*] Typical values for amorphous materials, such as glass and ceramics, are close to
the theoretical value of 0.25 derived by Poisson. The value for cork is nearly zero.

The quantity *Poisson's ratio* may be regarded as a material property and will be indicated in this text by ν. Expressed as an equation,

$$\nu = \left| \frac{\epsilon_{\text{tranverse}}}{\epsilon_{\text{longitudinal}}} \right| \qquad (1.11)$$

(The vertical bars in this equation indicate that only the magnitude, not the sign, is considered in defining Poisson's ratio.)

Two important points must be remembered in using Poisson's ratio:

1. The transverse strain will be of opposite sense to the longitudinal strain (negative sign must be added).
2. The ratio is a *strain* ratio, not a deflection ratio.

EXAMPLE 1.5. Assume that an element such as that shown in Fig. 1.7 is 20 in. long and $\frac{1}{2}$ in. square and that the strain in the x direction is $\epsilon_x = 0.0006$. The corresponding deflection would be $\delta_x = \epsilon_x L_x = 0.0006 \times 20 = 0.012$ in. The transverse *strain* is equal to $-\nu\epsilon_x$. Assuming a value of $\frac{1}{3}$ for ν gives $\epsilon_y = \epsilon_z = -0.0002$. The transverse *deflection* is therefore

$$\delta_y = \epsilon_y L_y = -0.0002 \times 0.5 = -0.0001 \text{ in.}$$

The negative value indicates a decrease in width.

It would obviously be wrong to calculate the transverse deflection as $-\nu\delta_x$, which would give -0.004 in.

Careful measurements of the lateral dimensions of a tensile-test specimen reveal that Poisson's ratio remains constant in the elastic range but gradually increases as the stress is raised above the proportional limit, approaching a value of $\frac{1}{2}$ for ductile materials.

1.6 Local elongation (necking)

Tensile tests of relatively ductile materials show that, up to the ultimate tensile stress (at maximum load), the strain is practically constant over the length of the specimen. (This would not be true, of course, if the cross-sectional area were not constant.) Consequently, test data on a short specimen can be used to predict the deflection of a long specimen, and vice versa.

Figure 1.4 shows that the stress decreases after reaching a maximum value and that actual rupture does not occur until a considerably higher strain has been reached. During this final stage the deflection tends to localize at one spot, forming a neck in the specimen, as shown in Fig. 1.8. Failure eventually occurs at the smallest cross section.

In metal forming, the total elongation that can be attained without failure is important. The strain distribution over the necked portion of the specimen is then of special interest. In Fig. 1.8 a curve of *local elongation* has been plotted alongside the specimen. The data for plotting this curve are usually obtained by photographing or scribing a fine grid or network of lines on the specimen before testing. After a load has been applied or failure has occurred, the grid is photographed, and the enlarged picture is then viewed through a microscope to determine the elongation over very short gauge lengths. The curve in Fig. 1.8 shows that high strains can be reached over short gauge lengths before failure occurs.

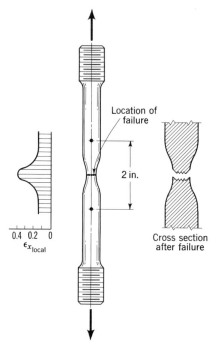

Figure 1.8. Local elongation and fracture in tension.

The phenomenon of necking is a form of instability in tension. The actions involved are complex and are of interest primarily in studies of material behavior under combined stresses (see Refs. 9 and 16).

Closely related to local elongation is the *reduction of area*. This term is usually applied to the percentage reduction of cross-sectional area, which is found by measuring the final cross section of the broken specimen at the point of failure. The reduction in area may be regarded as a limiting value for local elongation, as the gauge length approaches zero. Figure 1.8 shows a typical "cup-and-cone" type of fracture.

Since the cross-sectional area decreases rather rapidly during necking, the true stress does not drop off but continues to increase, as indicated in Fig. 1.4. It is evident that the average stress over the actual cross section which fails is considerably greater than the nominal ultimate tensile stress.

True strain is based on the concept that, at any stage of loading, a small increment of deflection is divided by the actual gauge length which existed just prior to the incremental deflection, not by the original gauge length. True strain can be obtained from engineering strain by the following transformation (see Ref. 9, p. 73):

$$\epsilon_{\text{true}} = \ln (1 + \epsilon) \tag{1.12}$$

This definition of strain is not used in this text.

1.7 Statistical aspects of stress-strain relationships

In predicting the strength or deflection of a structural element, it is necessary to use data obtained from tests. No two test specimens will ever be exactly alike in every respect; there will be unavoidable differences. The results of many tests of "identical" specimens will show deviations, or *scatter*. The range of such deviations may be large or small. For example, measured values of Young's modulus show negligibly small scatter for most structural materials. On the other hand, the compressive strength of concrete specimens varies over a wide range. Much of this scatter is the result of random variations in the controlling factors and therefore obeys certain statistical laws more or less closely. In subsequent chapters, statistical treatment will not be specifically included. It is to be understood that all data used are subject to variation and that this can be provided for by standard methods. (See also Appendix A.)

1.8 Empirical stress-strain formulas

Beyond the elastic range the strain ϵ can be separated into two distinct parts, *elastic* and *plastic*, as shown in Fig. 1.9. *Elastic strain ϵ_E is reversible* (recoverable); *plastic strain is irreversible*. The total strain is expressed by:

$$\epsilon = \epsilon_E + \epsilon_P \tag{1.13}$$

The elastic (reversible) strain is, from Hooke's law and the definition of Young's modulus,

$$\boxed{\epsilon_E = \frac{\sigma}{E}} \tag{1.14}$$

For uniaxial loading we can approximate the plastic stress-strain relationship by an empirical formula. The most common such formula is the *power law*:

$$\epsilon_P = C_\epsilon \sigma^n \tag{1.15a}$$

or

$$\epsilon_P = \left(\frac{\sigma}{B}\right)^n \tag{1.15b}$$

where C_ϵ (or B) and n are constants determined by curve fitting (plot ϵ_P versus σ on log-log paper). Equation (1.13) may now be expressed as

$$\epsilon = \frac{\sigma}{E} + \left(\frac{\sigma}{B}\right)^n \qquad (1.16a)$$

This is often called the Ramberg-Osgood equation, after the authors who used it in developing dimensionless strain-strain diagrams (Ref. 17).

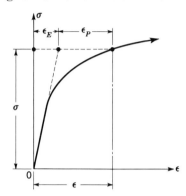

Figure 1.9. Elastic and plastic strains.

Table 1.1 lists some typical values of the stress-strain constants for various materials.

TABLE 1.1

Typical stress-strain constants (approximate)

Material	$E \times 10^{-6}$, psi	B, psi	n
Alloy steel: UTS = 100,000 psi; uniform elongation = 20%	29	122,400	25
Alloy steel: UTS = 180,000 psi; uniform elongation = 10%	29	202,000	30
Aluminum alloy 2024-T3: UTS = 65,000 psi; uniform elongation = 15%	10	72,300	10
Aluminum alloy 7075-T6: UTS = 83,000 psi; uniform elongation 10%	10	101,200	20
Magnesium alloy: UTS = 39,000 psi; uniform elongation = 15%	6.5	47,500	10

The Ramberg-Osgood equation in dimensionless form, as originally presented by the authors (Ref. 17), is

$$\frac{\epsilon}{\epsilon_0} = \frac{\sigma}{\sigma_0} + \frac{3}{7}\left(\frac{\sigma}{\sigma_0}\right)^n \qquad (1.16b)$$

where σ_0 = base stress

ϵ_0 = base strain = σ_0/E

n = empirical constant

In fitting this equation to an actual stress-strain curve, the base stress is selected at the point where a secant modulus line ($E_{\text{sec}} = 0.7E$) intersects the curve. The best value of n is obtained by curve fitting (see also Ref. 17). Figure 1.10 shows a dimensionless Ramberg-Osgood curve for $n = 10$.

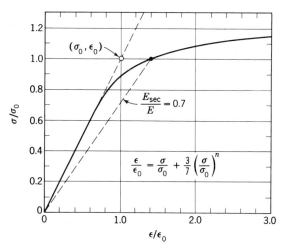

Figure 1.10. Dimensionless stress-strain diagram ($n = 10$).

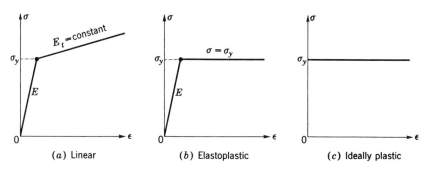

Figure 1.11. Approximate stress-strain diagrams.

Figure 1.11 shows three other types of approximate stress-strain diagrams, in the order of decreasing accuracy. Figure 1.11a shows a model that is sometimes referred to as the "linear strain-hardening model." The *elastoplastic* diagram (Fig. 1.11b) is frequently used. In the *ideally plastic* model the elastic strains are omitted. The latter model forms the basis for some theories of plasticity.

1.9 Axial deflection and energy of straight members

We create a general model of a straight member as one having a cross section of any shape. The centroids of all cross sections lie on the same straight line, called the *structural axis*. There may be a variation in cross-sectional area with length. (Abrupt variations cause stress concentrations but will not have a large effect on deflection.) The force P acts along the structural axis and may vary with length. Such a model is described by the following functions:

$$
\begin{array}{lc}
\text{Geometry} & A = f_A(x) \\
\text{Loading} & P = f_P(x) \\
\text{Stress-strain diagram} & \epsilon = f_\epsilon(\sigma)
\end{array}
$$

From Eq. (1.6),

$$
\delta = \int_0^L \epsilon \, dx \tag{1.17}
$$

If all the above functions (A, P, ϵ) are integrable, the deflection can be found mathematically. If not, a numerical method (such as Simpson's rule), or curve plotting, may be used.

The simplest case is that of the *straight member of uniform cross section in the elastic range, under constant load*. Then

$$
A = \text{constant}, \quad P = \text{constant}, \quad \sigma = \frac{P}{A}, \quad \epsilon = \frac{\sigma}{E}
$$

Equation (1.17) then reduces to the important equation

$$
\delta = \frac{PL}{AE} \tag{1.18}
$$

Trusses and framed structures are usually built up from members of constant cross section. The deflection at any point in the structure can be found by using Eq. (1.18) for each member and determining the geometric effects of these changes in length (see Chap. 15).

The *elastic energy* in a member of constant cross section, under load P, is found by substituting δ, from Eq. (1.18), in Eq. (1.4a):

$$
U_E = \frac{1}{2} \frac{P^2 L}{AE} \tag{1.19}
$$

For variable area or load, or both,

$$
U_E = \frac{1}{2} \int_0^L \frac{P^2}{AE} \, dx \tag{1.20}
$$

As shown in Sec. 1.5, the area under the stress-strain diagram represents *energy per unit volume* (u). Figure 1.12 shows how u can be plotted on the diagram. The volume of an element having length dx is

$$dV = A\,dx$$

Therefore

$$dU = uA\,dx$$

Then

$$U = \int_0^L uA\,dx \tag{1.21}$$

where u is determined by the stress, σ. Both σ and A may be functions of x.

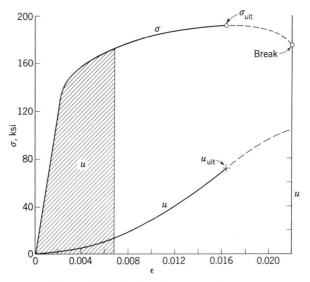

Figure 1.12. Inelastic-energy diagram.

EXAMPLE 1.6.   Find the deflection of a steel wire 1,000 ft long suspended at its upper end and loaded by its own weight only. Diameter is constant; $E = 29 \times 10^6$ psi; $A = 0.50$ in.²; density $w = 0.29$ lb/in.³; proportional limit = 50,000 psi. Let x be the distance from upper end,

$$P = (L - x)Aw \qquad \sigma = \frac{P}{A} = (L - x)w$$

Assuming elastic action,

$$\epsilon = \frac{\sigma}{E} = \frac{(L - x)w}{E}$$

$$\delta = \int_0^L \epsilon\,dx = \frac{w}{E}\int_0^L (L - x)\,dx$$

$$\delta = \frac{wL^2}{2E} = \frac{0.29 \times (1,000 \times 12)^2}{2 \times 29 \times 10^6} = 0.770 \text{ in.}$$

The stress at the upper end ($x = 0$) is

$$\sigma = Lw = 12{,}000 \times 0.29 = 3{,}480 \text{ psi}$$

Therefore the action is elastic, as assumed.

EXAMPLE 1.7 Constant-stress member.   For maximum efficiency the cross-sectional area of a tension member should be varied in such a way that $P/A = \sigma_{\text{allow}}$, where σ_{allow} represents the allowable tensile stress.

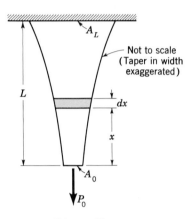

Figure E1.7

In Fig. E1.7 the member must transmit the initial force P_0 plus its own weight. The following relationships apply at station x (density $= w$):

$$dV = A \, dx$$
$$dP_{\text{appl}} = w \, dV = wA \, dx \tag{a}$$

The allowable load must increase at the same rate, that is,

$$dP_{\text{allow}} = \sigma_{\text{allow}} \, dA \tag{b}$$

Dropping subscript and equating,

$$\sigma \, dA = wA \, dx$$

or
$$\frac{dA}{A} = \frac{w}{\sigma} \, dx \tag{c}$$

Integrating both sides, we obtain

$$\ln A = \frac{w}{\sigma} x + C \tag{d}$$

To evaluate C let A_0 equal area at $x = 0$, which is equal to P_0/σ:

$$\ln A_0 = 0 + C \qquad \text{or} \qquad C = \ln A_0$$

Equation (*d*) becomes

$$\ln A - \ln A_0 = \frac{w}{\sigma} x$$

or

$$\ln \frac{A}{A_0} = \frac{w}{\sigma} x$$

This can be written:

$$A = A_0 e^{(w/\sigma)x} \tag{e}$$

Substituting for A_0,

$$A_{\text{req'd}} = \frac{P_0}{\sigma} e^{(w/\sigma)x} \tag{f}$$

Note that the quantity w/σ appearing in the exponent is the reciprocal of *specific strength* (σ/w), a quantity often used in comparing materials.

The deflection, at constant stress σ, is

$$\delta = \frac{\sigma L}{E} \tag{g}$$

The volume is

$$V = \int_0^L A \, dx = A_0 \int_0^L e^{(w/\sigma)x} \, dx = A_0 \frac{\sigma}{w} (e^{(w/\sigma)L} - 1)$$

$$= \frac{\sigma}{w} (A_L - A_0)$$

Let $\qquad L = 12,500$ ft

$\qquad\qquad P_0 = 30,000$ lb

$\qquad\qquad \sigma_{\text{allow}} = 30,000$ psi

$\qquad\qquad w = 0.30$ (lb/in.³)

Then $\qquad\qquad A_0 = 1$ in.² $\qquad$ Volume $= 348,000$ in.³

$\qquad\qquad A_L = 4.482$ in. $\qquad$ Weight $= 140,000$ lb

Check: $\qquad \sigma_L = \dfrac{P_L}{A_L} = \dfrac{140,000 + 30,000}{4.482} = 30,000$ psi

Figure E1.7 has been drawn to show the proper variation in width, for constant thickness. However, the length scale has been greatly compressed, for obvious reasons.

EXAMPLE 1.8. Figure E1.8 shows a tension member of variable cross section under constant load. If there is no simple mathematical expression for the area as a function of length, a numerical method of analysis may be used to find the deflection.

The simplest method is to imagine the member to be composed of short segments of constant area, as indicated in sketch *b*. A curve of stress is thus found (*c*). The corresponding strain is then determined (if in the inelastic range, use the stress-strain diagram, or an empirical equation). The change in length of each segment is then given by $\epsilon(\Delta L)$. Summation of these quantities gives the axial deflection of the member.

These calculations can be tabulated as shown in Table E1.8.

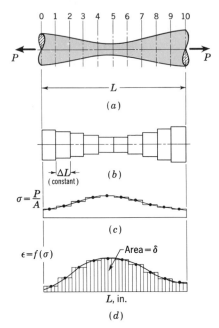

Figure E1.8

TABLE E1.8

Computation of axial deflection of nonuniform member

Station	P_i	A_i	$\sigma_i = \dfrac{(1)}{(2)}$	$\epsilon_i = f(\sigma_i)$	$\Delta \delta = (4)\Delta L$	Energy	
						u_i	$\Delta U = (6)(2)\Delta L$
	(1)	(2)	(3)	(4)	(5)	(6)	(7)
1							
2							
.							
.							
.							
10							
Σ					δ		U

To calculate the energy in the elastic range Eq. (1.4) may be used for the member as a whole.

If inelastic (plastic) strains are involved, the computed elongation cannot be used in Eq. (1.4), because the force-deflection diagram will not be a straight line. Equation (1.21) should then be used, as indicated in columns 6 and 7 of Table E1.8.

The method can be extended to include variable loading, where $P = f(x)$. The analysis of the blade of a rotating propeller, or of a helicopter, is an example. (It is also necessary, in such cases, to compute stresses due to bending, torsion, and other types of loading.)

1.10 Axis of resistance

For pure axial loading, the vector representing the resultant of the externally applied forces must be coaxial with the resultant representing the internal stresses. The location of the resultant on the cross section establishes the *axis of resistance*.

In the design of a tension member, the end fittings should be located in such a way that they cause the resultant of the externally applied forces to coincide with the axis of resistance. If this is not done, some of the stresses in the member will be greater than the value which would have been obtained for pure tension (P/A), as will be shown later.

For a straight axially loaded member the center of resistance of the cross section is found by applying the following postulates:

1. *Plane cross sections remain plane.* The cross sections are "cut" normal to the longitudinal axis. From experiments, it is known that such cross sections remain plane in an axially loaded member except for localized conditions such as those existing at points of concentrated loading.

Figure 1.13 shows a short section of a tension member having an "angle" cross section. Planes AA, BB, and so on, are passed through the member before loading. After application of a tensile force, the planes will be farther apart, and, according to the foregoing postulate, they will remain plane.

Pure axial deflection of an initially straight member requires that:

2. *Parallel cross sections remain parallel.* The change in length between planes AA and BB is indicated by δ_{AB} in Fig. 1.13b. Since the planes are assumed to remain plane and parallel, the value δ_{AB} will apply to every fiber* of the material between AA and BB.

The strain corresponding to δ_{AB} is, from Eq. (1.5),

$$\epsilon_{AB} = \frac{\delta_{AB}}{L_{AB}}$$

* The word "fiber" is frequently used to describe an imaginary element of the material for which the cross-sectional area approaches zero as a limit. Some materials actually are fibrous, but this is not what is meant by the term in the above context.

The assumption of plane parallel cross sections therefore results in *uniform strain* over the cross section for an initially straight member. For a homogeneous material, the stress distribution over the cross section will therefore be uniform. For example, if the value of the strain (ϵ) is known, the stress at every point on the cross section may be found by entering the stress-strain diagram at this value of strain. Even if the stress so determined should lie in the plastic range, the above statement still applies.

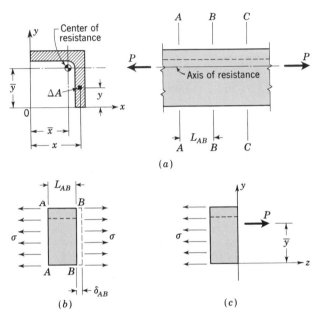

Figure 1.13. Member under pure axial loading.

The total resisting force is found by summation or integration of the forces acting on elements of area, such as ΔA in Fig. 1.13a. Applying the equation of equilibrium for forces along the z axis (Fig. 1.13c) and treating σ as a constant,

$$[\Sigma P = 0] \qquad P - \int \sigma \, dA = 0$$

$$P = \sigma A$$

This is used in inverse form to find the stress in pure axial loading of a homogeneous,* initially straight member (Eq. 1.7): $\sigma = P/A$.

The location of the resisting force with respect to any two orthogonal axes drawn in the plane of the cross section (x and y in Fig. 1.13a) may

---

* Homogeneous here implies uniform properties and constant temperature over the cross section.

be found by writing the equations of equilibrium for moments, for the element considered as a free body. Taking moments about the x axis,

$$[\Sigma M_x = 0] \qquad P\bar{y} - \int y\sigma \, dA = 0$$

from which,

$$\bar{y} = \frac{\int y \, dA}{A} \qquad (1.22a)$$

Similarly,

$$\bar{x} = \frac{\int x \, dA}{A} \qquad (1.22b)$$

These are the equations for the centroid of an area. The above analysis shows that *in pure axial loading of an initially straight homogeneous member, the axis of resistance passes through the centroids of area of the cross sections.* As a corollary, design for pure uniaxial loading requires that centroids of area of all cross sections lie on a straight line.

1.11 Curved members

The wrapping of a string around a finger, the transmission of a tensile force by a cable passing over a pulley, all are examples of curved axial loading. This state of loading is not pure tension, because a radial distributed force is necessary for equilibrium. The value of this radial *line force* can be derived by isolating an element of length ds along the arc and finding the force dP_r required to maintain equilibrium in a radial direction

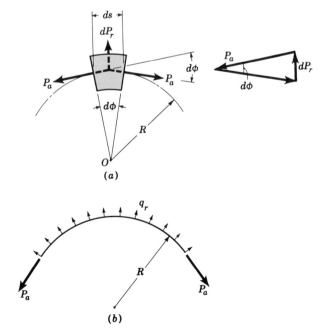

Figure 1.14. Equilibrium of a curved tension member.

(see Fig. 1.14). For indefinitely small values of $d\phi$ the following relationship is obtained (since $\sin d\phi \rightarrow d\phi$):

$$dP_r = P_a \, d\phi = P_a \frac{ds}{R}$$

Dividing by ds,

$$\frac{dP_r}{ds} = \frac{1}{R} P_a$$

A *line force* q_r is defined as dP_r/ds. Therefore

$$q_r = \frac{1}{R} P_a \qquad (1.23)$$

where q_r = distributed radial line force in plane of curvature
    $1/R$ = curvature
    P_a = axial force acting along curved axis in a plane

For large values of R (small curvature) q_r will be relatively small. We shall therefore omit its effect on the internal stresses, at this stage.

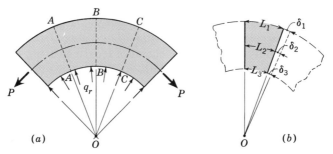

Figure 1.15. Tension in a curved member.

To find the center of resistance for a curved member under axial loading we "cut" the unloaded member by planes which pass through the axis of curvature, represented by point O in Fig. 1.15.

The following postulates are now made:

1. *Plane cross sections remain plane.*
2. *The radius of curvature remains constant.*
3. *Planes which passed through the original axis of curvature (under zero load) will continue to pass through this axis when the member is loaded.*

Figure 1.15 shows that the changes in lengths (δ_1, δ_2, δ_3, etc.) are proportional to their distance from the axis of curvature (at O). But the initial lengths (L_1, L_2, L_3, etc.) are also proportional to these distances. Therefore

$$\epsilon = \frac{\delta_1}{L_1} = \frac{\delta_2}{L_2} = \frac{\delta_3}{L_3} = \text{constant}$$

This result means that *in pure axial loading of a curved member the strain, and therefore the axial stress, is constant over the cross section.*

It follows that *the center of resistance of the curved member is located at the centroid of the cross-sectional area, as for a straight member.* From the above analysis we see also that

Pure axial deflection of a curved member involves change of length without change of curvature.

1.12 Thermal strains

A uniform increase in temperature usually causes a material to expand. The increase in a dimension, divided by the original dimension, is called *thermal strain.*

For many materials, the thermal strain varies approximately linearly with temperature. The rate of change of thermal strain with temperature is called the *linear coefficient of expansion.*[*] Therefore

$$\epsilon_T = \alpha \, \Delta T \tag{1.24}$$

where ϵ_T = thermal strain
α = linear coefficient of expansion
ΔT = change in temperature
Combining all three types of strain, we have

$$\epsilon = \epsilon_E + \epsilon_P + \epsilon_T \tag{1.25}$$

If a bar is constrained so that it cannot expand or contract longitudinally, $\epsilon = 0$. Then

$$\epsilon_E + \epsilon_P + \epsilon_T = 0$$

Replacing each term by expressions previously stated,

$$\frac{\sigma}{E} + \left(\frac{\sigma}{B}\right)^n + \alpha \, \Delta T = 0$$

In the elastic range $B = \infty$, and we have an expression for *thermal stress:*

$$\sigma_T = -E\alpha \, \Delta T \tag{1.26}$$

This conceptual model is somewhat unrealistic because it is not likely that complete constraint will be found in any structure. However, it gives a general idea of the magnitude of thermal stresses. The quantity $E\alpha$ is useful in comparing materials.

[*] Coefficients of expansion for several materials are given in Table A.1 of Appendix A.

1.13 Conceptual models and laws

Before undertaking the analysis of material behavior under multiaxial applied forces, we shall examine more closely the abstractions used in dealing with forces. The common representation of a force by vector, although extremely useful, is obviously not realistic; it implies that the force is applied over an area of zero. The corresponding stress would be infinite! By dividing force by area we achieve the more realistic abstraction of stress.

In many structural applications it is convenient to introduce an abstraction that is intermediate between force and stress. We imagine a force to be distributed over a line instead of a point. This situation is approached in transmitting forces by means of a membrane, or by the edge of a razor blade. Although no standard word has been adopted for the resulting abstraction we shall use the term *line force*,* designated by the symbol q. (The symbol N is usually used in advanced texts.)

Mathematically, *line force* is defined as

$$q = \lim_{\Delta s \to 0} \frac{\Delta P}{\Delta s}$$

which can be written

$$q = \frac{dP}{ds} \qquad (1.27)$$

(This equation was used in Sec. 1.11.)

Table 1.2 summarizes the three conceptual models that we shall use in subsequent chapters. Note particularly that the force vector obeys the laws of vector algebra, but that line force and stress do not. For example, the maximum stress under biaxial loading cannot be found by using the Pythagorean theorem. Mathematically, line force and stress are classified as *tensor* quantities. In the next chapter we shall learn how to handle these.

In all static (unaccelerated) situations the law of *equilibrium* must be satisfied, that is, in the absence of either translational or rotational acceleration the following equations represent a necessary condition

$$\Sigma \mathbf{P} = 0$$
$$\Sigma \mathbf{M} = 0 \qquad (1.28)$$

This law applies on all levels of abstraction. In some structural systems the internal forces can be found by using the equilibrium laws only. Such

---

* The term "stress resultant" is often used.

situations are classed as *statically determinate,* that is, the condition of equilibrium is a necessary and sufficient condition for analytical solution.

If the law of equilibrium represented by Eqs. (1.28) is not sufficient for analysis of internal forces, the situation is classified as *statically indeterminate.* It is then necessary to apply other laws or principles. One of these laws can be stated simply as a condition of *compatibility.* For example, in analyzing uniaxial behavior we implicitly assumed that no actual discontinuities were produced within the material by the action of the force. Another example is given in Prob. 1.11 where two concentric

TABLE 1.2

Conceptual models for force

	Force	Line force	Stress
Class →	vector	2-D tensor	3-D tensor
Applied over	point	line	area
Symbol	P	q	σ
Physical analogy	fiber	membrane	solid
Units (U. S. system)	lb	lb/in.	lb/in.^{2}

members are fastened together at their ends. "Compatible," in this case, means that there can be no change of length of one tube with respect to the other.

In statically indeterminate situations the mechanical behavior of the material will in general affect the internal force (or stress) distribution.

Note to Instructor: It is possible to begin the study of structural systems at this point (this subject is covered more fully in Chap. 15). The forces P_i in a statically determinate system of axially loaded members (truss) can be determined from the laws of statics. The axial deflection (δ_i) of each component can be calculated as shown in this chapter. The system (truss) deflection can be found from Eqs. (15.1) and (15.2), which require only elementary calculations.

If this subject is taken up at this point, Probs. 15.1 and 15.2, or similar problems, should be assigned.

PROBLEMS

(*Note:* See appendixes for material properties, section properties, etc.)

1.1. In Fig. P1.1, a curved structural member lying in the xy plane is loaded with two forces $\mathbf{F}_1$ and $\mathbf{F}_2$, which are transmitted to the wall. Find moments and force components in the xyz, $x'y'z'$, and $x''y''z''$ systems at

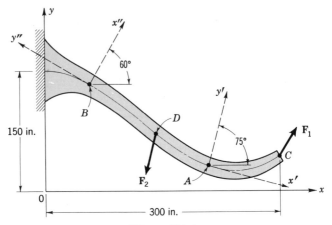

Figure P1.1

sections through points A and B, respectively. (z, z', and z'' axes are normal to the xy plane.) In the base xyz system (right-handed), the coordinates of points are $A = (210, 30)$ in., $B = (60, 130)$ in., $C = (300, 40)$ in., $D = (140, 75)$ in., and forces are $\mathbf{F}_1 = (300, 500, 0)$ lb and $\mathbf{F}_2 = (-400, -100, 100)$ lb.

1.2. A semicircular C clamp is tightened to exert a force of 400 lb on a block of wood, as shown in Fig. P1.2.

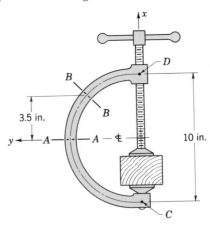

Figure P1.2

(*a*) Find moments and force components in directions parallel and perpendicular to "cuts" made at sections *AA* and *BB*. Cuts are made perpendicular to the center line of the member.

(*b*) Plot the variations of moment and force components along the center line of the member. Values may be calculated either by making additional "cuts" perpendicular to the center line at various points, or by formulating mathematical expressions for the desired quantities. Curves are to be drawn with respect to the developed length *s*, plotted horizontally between *C* and *D*.

1.3. A structural member is composed of two rigidly joined straight sections *AB* and *BC* and is loaded with a force **F** at *C*. The joint at *A* is rigidly attached to the base.

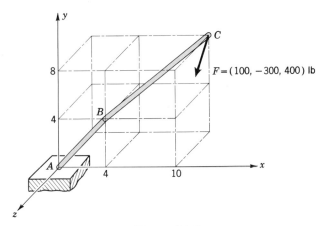

Figure P1.3

(*a*) Find the resultant moment and force at points *B* and *A*, respectively, in terms of an *x'*, *y'*, *z'* system in which the *x'* axis is in the direction of *AB*, the *z'* axis is parallel to the *z* axis, and the *y'* axis is normal to *x'* and *z'* axes. Coordinates of points are $A = (0,0,0)$ in., $B = (4,4,0)$ in., $C = (10,8,-4)$ in. (Answer to be in terms of components in primed system.)

(*b*) Find the axial force, transverse force, bending moment, and torsional moment at point *A*, for member *AB*.

(*c*) Repeat part *b* for member *BC* at point *C*. (Use *x''*, *y''*, *z''* system.)

1.4. A solid rod 100 ft long has a diameter of 0.25 in. It is suspended vertically from its upper end. A weight of 500 lb is attached at the lower end. Find the elastic deflection of the rod if it is made from (*a*) AISI 1025 steel and (*b*) 7075-T6 aluminum alloy. (Include the weight of the rod in calculations.)

1.5. A bar is suspended vertically from its upper end (lower end free). The cross-sectional dimensions vary linearly from zero at the lower end to some finite value at the upper end, i.e., the bar is conical, with a typical cross-sectional dimension b_0 at the upper end. Prove that the vertical deflection (elastic) at the lower end due to the weight of the bar is one-third that of a prismatic bar (no taper) of the same length and similar material.

1.6. *Variable cross section: elastic.* The solid member shown in Fig. P1.6 has a circular cross section, symmetrical about the center line. A compressive load P is applied along the centroidal axis. The profile is composed of two circular arcs. Find the maximum stress and the axial deflection over the entire length, assuming that stresses remain in the elastic

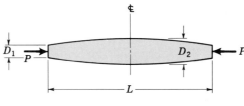

Figure P1.6

range. Calculate elastic energy in the member. Use assigned values from columns 1 to 3 of Table P1.6. (Omit buckling effects.) Plot a curve showing change of diameter as a function of length.

Suggestions: Alternative methods may be used, either singly or as a means of checking results. In the *semigraphical method*, divide the length into small increments and compute A and σ at each station. Divide σ by E

TABLE P1.6

Case	1	2	3	4	5	6
P, lb	30,000	20,000	6,000	60,000	25,000	30,000
D_1, in.	1.0	0.75	1.0	1.0	0.75	1.0
D_2, in.	2.0	2.0	2.0	2.0	2.0	2.0
L, in.	12	20	24	12	20	24
E, psi	10×10^6	30×10^6	2×10^6			
$\sigma - \epsilon$ diag.				A.1a	A.1d	A1.b
	For Prob. 1.6			For Prob. 1.9*		

* See Appendix A.

to obtain ϵ. (This operation can be placed last in elastic situations.) Plot ϵ (or σ) over the span and obtain the area under the curve (count squares or use planimeter or Simpson's rule). To save time, devise a tabular form for computations. In the *mathematical method*, write a function that closely describes the variation of D with x. (*Note:* In this problem $x = 0$ can be taken at the center line, because of symmetry.) For relatively "flat" circular arcs, a parabolic function gives a very close approximation. A sine function can also be used. The remaining calculations can then be accomplished by integration.

Note that since the relationship between ϵ and σ is linear at all stations, δ will remain proportional to P. Therefore, total elastic energy is easily determined from δ and P.

1.7. *Inelastic behavior.* Using the stress-strain diagram of Fig. A.1*a* (Appendix A):

(*a*) Find the total deflection of a 120 in. long bar with a uniform cross-sectional area of 0.50 in.^{2}, which is axially loaded up to a stress of 70,000 psi.

(*b*) Calculate the *elastic* energy stored in the bar (obtain E from diagram).

(*c*) Calculate *total* work done in elongating the bar (to $\sigma = 70,000$ psi).

(*d*) Calculate work converted into heat.

(*e*) Find the length of the bar after the load is removed.

1.8. (*a*) Given a bar of length 60 in., with uniform cross-sectional area of 0.6 in.^{2}, find the axial load required to increase the length of the bar by 0.30 in. Assume elastic behavior, with $E = 10 \times 10^6$ psi.

(*b*) Referring to the stress-strain diagram of Fig. 1.5, determine the axial load required to produce a *permanent* elongation of 0.5 in. in the above bar. What is the *total* elongation at this axial load?

1.9. *Variable cross section: inelastic.* Referring to Fig. P1.6 and using assigned values from columns 4 to 6 of Table P1.6,

(*a*) Find the total deflection of the member.

(*b*) Calculate the elastic energy stored in the member.

(*c*) Calculate total work done in deforming the bar.

(*d*) Calculate work converted into heat.

(*e*) Find length of member after load is removed.

1.10. (*a*) For each of the three bars shown in Fig. P1.10, apply an axial load P such that the maximum stress (P/A) is 35,000 psi. Assuming elastic behavior with $E = 29 \times 10^6$ psi, determine the *elastic* energy stored in each bar at this value of load.

(*b*) Construct an elastoplastic stress-strain diagram with $\sigma_y = 35,000$ psi, $E = 29 \times 10^6$ psi, and a maximum strain at failure of 0.10. Calculate the *total* energy absorbed by each bar at failure.

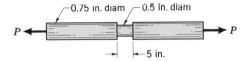

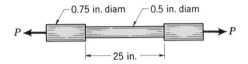

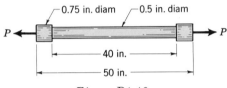

Figure P1.10

1.11. A circular tube of $1\frac{7}{8}$ in. outside diameter with 0.035 in. wall thickness is placed inside a 2.0 in. O.D. tube having a 0.049 in. wall thickness. The larger tube is made of aluminum alloy ($E = 10 \times 10^6$ psi) and the smaller tube is made of steel ($E = 29 \times 10^6$ psi). The length of both tubes is 40.00 in. In this configuration the tubes are loaded in compression by placing them between parallel flat surfaces of a testing machine. (Omit buckling considerations.)

(*a*) Assuming elastic behavior, determine the stress in each tube when the compressive load reaches 10,000 lb. (Omit buckling considerations.)

(*b*) Using the stress-strain curves of Figs. A.1*a* and A.1*d* (Appendix A) plot the composite load-deflection curve up to a point at which the stress in one of the tubes first reaches the ultimate value shown on its stress-strain diagram.

(*c*) Superimpose on the curve of part *b* the load-deflection curve obtained upon unloading the composite member.

1.12. Modify Prob. 1.11 so the steel tube has an original length of 39.96 in. while the other remains at 40.00 in. Parts *a*, *b*, and *c* are the same.

1.13. *Thermal stress.* A straight bar of length 100 in. and constant cross-sectional area of 0.75 in.² is "rigidly" attached at each end to a massive base, under zero stress, and at a temperature of 70°F. Calculate the stress caused by changing the bar temperature to 300°F. (Temperature of base unchanged.) Use each of the following materials: steel, aluminum, magnesium, titanium. Assume elastic action only. Values of E and α (coefficient of thermal expansion) are given in Table A.1.

1.14. A steel tube 8 ft long, with 2 in. outside diameter and 0.065 in. wall thickness (see Appendix B), encloses a solid round bar of titanium alloy of the same length, $\frac{1}{2}$ in. in diameter. The ends of the concentric members are rigidly attached to each other, but the composite member as a whole is free to expand or contract as the temperature changes. Assume elastic action only. Using properties from Appendix A, find the axial stresses and forces in the tubes when heated from 70°F (zero stress state) to 470°F. Also find the overall deflection of the composite member. (Omit consideration of buckling.)

Suggestion: Write the equation of equilibrium (one-dimensional). Write the equation for deflection of each member, assuming forces P_1 and P_2 to be both tensile and including thermal strains. Apply compatibility condition that $\delta_1 = \delta_2$ and solve for P_1, P_2, etc. (*Note:* This problem may be assigned for any combination of different materials for which E and α are given in Appendix A.)

1.15. Using the simplified stress-strain diagram of Fig. A.1a (Appendix A), plot the total stress-strain diagram for a rod which is stressed to 65 ksi at room temperature (70°F), then heated to 450°F (with stress remaining constant), then unloaded to zero stress (temperature at 450°F), and finally cooled back to 70°F. Calculate the energy per unit volume represented by the hysteresis loop (i.e., the enclosed area).

1.16. A single layer of fine steel wire is wrapped around a cylindrical ceramic bar so that adjacent strands touch each other. Bar diameter is 2 in. and wire diameter is 0.005 in. During wrapping, a constant tensile load of 10 lb is maintained in the wire. What radial pressure (psi) is thereby exerted on the ceramic? Assume that the ceramic bar does not change in diameter under this pressure. (After Chap. 4 is completed it will be possible to include the effects of bar contraction in such a situation.)

1.17. A steel ring has an initial mean radius of 10 in. and a cross-sectional area of 0.32 in.² Find the tension stress and increase in diameter when rotating at 1,800 rpm, assuming $E = 29 \times 10^6$ psi. (Repeat for other materials assigned from Appendix A.)

The radial acceleration is (from dynamics) $\alpha = \omega^2 R$, where ω = angular velocity (radians/sec) = $(2\pi \times 1,800)/60 = 60\pi$. The radial distributed force is the centrifugal force of an element of unit length:

$$q = m\alpha = \frac{W}{g}\alpha = \frac{Aw\alpha}{g} = \frac{Aw\omega^2 R}{g}$$

where m = mass density
W = weight per unit length
w = density (see Appendix A)

1.18. An object weighing 1,000 lb is to be suspended midway between two buildings, which are 50 ft apart. Two steel rods in the form of a flat V are to be used, with pin joint at center. The apex must lie 2.0 ft below a horizontal line joining the outer ends of the rods. Neglecting the weight of the rods, find the loads in the rods when in this position. Using an allowable stress of 30,000 psi, calculate the required cross-sectional area and the axial deflection in each rod ($E = 29 \times 10^6$ psi). Show by geometry (or by reference to Sec. 15.2) the approximate magnitude of the error involved in omitting the effect of the elastic deflections when dimensioning the rods on the production drawing (see Chap. 12 if necessary).

1.19. Derive the following approximate formula for the ratio of "true stress" to engineering stress in the elastic region. Note any assumptions made.

$$\frac{\sigma_{\text{true}}}{\sigma_{\text{eng}}} = \frac{1}{1 - 2\nu\sigma_{\text{eng}}/E}$$

Find the numerical value of this ratio for steel, aluminum, and magnesium, at $\sigma_{\text{eng}} = 100,00$ psi, with $\nu = \frac{1}{3}$.

Chapter 2

State of Stress

2.1 Stresses in uniaxial loading

In Chap. 1 we considered only the normal stress ($\sigma = P/A$) in a structural component or test specimen, where A represents the cross section that would be exposed by a "cut" normal to the line of force transmission. When the cut is made at some other angle, a different situation is observed. We shall analyze this situation, first for the case of uniaxial loading, after which biaxial and triaxial loading of an element will be investigated. The results will be useful in predicting the behavior of materials under any state of stress.

In Fig. 2.1 an imaginary cutting plane is passed through the z' axis at an angle θ with respect to the x axis. The coordinate system has been rotated through this angle and is denoted by x', y', z'. The "cut" area is A'.

A double subscript system is used here to identify forces and stresses. The first subscript identifies the stressed surface by stating the axis *normal* to it. The second subscript refers to the direction of the force or stress. Thus P_{xx} represents a force acting on a surface which is normal to the x axis. The second subscript tells us that this force acts in the x direction. The symbol P'_{xy} represents a force acting on a surface normal to the x' axis. (For printing convenience the prime is attached to P instead of to x and y.) This force acts in the y' direction, as shown in Fig. 2.1. Although the normal and shear forces (or stresses) are shown as if they act separately, it is important to remember that, in reality, they act simultaneously.

To obtain the stresses acting on the cut section, the first step is to resolve the force P_{xx} into components acting in the x' and y' directions. Since z' has the same direction as z,

$$P'_{xx} = P_{xx} \cos \theta \qquad (a)$$
$$P'_{xy} = -P_{xx} \sin \theta$$

The force P'_{xx} acts normal to the cross section, whereas P'_{xy} acts tangentially.

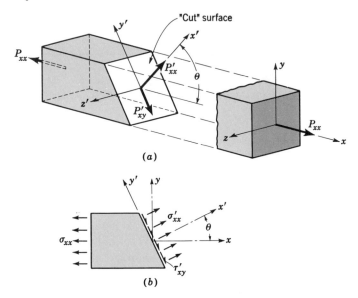

(a)

(b)

Figure 2.1. Stresses on a "cut" surface.

The cross-sectional area of the cut section is

$$A' = \frac{A}{\cos \theta} \qquad (b)$$

To find the stresses, divide the force components by A':

$$\sigma'_{xx} = \frac{P'_{xx}}{A'} = \frac{P_{xx} \cos \theta}{A/\cos \theta} = \sigma_{xx} \cos^2 \theta \qquad (2.1)$$

$$\tau'_{xy} = \frac{P'_{xy}}{A'} = -\frac{P_{xx} \sin \theta}{A/\cos \theta} = -\sigma_{xx} \sin \theta \cos \theta \qquad (2.2)$$

As previously noted, the symbol σ represents a *normal stress*; τ is used for a tangential or *shear stress*. A half arrowhead is used in Fig. 2.1*b*, to identify shear forces or stresses.

A clear understanding of the concept of shear stress is important. The word "shear" comes from the instrument used to cut wool, in which two blades *slip* over each other. The physical action associated with

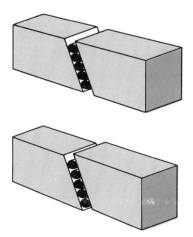

Figure 2.2. Model illustrating slip.

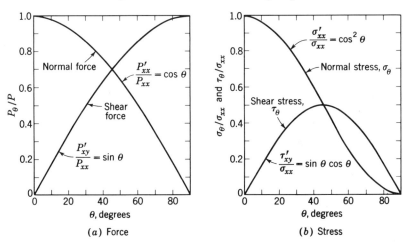

Figure 2.3. Variation of forces and stresses with angle (uniaxial loading).

shear stresses is one of slip. In the model shown in Fig. 2.2 the rollers are capable of transmitting compressive forces normal to the surface, but will move when a compressive force is applied at the ends.

Equations (2.1) and (2.2) may be normalized by dividing by σ_{xx}, giving

$$\frac{\sigma'_{xx}}{\sigma_{xx}} = \cos^2 \theta \qquad \frac{\tau'_{xy}}{\sigma_{xx}} = -\sin \theta \cos \theta$$

Figure 2.3a shows how the components of a force vector vary with rotation of axes. The force vector itself remains unchanged. Figure 2.3b shows the corresponding picture for stress.

2.2 State of stress at a point

A body transmitting forces can be "cut" along any section and the internal forces may be replaced by a resultant force vector, together

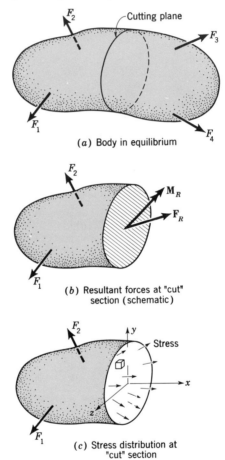

(a) Body in equilibrium

(b) Resultant forces at "cut" section (schematic)

(c) Stress distribution at "cut" section

Figure 2.4. Stresses on a "cut" section (general case).

with a resultant moment vector, as shown in Fig. 2.4. If the entire body is in static equilibrium, each cut portion will remain in equilibrium under the combined action of the external forces and the resultants of the stresses acting at the cut section, as shown in Fig. 2.4b.

To determine the *state of stress* at a point within a body that is transmitting forces, imagine that an infinitesimal* cubic element is isolated at the point in question, as indicated in Fig. 2.4c. An enlarged view of such an element is shown in Fig. 2.5. The state of stress is then described by stating the values of normal and shear stresses on three adjacent faces of the cube, relative to the coordinate system associated with the cube. (Only three faces need be examined, because the stresses on opposite faces must be equal and opposite. Infinitesimal changes between faces are omitted in establishing the state of stress.)

The normal stresses σ_{xx}, σ_{yy}, and σ_{zz} are shown as positive and represent tension. When acting in a negative sense, the normal stresses represent compression.

On each surface of the element, two components of shear stress are shown. There is no physical difference that distinguishes positive from negative shear stresses.

In applying the equations of equilibrium to the forces acting on the element of Fig. 2.5, it is found that the couple represented by the shear forces acting on two opposite faces of the cube must be balanced by another equal and opposite couple on the contiguous faces. The following important relationships are thereby revealed:

$$\begin{array}{|c|}
\hline
\tau_{xy} = \tau_{yx} \\
\tau_{yz} = \tau_{zy} \\
\tau_{zx} = \tau_{xz} \\
\hline
\end{array} \qquad (2.3)$$

To show that the above relationships are independent of the shape used for the element, the first equation will be derived for a rectangular parallelepiped, as shown in Fig. 2.6. The stresses are first converted to forces by multiplying by the magnitude of the surface area on which each stress acts.

Imagine that in drawing sketch b one draws first the force vector P_{xy}. To maintain $\Sigma P = 0$ in the y direction, it is necessary to apply a force $-P_{xy}$ on the opposite face. Now we have an unbalanced couple acting in a counterclockwise direction, having the value

$$M = P_{xy}a = abc\tau_{xy}$$

It is necessary to apply another couple to restore equilibrium, the value of which is

$$M = -P_{yx}c = -abc\tau_{yx}$$

For moment equilibrium,

$$abc\tau_{xy} - abc\tau_{yx} = 0$$

Therefore

$$\tau_{xy} = \tau_{yx}$$

* The concept of stress at a "point" is of course an abstraction and the use of an "infinitesimal" element of area is justified only when we intend to integrate over finite areas. When we are really interested in what happens on a minute scale, it is necessary to work with crystals, atoms, molecules, and so forth.

The nine stresses shown in Fig. 2.5 may be arranged in an orderly array (matrix) called the *stress tensor*, which represents the general state of stress at a point.

$$T_\sigma = \begin{bmatrix} \sigma_{xx} & \tau_{xy} & \tau_{xz} \\ \tau_{yx} & \sigma_{yy} & \tau_{yz} \\ \tau_{zx} & \tau_{zy} & \sigma_{zz} \end{bmatrix} \qquad (2.4)$$

The first horizontal row shows the stresses on the x face, the second row those on the y face, and so on.

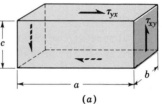

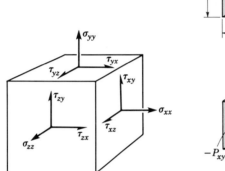

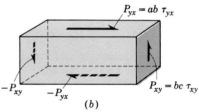

Figure 2.5. General state of stress at a point (stresses on opposite sides not shown—they are equal and opposite to those shown).

Figure 2.6. Equilibrium in pure (plane) shear.

In this tensor there are only six independent quantities, because of the relationships given by Eqs. (2.3). They are the *normal stresses* σ_{xx}, σ_{yy}, σ_{zz} and the *shear stresses* τ_{xy}, τ_{yz}, τ_{zx}. The tensor is symmetrical about the diagonal containing the normal stresses.

If the state of stress with reference to a set of orthogonal axes (x, y, z) is known, the same state of stress can be represented for a different set of axes (x', y', z'). Although the numbers appearing in the matrix will change as the reference axes are rotated, the *state* of stress remains invariant. The two matrices are said to be *similar*.

2.3 Principal directions and principal stresses

The general state of stress at a point, as depicted by Fig. 2.5, does not give a clear picture of the manner in which forces are transmitted by the element of material. The following theorems and definitions will clarify the situation.

1. In any state of stress at a point, an element can be oriented in such a way that the shear stresses become zero on all its surfaces. (Proved in next section for two-dimensional state.)

2. The three directions normal to the surfaces of the element so oriented are called the principal directions.

3. The three normal stresses (σ_1, σ_2, σ_3) *acting on such an element are called the principal stresses.*

Figure 2.7 shows graphically the nature of the transformation involved. It is clear that force transmission is accomplished along the principal axes, by the principal (normal) stresses.

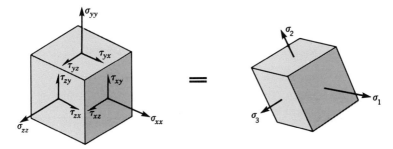

Figure 2.7. Transformation of axes to principal-axis system. (Balancing stresses on negative faces are not shown.)

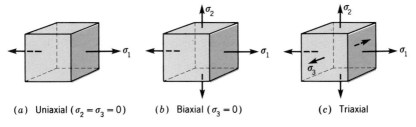

(*a*) Uniaxial ($\sigma_2 = \sigma_3 = 0$)　　(*b*) Biaxial ($\sigma_3 = 0$)　　　　(*c*) Triaxial

Figure 2.8. Types of force transmission (in terms of stress at a point).

Figure 2.8 shows three different types of force transmission, *uniaxial*, *biaxial*, and *triaxial*. The biaxial type is generally designated as a state of *plane stress*.

The basic stress tensor for the state of stress at a point can be written in terms of principal stresses, as follows:

$$T_{\sigma,\text{prin}} = \begin{bmatrix} \sigma_1 & 0 & 0 \\ 0 & \sigma_2 & 0 \\ 0 & 0 & \sigma_3 \end{bmatrix} \qquad (2.5)$$

Although Eq. (2.5) is not numerically equal to Eq. (2.4), it represents the same state of stress, referred to the principal directions.

2.4 Plane stress (biaxial loading)

Figure 2.9 shows an element in a state of plane stress (two opposite sides are free from stress). Such a state is frequently encountered in structures.

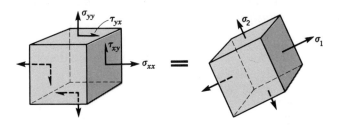

Figure 2.9. State of plane stress at a point.

As previously shown, this is equivalent to a *biaxial* state of stress. In tensor form the state is described as follows:

General:

$$T_\sigma = \begin{bmatrix} \sigma_{xx} & \tau_{xy} & 0 \\ \tau_{yx} & \sigma_{yy} & 0 \\ 0 & 0 & 0 \end{bmatrix} \tag{2.6a}$$

Referred to principal axes:

$$T_{\sigma,\text{prin}} = \begin{bmatrix} \sigma_1 & 0 & 0 \\ 0 & \sigma_2 & 0 \\ 0 & 0 & 0 \end{bmatrix} \tag{2.6b}$$

In Fig. 2.10a the square element is subjected to a state of plane stress, in which $\sigma_{zz} = 0$, $\tau_{yz} = 0$, $\tau_{zx} = 0$. Another element is "cut" in such a way that the x' and y' axes are rotated through an angle θ, about the z axis; that is, the z' axis is identical with the z axis. To find the stresses on the x' face of the rotated element a triangular portion is used, as indicated. Sketch b shows the stresses acting on this element, the sides* of which have the lengths dx, dy, and ds. Sketch c shows the forces.

The equations of equilibrium will be written with respect to the x' and y' axes. See Fig. 2.10c for forces.

---

* Note that dx does *not* represent the x face of the element, in this figure.

For the x' direction ($\Sigma P'_x = 0$),

$$\sigma'_{xx}t\,ds - \sigma_{xx}t\,dy\cos\theta - \sigma_{yy}t\,dx\sin\theta - \tau_{xy}t\,dy\sin\theta - \tau_{yx}t\,dx\cos\theta = 0$$

Dividing through by $t\,ds$ and noting that $dx/ds = \sin\theta$, $dy/ds = \cos\theta$, and $\tau_{yx} = \tau_{xy}$, we obtain

$$\sigma'_{xx} = \sigma_{xx}\cos^2\theta + \sigma_{yy}\sin^2\theta + 2\tau_{xy}\sin\theta\cos\theta \qquad (2.7)$$

For the y' direction ($\Sigma P'_y = 0$), a similar procedure gives

$$\tau'_{xy} = (-\sigma_{xx} + \sigma_{yy})\sin\theta\cos\theta + \tau_{xy}(\cos^2\theta - \sin^2\theta) \qquad (2.8)$$

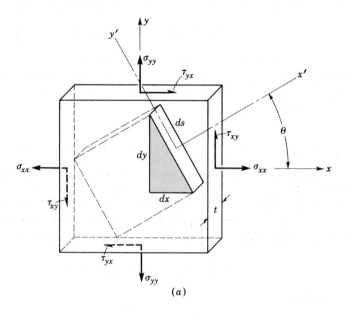

(a)

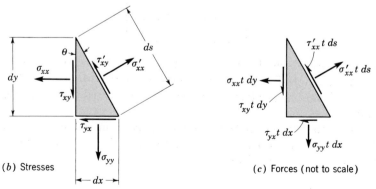

(b) Stresses

(c) Forces (not to scale)

Figure 2.10. Analysis of plane stress.

These equations can be simplified by using the following identities:

$$\cos^2 \theta = \frac{\cos 2\theta + 1}{2}$$

$$\sin^2 \theta = \frac{1 - \cos 2\theta}{2}$$

$$2 \sin \theta \cos \theta = \sin 2\theta$$

$$\cos^2 \theta - \sin^2 \theta = \cos 2\theta$$

The equations then become

$$\sigma'_{xx} = \frac{\sigma_{xx} + \sigma_{yy}}{2} + \frac{\sigma_{xx} - \sigma_{yy}}{2} \cos 2\theta + \tau_{xy} \sin 2\theta \qquad (2.9)$$

$$\tau'_{xy} = -\frac{\sigma_{xx} - \sigma_{yy}}{2} \sin 2\theta + \tau_{xy} \cos 2\theta \qquad (2.10)$$

To find the stresses on the y' face of the rotated element, a similar procedure can be used, but it is simpler to substitute $\theta + \pi/2$ for θ in the above equations.

2.5 Principal axes and principal stresses (plane stress)

By definition, all shear stresses on the surfaces of the element vanish when the element is oriented in the principal directions. In plane stress one of the principal axes is normal to the surface of zero stress (z axis in Fig. 2.10). The other two principal directions may be found by setting the shear stress of Eq. (2.10) equal to zero and solving for θ:

$$-\frac{\sigma_{xx} - \sigma_{yy}}{2} \sin 2\theta + \tau_{xy} \cos 2\theta = 0$$

From which

$$\tan 2\theta = \frac{2\tau_{xy}}{\sigma_{xx} - \sigma_{yy}} \qquad (2.11)$$

Two angles which differ by π radians have the same value of the tangent. Therefore Eq. (2.11) represents two angles, θ_1 and θ_2, which are 90° apart. These angles locate the two other principal axes, which are in the xy plane.

To prove that the normal stresses have maximum and minimum values with respect to the principal axes, differentiate Eq. (2.9) with respect to θ and set the result equal to zero:

$$\frac{d\sigma'_{xx}}{d\theta} = -2\left(\frac{\sigma_{xx} - \sigma_{yy}}{2}\right) \sin 2\theta + 2\tau_{xy} \cos 2\theta = 0$$

From which

$$\tan 2\theta = \frac{2\tau_{xy}}{\sigma_{xx} - \sigma_{yy}}$$

This is identical to Eq. (2.11), thereby proving that, in a state of plane stress, the maximum and minimum normal stresses occur on those surfaces normal to the principal axes.

The values of the principal stresses are found by substituting in Eq. (2.9) the values of 2θ corresponding to the directions of the principal

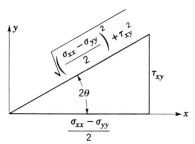

Figure 2.11. Geometric relationships.

axes, from Eq. (2.11). As shown in Fig. 2.11, the following relationships can be derived from Eq. (2.11):

$$\sin 2\theta = \pm \frac{\tau_{xy}}{\sqrt{\left(\frac{\sigma_{xx} - \sigma_{yy}}{2}\right)^2 + \tau_{xy}^2}}$$

$$\cos 2\theta = \pm \frac{\frac{1}{2}(\sigma_{xx} - \sigma_{yy})}{\sqrt{\left(\frac{\sigma_{xx} - \sigma_{yy}}{2}\right)^2 + \tau_{xy}^2}}$$

Substituting these identities in Eq. (2.9) gives the desired answer, as follows:

$$\sigma_{max,min} = \frac{\sigma_{xx} + \sigma_{yy}}{2} \pm \sqrt{\left(\frac{\sigma_{xx} - \sigma_{yy}}{2}\right)^2 + \tau_{xy}^2} \qquad (2.12)$$

When this equation is evaluated with positive and negative signs, respectively, we obtain the values of two of the principal stresses in a state of plane stress. The third value is zero.

The maximum shear stress on any plane cut parallel with the z axis (Fig. 2.10) is found by setting the derivative of Eq. (2.10) equal to zero. This gives the values of θ at which τ'_{xy} has extreme values, as follows:

$$\tan 2\theta_s = -\frac{\sigma_{xx} - \sigma_{yy}}{2\tau_{xy}} \qquad (a)$$

By a procedure similar to that used to derive Eq. (2.12) the values of $\tau_{max,min}$ are found to be

$$\tau_{max,min} = \pm \sqrt{\left(\frac{\sigma_{xx} - \sigma_{yy}}{2}\right)^2 + \tau_{xy}^2} \qquad (2.13)$$

Comparison of Eq. (*a*) with Eq. (2.11) shows that the values of 2θ for maximum normal and maximum shear stresses, respectively, differ by 90° (see Fig. 2.12 for this relationship). Consequently, *the planes of maximum shear stress are located at 45° from the principal planes; that is, a plane of maximum (or minimum) shear stress bisects the 90° angle between two principal planes.*

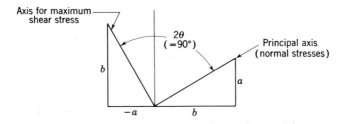

Figure 2.12. Relationship between principal axis and axis for maximum shear stress, in terms of 2θ.

In the foregoing analysis of *plane stress* the cutting plane is always parallel with the z axis (see Fig. 2.10). However, planes can be passed through the element at other angles. If the stresses σ_{xx} and σ_{yy} both have the same sign, Eq. (2.13) will *not* give the absolute maximum value of the shear stress, even though $\sigma_{zz} = 0$. The reason for this is explained later.

EXAMPLE 2.1.   A square plane element is stressed as shown in Fig. E2.1. The equations for plane stress apply. The location of the principal axes is given by

$$\tan 2\theta = -\frac{2 \times 1,000}{2,000 - 1,000} = -2$$
$$2\theta = -63.45°$$

Another value of 2θ is given by $2\theta = -63.45 + 180 = 116.55°$. The principal axes are therefore located at

$$\theta = -\frac{63.45}{2} = -31.72° \qquad \theta = +\frac{116.55}{2} = +58.28°$$

The location of these axes for this particular case is shown in Fig. E2.1. Sketch *a* shows the original element, which was cut with respect to the x and y axes. Sketch *b* shows an element cut with respect to the principal axes. It is important to realize that these two sketches represent the same loading condition; the only difference is in the orientation of the element.

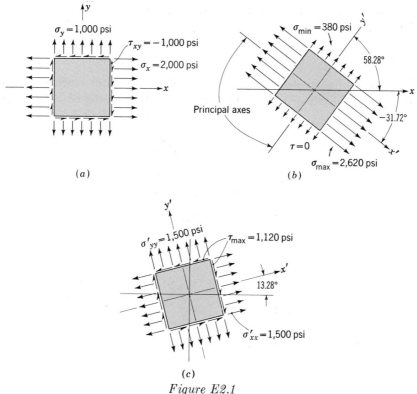

(a)

(b)

(c)

Figure E2.1

The maximum and minimum values of σ are found by substituting the given values of σ_{xx}, σ_{yy}, and τ_{xy} in Eq. (2.12), as follows:

$$\sigma_{\text{max,min}} = \frac{2,000 + 1,000}{2} \pm \sqrt{\left(\frac{2,000 - 1,000}{2}\right)^2 + (-1,000)^2}$$

from which

$$\sigma_{\text{max}} = 2620 \text{ psi} \qquad \sigma_{\text{min}} = 380 \text{ psi}$$

The direction of σ_{max} can be checked by using Eq. (2.9).

The location of the axes for maximum and minimum shear stresses is given by

$$\tan 2\theta = -\frac{2,000 - 1,000}{2 \times 2,000} = \frac{1}{2} \qquad 2\theta = 26.55°$$

Another value of 2θ is given by $2\theta = 26.55 + 180 = 206.55°$. The directions of the axes for maximum and minimum shear stresses are therefore

$$\theta = \frac{26.55}{2} = 13.28° \qquad \theta = \frac{206.55}{2} = 103.28°$$

Sketch *c* shows an element which has been cut at these angles. The maximum and minimum values of τ are found from Eq. (2.13), giving $\tau_{\max} = 1,120$ psi and $\tau_{\min} = -1,120$ psi. Note that the normal stresses on this element are not zero but are the *average* of the two normal stresses σ_{xx} and σ_{yy}. This can be proved to be true generally by using Eq. (2.9).

2.6 Mohr's circle

In 1866 Culmann discovered a graphical method that represented the foregoing analysis of plane stress. Mohr further developed the method

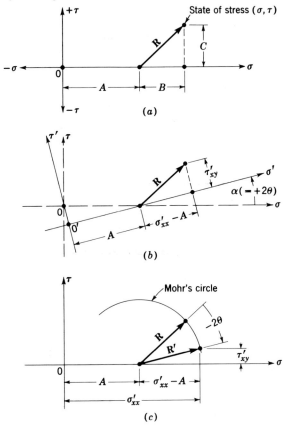

Figure 2.13. Rotation of coordinate system.

(Ref. 1, pp. 195 and 285). It consists of representing the complete state of plane stress by a circle plotted in the $\sigma\tau$ plane.

The state of plane stress at a point is represented by Eqs. (2.9) and (2.10). These can be simplified by making the following substitutions:

$$A = \frac{\sigma_{xx} + \sigma_{yy}}{2} \qquad B = \frac{\sigma_{xx} - \sigma_{yy}}{2}$$

$$C = \tau_{xy} \qquad \alpha = 2\theta$$

Equations (2.9) and (2.10) become

$$\sigma'_{xx} - A = B \cos \alpha + C \sin \alpha$$
$$\tau'_{xy} = -B \sin \alpha + C \cos \alpha$$

These equations represent the manner in which the components of a vector are transformed when the coordinate system is translated through a positive value A and rotated through the positive angle α, the vector remaining invariant. (See Example 1.3 for rotation matrix.) Figure 2.13a shows this diagrammatically. In sketch b the coordinate system has been

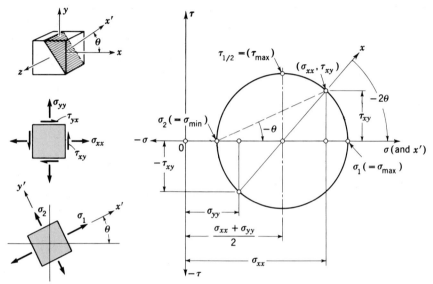

Figure 2.14. Mohr's circle for plane stress (for "cuts" parallel with z axis).

rotated through the positive angle α (= $+2\theta$). However, in constructing the diagram it is easier to retain the original coordinate axes and to rotate the vector **R** in a *negative* direction, as shown in sketch c. As the element angle θ is then varied through 180° the point representing the constant vector **R** will describe a circle. The coordinates of a point on the circle represent the normal and shear stresses on one surface of the element.

The magnitude of **R** is, from sketch a,

$$|\mathbf{R}| = \sqrt{B^2 + C^2} = \sqrt{\left(\frac{\sigma_{xx} - \sigma_{yy}}{2}\right)^2 + \tau_{xy}{}^2}$$

This equation shows that $|\mathbf{R}|$ has the value of the maximum shear stress.

Figure 2.14 shows Mohr's circle for a state of plane stress. To construct the figure, the two points representing the stresses acting on the x and y faces are plotted and connected by a straight line, which is the diameter of the circle. The shear stress on the y face is plotted negatively. The reason for this is that when the element is rotated through $\theta = +90°$ (counterclockwise) the direction of τ'_{xy} will be to the left, which is negative with respect to the shear stress that must actually be acting on that face (see sketch on Fig. 2.14). The stresses acting on the x' face of the element are found by moving around the circle in a negative (clockwise) direction through the angle 2θ.

On Mohr's circle the values of two of the principal stresses occur at the points where the circle intersects the σ axis. The maximum shear stress obviously corresponds to a point at the top of the circle.

Mohr's circle construction is of fundamental importance because it applies to all (two-dimensional) tensor quantities (for example, *line force, stress, strain, moment of inertia*). However, *a single Mohr's circle does not represent completely the state of stress at a point.* The state of stress is three-dimensional; therefore *three Mohr's circles are required,* as will be shown in the next section.

2.7 Mohr's circles for the general state of stress

In Sec. 2.3 and Fig. 2.7 it was shown that in any state of stress three principal directions exist and that the complete state of stress is given by the values of the principal stresses. The analytical determination of the principal stresses for the general case is seldom required in routine analysis. This is because in most situations one of the principal stresses is known, or is zero (as in plane stress). We can then find all three principal stresses by using the foregoing methods. (*Note:* A method for the general three-dimensional case is presented in Sec. 2.10.)

The *principal shear stresses* are defined as follows:

$$\tau_{1/2} = \frac{\sigma_1 - \sigma_2}{2}$$
$$\tau_{2/3} = \frac{\sigma_2 - \sigma_3}{2} \qquad (2.14)$$
$$\tau_{3/1} = \frac{\sigma_3 - \sigma_1}{2}$$

Note: The subscript 1/2 does not represent a fraction, but is used to indicate that the shear stress is on the plane which makes an angle of 45° with the σ_1 and σ_2 planes, as shown in Fig. 2.15.

The maximum shear stress in the element is the largest absolute value found from Eqs. (2.14). If the values of the principal stresses are arranged in such an order that $\sigma_1 > \sigma_2 > \sigma_3$, we have

$$|\tau_{max}| = \left|\frac{\sigma_1 - \sigma_3}{2}\right| \qquad (2.15)$$

Three Mohr's circles can be drawn if the values of σ_1, σ_2, and σ_3 are known, as shown in Fig. 2.16. It can be proved that the stress conditions on any plane cut through the element are all included in the shaded area between the largest circle and the other two, as shown in Fig. 2.16.

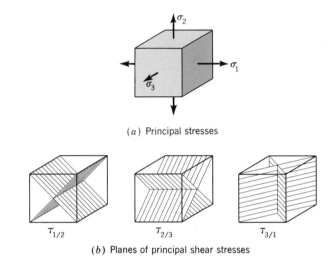

(*a*) Principal stresses

(*b*) Planes of principal shear stresses

Figure 2.15. Principal shear planes.

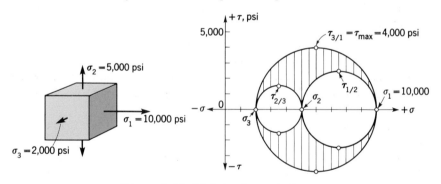

Figure 2.16. Mohr's stress circles.

EXAMPLE 2.2. Figure E2.2 shows the graphical solution for a state of stress in which one principal stress is known (i.e., one pair of opposite surfaces is free of shear stress). (A single subscript is used here for normal stresses, instead of the double symbol previously employed. This practice does not introduce any ambiguity and is frequently used.) Mohr's circle for the xy plane is found in the usual manner (by laying off σ_x, σ_y, and τ_{xy}). The intercepts of this circle on the σ axis give the principal stresses in the xy plane. Since σ_z is a principal stress (shear stress τ_{zy} and $\tau_{zx} = 0$), the location of σ_z gives the point through which the remaining two circles are drawn.

This operation can be carried out mathematically by combining Eqs. (2.12) and (2.14). In problems of this type, it is a good idea to draw Mohr's circles, at least roughly, before calculating the values from equations. The graphical picture

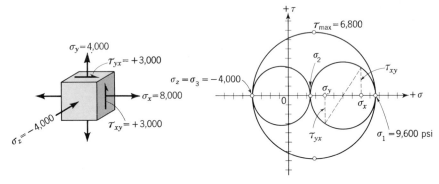

Figure E2.2

will immediately show whether the addition of the third stress (σ_z in this example) will increase the maximum shear stress.

2.8 Special states of stress

Figure 2.17 shows Mohr's circles for a number of important states of stress as follows (letters refer to the sketches):

(a) *Pure tension.* Two of the circles have degenerated to a point ($\sigma_y = \sigma_z = 0$). The maximum shear stress is one-half the tensile stress and occurs on the x/y and x/z planes (at 45°). Because of symmetry, this same value of the maximum shear stress will occur on any plane which makes an angle of 45° with the tension axis.

(b) *Pure compression.* This is identical to pure tension, except that the signs are reversed.

(c) *Equal biaxial tension.* The tensile stresses σ_x and σ_y are equal, and $\sigma_z = 0$. The x–y circle has degenerated to a point, showing that there is no shear stress on any plane parallel with the z axis. This also shows that the tensile stress in any direction in the xy plane (any value of θ) is the same. The circle which can be seen is actually two circles, the x–z circle and the y–z circle. Note that the maximum shear stress occurs on two systems of planes, $\tau_{x/z}$ and $\tau_{y/z}$.

(d) *Equal triaxial tension.* All three Mohr's circles have degenerated to points, which are superimposed. *No shear stress exists on any plane.* The tensile stress in any direction is the same. The same situation exists for *equal triaxial compression*, such as that found in a small element of a fluid under static pressure. Equal triaxial tension is sometimes called *hydrostatic* tension.

(e) *Equal tension and compression.* The applied stresses are shown in the xy plane ($\sigma_z = 0$). Mohr's circle for this plane is centered at the origin. The maximum

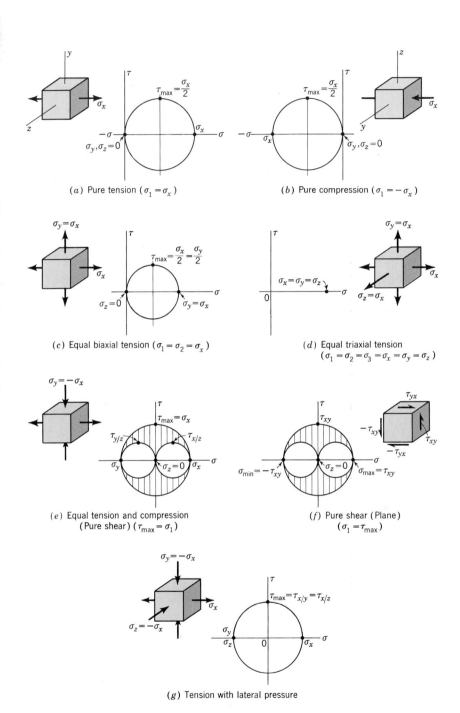

(a) Pure tension ($\sigma_1 = \sigma_x$)

(b) Pure compression ($\sigma_1 = -\sigma_x$)

(c) Equal biaxial tension ($\sigma_1 = \sigma_2 = \sigma_x$)

(d) Equal triaxial tension
($\sigma_1 = \sigma_2 = \sigma_3 = \sigma_x = \sigma_y = \sigma_z$)

(e) Equal tension and compression
(Pure shear) ($\tau_{max} = \sigma_1$)

(f) Pure shear (Plane)
($\sigma_1 = \tau_{max}$)

(g) Tension with lateral pressure

Figure 2.17. Mohr's circles for various states of stress.

shear stress equals the tensile stress. The maximum shear stress is twice as great as for pure tension.

(*f*) *Pure shear* (*plane*). The state of stress is identical to that of equal tension and compression. An element in the latter condition can be converted to a condition of pure shear by rotating it 45°.

(*g*) *Tension with lateral pressure*. This condition is produced by applying lateral (or radial) compressive stresses equal in magnitude to the tension stress. The y–z circle has degenerated to a point, leaving two circles (x–y, x–z) which coincide.

The various cases of combined stress described above furnish a basis for analyzing the behavior of material under different states of stress. The student should be able to reproduce all the figures shown in Fig. 2.17 by simple reasoning. In any discussion of the behavior of materials under certain stress conditions, Mohr's circles should be drawn. Failure to do this may result in overlooking one or more of the important stresses in the three-dimensional picture.

2.9 Membrane theory

For structures such as thin-walled shells or pressure vessels, it is convenient to express a state of plane stress in terms of *line force*, which was defined in Sec. 1.13 as

$$q = \frac{dP}{ds} \qquad (2.16)$$

where ds represents an indefinitely small length of a line over which the force is distributed. A line force can be thought of as a two-dimensional abstraction in which the force is distributed over a membrane of "zero" thickness.

For a plate of thickness t, under uniform stress, the relationship between line force and stress is

$$q = \sigma t \qquad (2.17)$$

In the derivation of Eqs. (2.9) and (2.10), the equations of equilibrium for an element were written in a form containing terms such as $\sigma_{xx} t \, dy \cos \theta$. From Eq. (2.17) it is evident that the quantity $\sigma_{xx} t$ represents the line force q_{xx}, when the element is reduced to a two-dimensional membrane. Therefore the equation of equilibrium for $\Sigma P'_x = 0$ can be written, for the membrane, as

$$q'_{zz} ds - q_{xx} \, dy \cos \theta - q_{yy} \, dx \sin \theta - q_{xy} \, dy \sin \theta - q_{yx} \, dx \cos \theta = 0$$

Dividing through by ds and making the substitutions $dx/ds = \sin \theta$,

$dy/ds = \cos\theta$, and $q_{yx} = q_{xy}$, we obtain

$$q'_{xx} = q_{xx}\cos^2\theta + q_{yy}\sin^2\theta + 2q_{xy}\sin\theta\cos\theta \qquad (2.18)$$

This equation is identical with Eq. (2.7) except that all stresses are replaced by the corresponding line forces. It can be similarly demonstrated that the correspondence carries through the entire analysis of plane stress, including Mohr's circle. We have, in fact, demonstrated that line force is a tensor quantity and that the state of line force at a point can be expressed by the tensors

General:

$$T_q = \begin{bmatrix} q_{xx} & q_{xy} \\ q_{yx} & q_{yy} \end{bmatrix} \qquad (2.19a)$$

Referred to principal axes:

$$T_{q,\text{prin}} = \begin{bmatrix} q_1 & 0 \\ 0 & q_2 \end{bmatrix} \qquad (2.19b)$$

where q_1 and q_2 are the principal line forces.

EXAMPLE 2.3. The cylindrical pressure vessel of Fig. E2.3 will be analyzed by using membrane theory. A conceptual model is developed by representing the walls of actual thickness t by a membrane of "zero" thickness. Since Eq. (2.17) is based on the assumption that the stress is uniformly distributed over the thickness the membrane must be located at midthickness; that is, the *average* value of the inside and outside diameters must be used for the conceptual model, as shown in Fig. E2.3b. The values of q_x and q_y are found as follows, for a net pressure p.

$[\Sigma P_x = 0]$ $\qquad\qquad pD_{av}\,dy - 2q_x\,dy = 0$

$$q_x = \frac{pD_{av}}{2} = pR_{av}$$

From Eq. (2.17) the circumferential (so-called "hoop tension") stress is (see sketch c)

$$\sigma_x = \frac{q_x}{t} = \frac{pR_{av}}{t} \qquad (a)$$

For a closed cylinder, the longitudinal stress is found by writing the equation of equilibrium for the "free body" shown in sketch d. The internal force in the y direction is not shown, but is equal to the net pressure times the projected area of the end closure.

$[\Sigma P_y = 0]$ $\qquad\qquad -q_y 2\pi R_{av} + p\pi R_{av}^2 = 0$

$$q_y = \tfrac{1}{2}pR_{av}$$

$$\sigma_y = \frac{q_y}{t} = \frac{1}{2}\frac{pR_{av}}{t} \qquad (2.20)$$

The state of stress for an element of the cylindrical shell is shown in sketch e.

The formula for σ_y also applies to a *spherical shell*, as can easily be proved by "cutting" such a shell in half and writing the equation of equilibrium as above.

The above formulas are widely used in engineering. They are approximate, as compared with the solution obtained from the theory of elasticity (Lamé's formulas). The error increases with increasing ratio of t/R_{av}.

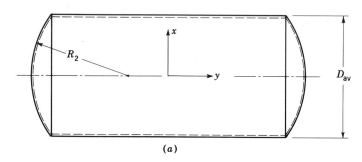

(a)

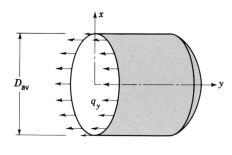

(b) Membrane

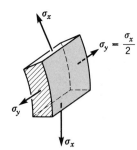

(c) Element (q_y not shown; pressure not shown)

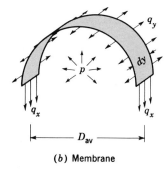

(d) Longitudinal forces (pressure not shown)

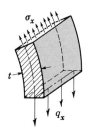

(e) State of stress (pressure not shown)

Figure E2.3

The hoop-tension formula, Eq. (a), is often erroneously derived by using the inside radius in writing the equation $\Sigma P_x = 0$. This is incorrect, because it involves a mixing of different levels of abstraction. One cannot assume that the stress is uniformly distributed over the thickness, giving a resultant at midthickness, and at the same time represent the shell by a membrane located at the inner radius. Such a conceptual model would create a moment at the cut section, which is inadmissible in membrane theory.

To show the practical effects of making such an error in the conceptual model three methods will be compared for a vessel having a value of $t/R_{\text{av}} = 0.2$, which would be classed as "thick-walled."

1. Membrane theory using R_{av}:

$$\sigma_x = p \frac{R_{\text{av}}}{0.2R_{\text{av}}} = 5.00p$$

2. Membrane theory using R_i (wrong):

$$R_i = R_{\text{av}} - \frac{t}{2} = R_{\text{av}} - \frac{0.2R_{\text{av}}}{2} = 0.9R_{\text{av}}$$

$$\sigma_x = \frac{pR_i}{0.2R_{\text{av}}} = p \frac{0.9R_{\text{av}}}{0.2R_{\text{av}}} = 4.50p$$

3. Lamé formula ("exact") (Ref. 2):

Let

$$k = \frac{R_{\text{outer}}}{R_{\text{inner}}} = \frac{1.1R_{\text{av}}}{0.9R_{\text{av}}} = 1.222$$

$$\sigma_{x,\text{max}} = p \frac{k^2 + 1}{k^2 - 1} = 5.06p$$

The correct membrane theory (with R_{av}) underestimates the maximum stress by about 1 percent for this cylinder. The use of the inside radius causes an underestimate of about 11 percent.

If the end closure of a cylindrical vessel is a segment of a thin-walled sphere, the average radius of the end closure can be used in the above Eq. (2.20). However, the situation at the juncture of the end closure and the cylindrical wall involves localized effects that cannot be computed by membrane theory.

2.10 Principal stresses in the general state of stress*

The type of analysis used in Sec. 2.4 can be extended to a three-dimensional state of stress, but the procedure is complicated. A simpler procedure is to *diagonalize* the stress tensor, following the rules developed in matrix algebra. (This procedure can of course be used also for the two-dimensional case.)

* This section should be omitted if students have not received training in elementary matrix algebra.

The state of stress is represented by the tensor of Eq. (2.4):

$$T_\sigma = \begin{bmatrix} \sigma_{xx} & \tau_{xy} & \tau_{xz} \\ \tau_{yx} & \sigma_{yy} & \tau_{yz} \\ \tau_{zx} & \tau_{zy} & \sigma_{zz} \end{bmatrix}$$

A diagonal matrix representing the same state of stress is found by rotating the axis system to a new orientation x', y', z' such that

$$T_{\sigma,\text{prin}} = \begin{bmatrix} \sigma_1 & 0 & 0 \\ 0 & \sigma_2 & 0 \\ 0 & 0 & \sigma_3 \end{bmatrix}$$

where σ_1, σ_2, and σ_3 are the principal stresses.

The procedure* is to set the following determinant equal to zero:

$$\begin{vmatrix} (\sigma_{xx} - \lambda) & \tau_{xy} & \tau_{xz} \\ \tau_{yx} & (\sigma_{yy} - \lambda) & \tau_{yz} \\ \tau_{zx} & \tau_{zy} & (\sigma_{zz} - \lambda) \end{vmatrix} = 0$$

Expansion of this determinant gives a cubic equation in λ, the roots of which are all real (this is true for all tensors). The three roots represent the principal stresses.

EXAMPLE 2.4. A particular stress tensor is represented by the following stresses in ksi:

$$T_\sigma = \begin{bmatrix} 3 & 1 & 2 \\ 1 & 2 & 2 \\ 2 & 2 & 1 \end{bmatrix}$$

Write the following equation:

$$\begin{vmatrix} (3 - \lambda) & 1 & 2 \\ 1 & (2 - \lambda) & 2 \\ 2 & 2 & (1 - \lambda) \end{vmatrix} = 0$$

After expanding the determinant we have the *characteristic equation*

$$\lambda^3 - 6\lambda^2 + 4\lambda + 7 = 0$$

The roots of this equation† give the principal stresses, as follows:

$$\sigma_1 = \lambda_1 = 4.89 \text{ ksi } (= 4{,}890 \text{ psi, tension})$$
$$\sigma_2 = \lambda_2 = -0.76 \text{ ksi } (= -760 \text{ psi, compression})$$
$$\sigma_3 = \lambda_3 = 1.875 \text{ ksi } (= 1{,}875 \text{ psi, tension})$$

---

* See any textbook that includes matrix algebra; for example, Ref. 12, p. 88.
† A convenient method of finding the roots can be found in Ref. 12.

The principal shear stresses are found from Eqs. (2.14):

$$\tau_{1/2} = \frac{4,890 - 1,875}{2} = 1,508 \text{ psi}$$

$$\tau_{2/3} = \frac{1,875 - (-760)}{2} = 1,318 \text{ psi}$$

$$\tau_{3/1} = \frac{-760 - 4,890}{2} = -2,825 \text{ psi}$$

from which, disregarding sign,

$$\tau_{max} = 2,825 \text{ psi}$$

The diagonalized stress tensor is

$$T_{\sigma, \text{prin}} = \begin{bmatrix} 4,890 & 0 & 0 \\ 0 & -760 & 0 \\ 0 & 0 & 1,875 \end{bmatrix}$$

The arbitrary convention that σ_1 and σ_3 represent respectively maximum and minimum principal stresses is obviously in conflict with the above result. If we use such a convention σ_3 would become -760 and σ_2 would be 1,875 psi.

As a check, note that the sum of the principal diagonal elements of a tensor (called the *trace*) is an invariant. For the original matrix, the trace is

$$3,000 + 2,000 + 1,000 = 6,000 \text{ psi}$$

For the diagonal matrix,

$$4,890 + 1,875 - 760 = 6,005 \text{ psi}$$

The directions of the principal stresses can be calculated by methods developed in matrix algebra. These calculations are omitted because there is seldom any need for this knowledge in predicting the behavior of structural components.

PROBLEMS

2.1. A bar of uniform rectangular cross section, 2 in. by 3 in., and 30 in. long, transmits a pure tension force of 30,000 lb in the x direction (see Fig. 2.1). Find the values of normal and shear stresses on three different cross sections which are "cut" at $\theta = 30°$, $45°$, and $60°$, respectively. (Work analytically and check answers by drawing Mohr's circle.)

2.2. Calculate the principal stresses and the maximum shear stress for an assigned set of values from the following table. Also draw Mohr's circles (3) to scale. (Note that all states represent plane stress.)

TABLE P2.2

	1	2	3	4	5	6	7
σ_{xx}, ksi	20	-8	9	-30	-6	13	-4
σ_{yy}, ksi	12	15	-7	-10	-18	7	0
τ_{xy}, ksi	6	7	12	5	20	-10	16

2.3. (*a*) A spherical pressure vessel has an average radius R and thickness t. It is subjected to an internal (gauge) pressure p at ground level. Using an assigned set of values from Table P2.3, calculate the maximum normal and shear stresses in the material. Also draw Mohr's stress circles and designate on them the stresses σ_1, σ_2, σ_3, and τ_{max}.

(*b*) What will the stresses be if this sphere is transported to outer space? (Neglect any effect of change in size of vessel and assume internal pressure unchanged.)

TABLE P2.3

	1	2	3	4	5	6
R, in.	100	80	50	25	10	10
t, in.	0.050	0.050	0.050	0.075	0.05	0.250
p, psi	10	50	100	500	1,000	5,000

2.4. Figure P2.4 shows a cylindrical pressure vessel with closed ends, subjected to a pressure difference p between inside and outside and an axial load P. For an assigned set of values from Table P2.4:

(*a*) Find the principal stresses for an element of the cylinder midway between the ends.

(*b*) Find the stresses for an element the orientation of which is defined by the angle θ shown in Fig. P2.4. (Omit possible effects of buckling under compressive loads.)

TABLE P2.4

	1	2	3	4	5	6
D_{av}, in.	12	12	12	120	120	120
t, in.	0.1	0.1	0.1	0.6	0.6	0.6
p, psi	500	500	$-500*$	100	50	50
P, kips	0	56.5	-100	$-3,400$	$-3,400$	3,400
θ	30°	30°	45°	45°	45°	60°

* External pressure.

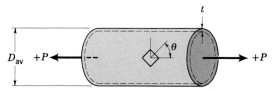

Figure P2.4

2.5. (*a*) In the design of a certain cylindrical pressure vessel a maximum (limit) pressure differential (p_1) is specified. The design criteria also require a *factor of safety* of 2.0 against yielding. Assume that yielding will occur when the maximum shear stress in the material reaches a certain value τ_1. Derive a design formula by which the required ratio R/t for the cylinder can be determined as a function of p_1 and τ_1.

(*b*) Repeat for a spherical vessel.

[*Notes:* (1) Omit consideration of joints; (2) multiply p_1 by factor of safety; (3) R is mean radius.]

2.6. A tank is constructed by wrapping a 12 in. wide plate into a spiral to form a cylinder. (Edges of plate are welded together.) The mean diameter of the cylinder is 24 in. Find the *line forces q* normal and tangential to the joint, for a pressure differential of 200 psi. Check by Mohr's circle.

2.7. In a certain structure it is known that a flat plate $\frac{1}{8}$ in. thick is subjected to the line forces $q_{xx} = 1,000$ lb/in., $q_{yy} = 700$ lb/in., $q_{xy} = 500$ lb/in. Find principal line forces q_1 and q_2. Also find the principal stresses and maximum shear stress in material. (Check stresses by Mohr's circles.)

2.8. Determine the principal normal and shear stresses by diagonalization, for the following stress tensors. All values are in ksi.

$$\begin{bmatrix} 8 & 3 & 0 \\ 3 & 4 & 0 \\ 0 & 0 & -4 \end{bmatrix} \qquad \begin{bmatrix} 18.75 & -6.5 & 0 \\ -6.5 & 26.25 & 0 \\ 0 & 0 & 0 \end{bmatrix}$$
$$(a) \qquad\qquad\qquad\qquad (b)$$

$$\begin{bmatrix} -35.83 & -5.83 & 0 \\ -5.83 & -35.83 & 0 \\ 0 & 0 & 0 \end{bmatrix}$$
$$(c)$$

[*Note:* Compare (*a*) with Example 2.2.]

2.9. In the analysis of the behavior of single crystals it is necessary to be able to find the "resolved" shear stress on a plane the normal to which makes an angle of θ with the axis along which a pure tensile stress σ is applied. The "resolved" shear stress is a measurement of the tendency to slip *in a certain direction* on the θ plane. Let this direction be described by the angle β, as shown in Fig. P2.9. Prove that the resolved shear stress is given by

$$\tau_r = \sigma \cos \theta \cos \beta$$

where $\sigma = P/A$.

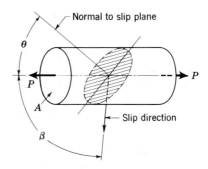

Figure P2.9

2.10. *Optional.* The stress tensor obeys a transformation law which may be expressed in matrix algebra as

$$T' = RTR^*$$

where T = original tensor in xyz system
T' = transformed tensor in $x'y'z'$ system
R = rotation matrix (see Example 1.3)
R^* = transpose of R (change rows of R to columns)
Derive Eqs. (2.9) and (2.10) by this method.

Chapter 3

State of Strain

3.1 Normal strain

In Chap. 1 strain was defined as *change of length per unit length,* or *rate of axial deformation.* In that chapter only the uniaxial state of loading was considered. In general, one can imagine any two points located in the interior of a body on the "cut" surface, before and after deformation, as indicated by A and B of Fig. 3.1a. Let L_0 represent the original length of a straight line between these two points. After the body has been deformed, the points have moved relative to each other, to positions A' and B'. The change in L_0 is the *normal deformation* and is designated by δ, as before.

The word "normal" is used to distinguish this type of deformation from "shear" deformation and to agree with the definition of normal stress. So far as two *points* are concerned there can be only one kind of deformation, a change of length of the line joining the two points. The definitions of strain given by Eqs. (1.5) and (1.6) are applicable. Equation (1.6) is rewritten below, for average "engineering" normal strain:

$$\epsilon = \frac{\delta}{L_0} \tag{3.1}$$

where δ is the change in length, and L_0 is the distance between points, measured *before* deformation. When the intensity of strain varies from point to point, the original length L_0 is imagined to become indefinitely small, leading to the general definition of normal strain:

$$\boxed{\epsilon = \frac{d\delta}{dx}} \tag{3.2}$$

69

It can be shown that the concept of normal strain is sufficient to describe the state of strain at any point in a deformed body. It is necessary only to determine the three *principal strains* (ϵ_1, ϵ_2, ϵ_3) and the directions of the principal axes for strain. However, it is useful to describe the state of strain in a more general manner, as has already been done for stress.

Imagine a cube of initial dimensions L_0 on each edge. The cube is increased in size by changes δ in these lengths along the three axes. If

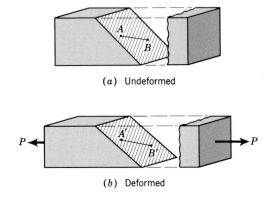

(a) Undeformed

(b) Deformed

Figure 3.1. Interior deformation (schematic).

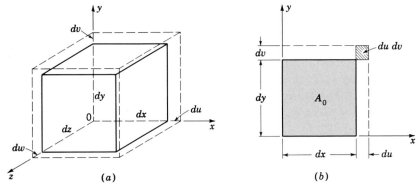

(a)   (b)

Figure 3.2. Strains at a point.

δ_x, δ_y, and δ_z are different in magnitude (or sign or both), the cube becomes a rectangular parallelepiped. (Note that the double subscript is not necessary for normal strains and will be dropped in accordance with American practice.)

To agree with standard conventions and to eliminate subscripts, the axial deformations δ_x, δ_y, δ_z will be designated respectively by u, v, w. (In general these symbols refer to displacements and include rigid body translations, but in the following they are treated as normal deformations.)

Figure 3.2 shows an "infinitesimal" element, for which the original length L_0 has been imagined to become indefinitely small. Figure 3.2b shows a two-dimensional view of the surface normal to the z axis. Normal strains at a point are then defined as

$$
\boxed{
\begin{aligned}
\epsilon_x &= \frac{\partial u}{\partial x} \\[2mm]
\epsilon_y &= \frac{\partial v}{\partial y} \\[2mm]
\epsilon_z &= \frac{\partial w}{\partial z}
\end{aligned}
}
\tag{3.3}
$$

The partial derivative $\partial u/\partial x$ refers *only* to the change of u with respect to x, even though u may also change with respect to the other directions. These strains are sometimes called *extensional*, or *axial*.

EXAMPLE 3.1. Consider a cubic element having dimensions L_0 on each edge. The increase in length is given by ϵL. The deformed area of the surface normal to the z axis is

$$ A = L_x L_y = L_0(1 + \epsilon_x)L_0(1 + \epsilon_y) $$

The *area strain* (not a common term) is given by

$$ \frac{\Delta A}{A_0} = \frac{A}{A_0} - 1 = \frac{L_0^2(1 + \epsilon_x)(1 + \epsilon_y)}{L_0^2} - 1 $$
$$ = \epsilon_x + \epsilon_y + \epsilon_x \epsilon_y $$

For most structural materials, the maximum strain developed will be in the range of 0.001 to 0.005, and the product $\epsilon_x \epsilon_y$ will be negligible. The "area strain" (normal to z axis) is then given approximately by

$$ \frac{\Delta A}{A_0} = \epsilon_x + \epsilon_y \tag{a} $$

(In Fig. 3.2b the neglected area is designated as $du\,dv$.)

Similarly, the *volumetric strain* can be shown to be approximately

$$ \frac{\Delta V}{V_0} = \epsilon_x + \epsilon_y + \epsilon_z \tag{b} $$

3.2 General state of strain

Figure 3.3 shows an element of surface as deformed in three different ways. The first two sketches represent pure normal strains in the x and y directions, respectively. Note that there are *no changes in angles;* that is, right angles remain right angles. In sketch c the geometric *shape* of the element is distorted; there is angular change but no change in the length of any lines originally parallel with either L_x or L_y. This type of deformation is called *shear*.* The *shear strain* γ is, for the case shown, defined by

$$\gamma_{xy} = \frac{\delta_y}{L_x} \tag{a}$$

Note that *the subscripts for δ_y and L_x are not the same.*

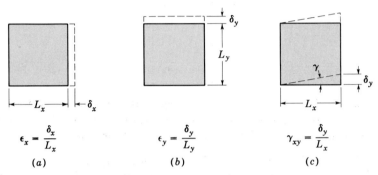

$$\epsilon_x = \frac{\delta_x}{L_x} \qquad\qquad \epsilon_y = \frac{\delta_y}{L_y} \qquad\qquad \gamma_{xy} = \frac{\delta_y}{L_x}$$

(a)   (b)   (c)

Figure 3.3. Types of surface strain.

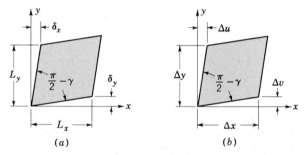

(a)   (b)

Figure 3.4. Definition of shear strain.

In defining shear deformation, we must exclude rigid body rotations (just as we excluded translations in defining normal deformation). Figure 3.4 shows a more general case in which the element of Fig. 3.3c has been rotated with respect to the reference axes. The shear strain is now given by

$$\gamma_{xy} = \frac{\delta_y}{L_x} + \frac{\delta_x}{L_y} \tag{3.4}$$

To provide for situations in which the shear strain varies from point to point, we allow L_x and L_y to become indefinitely small (Δx approaches zero, in Fig. 3.4), giving the standard definition of shear strain

$$\gamma_{xy} = \frac{\partial v}{\partial x} + \frac{\partial u}{\partial y} \tag{3.5}$$

* Sometimes called *simple shear*.

Figure 3.4 represents the distortion caused by a state of positive shear strain. (The original right angle becomes smaller.)

The above definition of shear strain applies to a single surface, or plane. To describe completely the *state of shear strain at a point*, we look at all three surfaces of the cubic element, applying the above definition to each. This gives three values of shear strain, as follows:

$$\gamma_{xy} = \frac{\partial v}{\partial x} + \frac{\partial u}{\partial y}$$

$$\gamma_{yz} = \frac{\partial w}{\partial y} + \frac{\partial v}{\partial z} \qquad (3.6)$$

$$\gamma_{zx} = \frac{\partial u}{\partial z} + \frac{\partial w}{\partial x}$$

If the values of normal strain (ϵ_x, ϵ_y, ϵ_z) and shear strain (γ_{xy}, γ_{yz}, γ_{zx}) are known at a point, the increase in size and the change of shape of an element at that point are completely determined.

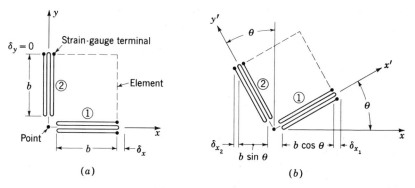

Figure 3.5. Measurement of surface strains.

We now confine our attention to *surface strains;* that is, we consider only the two-dimensional aspect of strains. The object is to develop a method by which the three strains ϵ_x, ϵ_y, and γ_{xy} can be determined for any orientation of the element, given the values for a particular orientation.

It can be proved that *strain is a tensor quantity;* therefore the formulas already developed for stress can be used directly. A general proof will not be given (this is done in more advanced treatments of the theory of deformable solids). We shall, however, analyze the case of uniaxial normal strain and show that the equations obtained are identical in form to those obtained for uniaxial stress in Chap. 2.

To make the situation realistic, consider a plane surface such as shown in Fig. 3.5. The conceptual model corresponds to a plate or membrane of zero thickness. (The page of the book can be thought of as the membrane.)

Imagine that this membrane is caused to increase in length in the x direction *only* (the y dimension is held constant). There are no angular changes. This represents a state of *uniaxial normal strain* in which

$$\epsilon_x = \frac{\Delta L}{L_0} \qquad \epsilon_y = 0$$

In Fig. 3.5a two electric-resistance gauges* are cemented to the membrane, along the x and y axes. If the gauge length is b, the deflection of gauge 1 will be

$$\delta_x = \epsilon_x b$$

Gauge 2 will have no deflection, since $\delta_y = 0$. (*Note:* the deformed shape of the element is not shown in Fig. 3.5; it must be imagined.)

In Fig. 3.5b two gauges have been placed at angles θ with respect to the reference axes of sketch a. When the membrane is elongated, gauge 1 will be subjected to a relative lateral displacement of

$$\delta_x = \epsilon_x b_x = \epsilon_x b \cos \theta \tag{a}$$

This distance is now resolved into components relative to the x' and y' axes. Using primes for quantities referred to the x' and y' axes,

$$\delta'_x = \delta_x \cos \theta = \epsilon_x b \cos^2 \theta \tag{b}$$

Since the initial length of the gauge is b,

$$\epsilon'_x = \frac{\delta'_x}{b} = \epsilon_x \cos^2 \theta \tag{c}$$

Compare this with Eq. (2.1) for stress. The value of ϵ'_y can be found by the same method, but we are not interested in it for the moment.

Equation (3.4) may be used to find the shear strain in the rotated element. For the case in question,

$$\gamma'_{xy} = \frac{\delta'_y}{b} + \frac{\delta'_x}{b} \tag{d}$$

For gauge 1,
$$\delta'_y = - \delta_x \sin \theta = - \epsilon_x b \sin \theta \cos \theta \tag{e}$$

For gauge 2,
$$\delta'_x = - \delta_x \cos \theta = - \epsilon_x b \sin \theta \cos \theta \tag{f}$$

Substituting these values in (d),

$$\gamma'_{xy} = - \frac{\epsilon_x b \sin \theta \cos \theta}{b} - \frac{\epsilon_x b \sin \theta \cos \theta}{b}$$

which gives

$$\gamma'_{xy} = - 2\epsilon_x \sin \theta \cos \theta \tag{g}$$

---

* This type of gauge consists of a length of fine wire or strip of foil which changes its resistance in proportion to change of length.

This derivation shows that the total shear strain is composed of two *equal* parts, one from the rotation of the x' edge of the element, the other from the rotation of the y' edge. These partial shear strains are designated as γ'_{xy} and γ'_{yx}, respectively. To make Eq. (*g*) correspond with Eq. (2.2) for shear stress, we therefore divide by two, giving

$$\frac{\gamma'_{xy}}{2} = -\epsilon_x \sin \theta \cos \theta \qquad (h)$$

This reveals an important rule:

The shear strain (change of angle) at the corner of an element must be distributed equally between adjacent sides of the element, in treating shear strain as a tensor quantity.

Figure 3.6 shows how shear stresses and shear strains compare. The state of strain shown on the right in Fig. 3.6 is called *pure shear* strain.

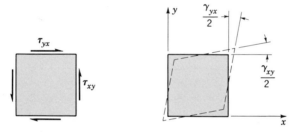

Figure 3.6. Comparison of pure shear stress and pure shear strain.

It can be proved that all equations and graphical constructions previously developed for a state of stress are identical with those for a state of strain. It is only necessary to make the following changes in symbols:

$$\sigma \rightarrow \epsilon \qquad \text{and} \qquad \tau \rightarrow \frac{\gamma}{2}$$

Certain statements applicable to the general state of stress can also be extended to three-dimensional strain as follows:

The principal directions for strain are defined as those directions for which all shear strains vanish.

Axial strains will be maximum and minimum with respect to two of the principal axes. (For two-dimensional strain the principal strains represent the extreme values.)

The maximum shear strain (distortion) is given by the maximum difference between principal normal strains.

For example, in three dimensions,

$$\gamma_{max} = \epsilon_1 - \epsilon_3$$

The equations for principal normal strains and maximum shear strains are obtained directly by transforming Eqs. (2.11), (2.12), and (2.13):

$$\tan 2\theta_{\text{prin}} = \frac{\gamma_{xy}}{\epsilon_x - \epsilon_y} \tag{3.7}$$

$$\epsilon_{\text{max,min}} = \frac{\epsilon_x + \epsilon_y}{2} \pm \sqrt{\left(\frac{\epsilon_x - \epsilon_y}{2}\right)^2 + \left(\frac{\gamma_{xy}}{2}\right)^2} \tag{3.8}$$

$$\left(\frac{\gamma}{2}\right)_{\text{max,min}} = \pm \sqrt{\left(\frac{\epsilon_x - \epsilon_y}{2}\right)^2 + \left(\frac{\gamma_{xy}}{2}\right)^2} \tag{3.9}$$

Similarly, Mohr's circle can be employed, as shown in Fig. 3.7.

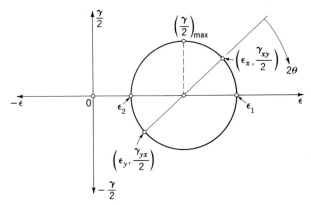

Figure 3.7. Mohr's circle for two-dimensional state of strain.

For the *three-dimensional* element the state of strain is represented by the symmetric strain tensor (double subscripts used)

$$T_\epsilon = \begin{bmatrix} \epsilon_{xx} & \left(\dfrac{\gamma}{2}\right)_{xy} & \left(\dfrac{\gamma}{2}\right)_{xz} \\ \left(\dfrac{\gamma}{2}\right)_{yx} & \epsilon_{yy} & \left(\dfrac{\gamma}{2}\right)_{yz} \\ \left(\dfrac{\gamma}{2}\right)_{zx} & \left(\dfrac{\gamma}{2}\right)_{zy} & \epsilon_{zz} \end{bmatrix} \tag{3.10}$$

EXAMPLE 3.2. Find the principal (normal) strains in pure plane shear, given the shear strain γ. From Eq. (3.8),

$$\epsilon_{max,min} = \frac{0+0}{2} \pm \sqrt{\left(\frac{0-0}{2}\right)^2 + \left(\frac{\gamma}{2}\right)^2}$$

$$\epsilon_1 = +\frac{\gamma}{2}$$

$$\epsilon_2 = -\frac{\gamma}{2}$$

Mohr's circle confirms these results, as shown in Fig. E3.2.

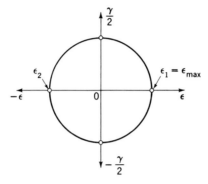

Figure E3.2

3.3 Conversion of strain-gauge readings

If the directions of the principal strains are known at a point, the state of two-dimensional strain can be determined experimentally by applying two strain gauges, one along each of the principal directions. (The gauges actually give the average deformation over the gauge length.) For example, in pure tension one gauge is placed along the direction of tensile

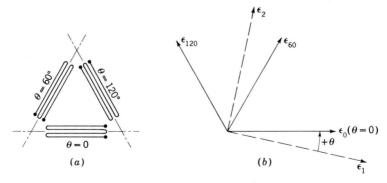

Figure 3.8. Rosette strain gauge (60° type).

loading, the other normal to it. In pure shear the gauges would be placed along lines 45 degrees from the axis of maximum shear strain.

When the principal directions are not known, the usual procedure is to employ three strain gauges, each in a different direction. A typical arrangement, called a 60° *strain rosette*, is shown in Fig. 3.8.

One of the gauges is selected to serve as a base for angular measurement. In sketch *b* the principal strain axes are drawn arbitrarily, at an unknown angle θ with respect to one of the gauges. We now write the equations for the three strains in terms of the unknown principal strains ϵ_1 and ϵ_2 and the unknown angle θ. The equation to be used is that for normal stresses, Eq. (2.12), with the substitutions noted in Sec. 3.2. (Single subscripts will be used for normal strains.) Thus we have

$$\epsilon'_x = \frac{\epsilon_x + \epsilon_y}{2} + \frac{\epsilon_x - \epsilon_y}{2} \cos 2\theta + \frac{\gamma_{xy}}{2} \sin 2\theta \qquad (3.11)$$

By definition, when ϵ_x and ϵ_y are principal strains, $\gamma_{xy} = 0$, and the above equation becomes

$$\epsilon'_x = \frac{\epsilon_1 + \epsilon_2}{2} + \frac{\epsilon_1 - \epsilon_2}{2} \cos 2\theta \qquad (a)$$

For convenience let

$$m = \frac{\epsilon_1 + \epsilon_2}{2} \qquad (b)$$

$$n = \frac{\epsilon_1 - \epsilon_2}{2} \qquad (c)$$

Now write equations for the strains in the gauges as follows:

$$\epsilon_0 = m + n \cos 2\theta \qquad (d)$$
$$\epsilon_{60} = m + n \cos 2(\theta + 60°) \qquad (e)$$
$$\epsilon_{120} = m + n \cos 2(\theta + 120°) \qquad (f)$$

To reduce terms to 2θ we use the relationship

$$\cos (\alpha + \beta) = \cos \alpha \cos \beta - \sin \alpha \sin \beta$$

together with the values for $\cos 60°$, $\sin 60°$, and so forth. Making these substitutions and solving Eqs. (*d*), (*e*), and (*f*) simultaneously give

$$m = \frac{\epsilon_0 + \epsilon_{60} + \epsilon_{120}}{3} \qquad (3.12)$$

$$n = + \sqrt{(\epsilon_0 - m)^2 + \frac{(\epsilon_{120} - \epsilon_{60})^2}{3}} \qquad (3.13)$$

(The negative root is extraneous.)

The principal strains and directions are given by

$$\epsilon_1 = m + n \qquad \gamma_{max} = 2n$$
$$\epsilon_2 = m - n \qquad \cos 2\theta = \frac{\epsilon_0 - m}{n} \qquad (3.14)$$

It can also be shown that when the gauges are placed at 45° the following equations apply:

$$m = \frac{\epsilon_0 + \epsilon_{90}}{2} \qquad (3.15)$$

$$n = + \sqrt{(\epsilon_0 - m)^2 + (m - \epsilon_{45})^2} \qquad (3.16)$$

These values are substituted in Eqs. (3.14) to find the principal strains.

PROBLEMS

3.1. From tests in pure tension the lateral strain ϵ_y (contraction) is usually found to be about one-third of the longitudinal strain ϵ_x in the elastic range. Draw Mohr's strain circle for this state, assuming $\epsilon_x = 0.001$ and $\epsilon_y = -0.00033$. Using the circle as a basis, derive an expression for the maximum shear strain (γ_{max}) in terms of ϵ_x and ϵ_y and evaluate it. Repeat for the case of "ideal plasticity" in which $\epsilon_y = -0.5\epsilon_x$ (see Chap. 5).

3.2. Table P3.2 lists several states of strain at a point on the surface of a body. For an assigned column:

(a) Find the principal strains and directions of the principal axes (in degrees, measured from x axis).

(b) Find the axial and shear strains on an element whose orientation is such that the x' axis is at an angle of θ with respect to the x axis.

TABLE P3.2

	1	2	3	4	5	6	7
ϵ_x, μ	120	210	−420	−360	310	−150	−100
ϵ_y, μ	85	−400	100	−100	120	210	−80
γ_{xy}, μ	180	80	−200	120	−80	100	80
θ, deg	30	10	−40	−30	15	10	20

Note: $\mu = 10^{-6}$. *Example:* $120\mu = 0.000120$

3.3. Strain readings from a 60° rosette gauge are listed in Table P3.3. Find magnitudes and directions of principal strains. Sketch Mohr's circle, showing locations of rosette readings on the circle. (*Note:* In addition to the analytical solution presented in Sec. 3.3, various graphical solutions based on Mohr's circle are available. For example, see Ref. 19, page 109, Ref. 6, page 158, or any book on experimental stress analysis.)

TABLE P3.3

	1	2	3	4	5	6	7
ϵ_0	+0.001	+0.004	+0.006	+0.008	−0.002	+0.003	−0.007
ϵ_{60}	−0.003	−0.005	−0.007	−0.009	+0.005	−0.006	−0.004
ϵ_{120}	+0.007	−0.009	−0.006	−0.004	+0.003	−0.001	−0.002

3.4. The normal strains in an object subjected to extremely high pressures (as in the atomic bomb or in the manufacture of synthetic diamonds) may reach large values. Equation (*b*) of Example 3.1 then becomes too inaccurate. For "hydrostatic" pressure let $\epsilon_1 = \epsilon_2 = \epsilon_3 = \epsilon$. Prove that the relative error in calculating volume is closely approximated by the value of ϵ itself, if ϵ^3 is neglected.

3.5. In a tension test of a flat-plate coupon, it is desired to place an electrical strain gauge at such an angle that *zero* strain will be recorded under load. If the action is purely elastic, with $v = \frac{1}{3}$, find the angle at which the gauge should be placed with respect to the longitudinal axis. Repeat the calculation assuming that $v = 0.50$ (approximately correct for large plastic strains; see Chap. 5).

3.6. Derive Eqs. (3.15) and (3.16) for the 45° strain rosette.

Chapter 4

Elastic Stress-Strain Relationships

4.1 Classification of strain as to cause

In Chap. 1 three kinds of strain were described for uniaxial loading: *elastic*, *plastic*, and *thermal*. The total strain is the sum of these:

$$\epsilon = \epsilon_E + \epsilon_P + \epsilon_T \tag{4.1}$$

To clarify the physical action, a model of a two-dimensional "crystal" is shown in Fig. 4.1. Such a model will serve as a basis for explaining the behavior of polycrystalline materials, which are composed of very small crystals having more or less random orientation.

In Fig. 4.1*a* the hypothetical atoms are in close-packed arrangement, typical of many metals. The distance between each atom and any neighbor is the same at all points. In (*b*), a tensile stress has been applied. The atoms have been pulled farther apart in the *x* direction. At the same time, the width of the specimen has decreased. All the atoms remain in the same general positions relative to each other. This is typical of elastic deformation.

In (*c*), *slip* has occurred along a diagonal line. On either side of this line the atoms have changed partners; that is, there has been a change of relative position. However, the distances between atoms have *not* been changed. The over-all length of the specimen has been increased by this slip. The strain thus produced is typical of plastic deformation, which is the result of slip on many different planes. (Note that in Fig. 4.1*c* there are many other possible slip lines parallel to the one shown; also there is another complete set at 60°.)

In (*d*) the temperature of the specimen has been increased. All the atoms have moved farther apart because of increased intensity of atomic vibration. Both length and width of the specimen have been increased. No change of relative position is involved. This model illustrates thermal strain.

The model of Fig. 4.1 can be made three dimensional by using spheres. In piling up balls to make a three-dimensional model of a crystal, the balls in the second layer naturally fall into the "valleys" between those of the first. However, when the third layer is started, we have a choice of placing the first ball in two ways: (1) directly above a ball in the first layer, or (2) directly above a "hole" (between three balls) in the first layer. In case (1) the resulting crystalline arrangement is

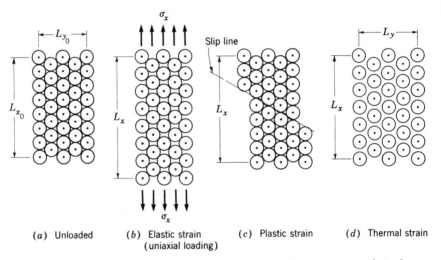

(a) Unloaded (b) Elastic strain (c) Plastic strain (d) Thermal strain
(uniaxial loading)

Figure 4.1. Two-dimensional model illustrating different types of strain.

called "face-centered cubic" (copper, aluminum, gamma iron, gold, platinum, silver, and others). In case (2) the arrangement is called "close-packed hexagonal" (magnesium, titanium, zinc, cadmium, cobalt, beryllium, and others). One difference between the two arrangements is that the number of different orientations of planes of "easy slip" is not the same. These matters are dealt with in textbooks and courses on properties of materials, or metallurgy.

4.2 Elastic stress-strain relationships (uniaxial loading)

Although Hooke's law implies that the relationship between stress and strain is linear, this is only approximately true. In atomic physics it is found that the fundamental relationship is something like that shown in Fig. 4.2. This can be thought of as a stress-strain diagram on the atomic level, where r represents the distance between atoms and stress represents the force between atoms. The curve is continuous and has a maximum value very much greater than the stresses at which an ordinary specimen will fail. In this sense the maximum interatomic force represents the potential strength. Tests of very thin filaments ("whiskers") have shown that stresses of several million psi (on the order of one-tenth of Young's modulus) can actually be developed. Other materials (such as glass) also exhibit very high strengths in this form.

Although the atomic stress-strain diagram is curved, the departure from linearity is imperceptible in the stress range found in ordinary structures. This justifies the use of Hooke's law and Young's modulus for the elastic part of the strain.

Another important fact made clear by the model is the *reversibility* of elastic (and thermal) deformation. Since the atoms have not changed

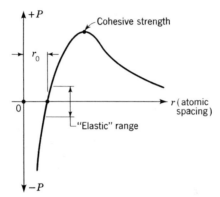

Figure 4.2. Interatomic force-deflection diagram (schematic).

their relative positions, they return to their original positions when the stress is removed or original temperature restored. For loading rates below the speed of sound in the material *the relationship between elastic strain and stress may be regarded as time-independent.*

Poisson's ratio ν can be calculated roughly by means of the two-dimensional elastic model.* Figure 4.3b shows four "atoms" in the close-packed arrangement (rotated 90° from Fig. 4.1b). In (c) the two horizontal atoms have been pulled apart by a force P_x. If the two vertical atoms remained in their original positions, the diagonal distances between atoms would increase. This increase would require tensile forces along the diagonal lines. But since there are no external tensile forces in the y direction, such extension is impossible. Therefore in sketch (b) the vertical atoms must move toward each other until the diagonal distances return to their original values, as shown in (c). (The experiment can be performed with four coins.)

---

* Poisson originally calculated the ratio by means of a theory of elasticity, obtaining the value of *one-fourth*.

It can easily be proved (Ref. 19) that, for relatively small movements, the strain ϵ_y (which is δ_y/L_y) is equal to $-\frac{1}{3}\epsilon_x$. There are several orientations of planes in a close-packed three-dimensional crystal on which the conditions shown by this model are found. Therefore it is reasonable to expect that Poisson's ratio for metals would be in the neighborhood of *one-third*. (It usually lies between 0.30 and 0.33.) For amorphous materials (having no regular crystal structure) the value is usually close to 0.25. For materials in which the diagonal effects are

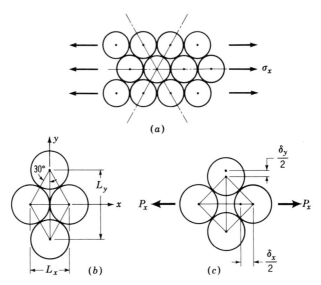

Figure 4.3. Physical model for lateral contraction (Poisson's ratio).

negligible (porous materials), the value of ν approaches zero (cork is an example). For rubber the value is roughly one-half.

4.3 Three-dimensional elastic strain

We now take up elastic strain in three dimensions. The model we shall deal with is *isotropic* (identical properties in all directions at a point) and *homogeneous* (no variation in properties from point to point). This is closely approached in bulk by most polycrystalline structural metals.*

In the elastic (linear) range the principle of superposition may be applied. If a small element is subjected to principal stresses σ_1, σ_2, and σ_3, the total deformation may be found by adding algebraically all the strains produced by each stress acting separately.

---

* For orthotropic materials (such as wood) see Ref. 6.

For example, σ_1 acting alone produces the following normal strains: $\epsilon_1 = \sigma_1/E$, $\epsilon_2 = -\nu\epsilon_1$, and $\epsilon_3 = -\nu\epsilon_1$. When all three principal stresses are acting, the following principal strains are found by superposition.

$$\epsilon_1 = \frac{1}{E}(\sigma_1 - \nu\sigma_2 - \nu\sigma_3)$$

$$\epsilon_2 = \frac{1}{E}(-\nu\sigma_1 + \sigma_2 - \nu\sigma_3) \qquad (4.2)$$

$$\epsilon_3 = \frac{1}{E}(-\nu\sigma_1 - \nu\sigma_2 + \sigma_3)$$

To provide for thermal strains, add $\alpha(\Delta T)$ to each equation.

From the definition of principal stress, there are no shear stresses on the sides of the element; therefore Eqs. (4.2) represent the total state of elastic strain.

When the element is *not* oriented along the principal directions, there will be shear stresses acting on either four or all six faces of the element, as shown in Chap. 2. Equations (4.2) can still be used to calculate the elastic strains caused by σ_x, σ_y, and σ_z, because the shear stresses do not change the lengths of elements in the x, y, z directions. The element will,

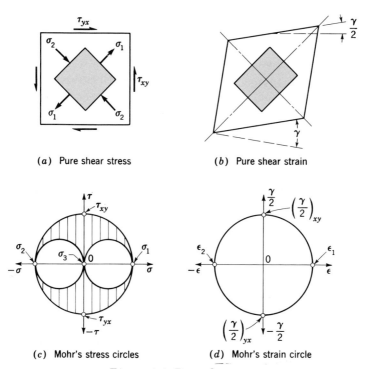

(a) Pure shear stress   (b) Pure shear strain

(c) Mohr's stress circles   (d) Mohr's strain circle

Figure 4.4. Pure shear.

however, be distorted by the shear stresses. To calculate this change in shape, we omit the normal stresses and work only with the shear stresses τ_{xy} and τ_{yz}, as shown in Fig. 4.4. Such a state of stress is called *pure shear*.

From Eq. (2.12) the principal stresses in pure (plane) shear are

$$\sigma_1 = \tau_{xy} \qquad \text{tension}$$
$$\sigma_2 = -\tau_{xy} \qquad \text{compression}$$
$$\sigma_3 = 0$$

This is also shown by Mohr's stress circle (Fig. 4.4c). The principal directions are at 45°. To find the principal strains, we use Eqs. (4.2):

$$\epsilon_1 = \frac{1}{E}(\sigma_1 - \nu\sigma_2) = \frac{\tau_{xy}}{E}(1 + \nu)$$

$$\epsilon_2 = \frac{1}{E}(-\nu\sigma_1 + \sigma_2) = -\frac{\tau_{xy}}{E}(1 + \nu)$$

$$\epsilon_3 = \frac{1}{E}(\nu\sigma_1 - \nu\sigma_2) = 0$$

From the general strain equations, or from Mohr's strain circle (Fig. 4.4d), we know that

$$\frac{\gamma}{2} = \epsilon_1 \qquad\qquad (a)$$

Therefore
$$\gamma = 2\epsilon_1 = \frac{2\tau_{xy}}{E}(1 + \nu) \qquad\qquad (b)$$

The relationship between shear strain and shear stress is given by this equation. It is customary to write this linear relationship in the general form

$$\boxed{\gamma = \frac{\tau}{G}} \qquad\qquad (4.3)$$

The quantity G is the *modulus of elasticity for pure shear*. It is sometimes called the *modulus of rigidity*.* From Eqs. (b) and (4.3),

$$\boxed{G = \frac{E}{2(1 + \nu)}} \qquad\qquad (4.4)$$

The shear distortion of the element, for each surface, is found by substituting the three shear stresses τ_{xy}, τ_{yz}, τ_{zx} in Eq. (4.3). Grouping these equations with the equations for normal strains, we have the following *general equations for an elastic isotropic material* (generalized

---

* This name is not entirely logical, in view of the classical definition of a rigid body.

form of Hooke's law on a stress-strain basis):

$$
\begin{array}{ll}
\epsilon_x = \dfrac{1}{E}\left(\sigma_x - \nu\sigma_y - \nu\sigma_z\right) & \gamma_{xy} = \dfrac{\tau_{xy}}{G} \\[2mm]
\epsilon_y = \dfrac{1}{E}\left(-\nu\sigma_x + \sigma_y - \nu\sigma_z\right) & \gamma_{yz} = \dfrac{\tau_{yz}}{G} \\[2mm]
\epsilon_z = \dfrac{1}{E}\left(-\nu\sigma_x - \nu\sigma_y + \sigma_z\right) & \gamma_{zx} = \dfrac{\tau_{zx}}{G}
\end{array}
\tag{4.5}
$$

To provide for thermal strains add $\alpha(\Delta T)$ to each of the equations for normal strains. (No shear strains are caused by ΔT.)

If the element is oriented with respect to the principal axes, the above equations reduce to Eqs. (4.2), since the shear stresses become zero. When the stresses are referred to the principal axes, we have

$$\tau_{xy} = \tau_{yz} = \tau_{zx} = 0$$

Equations (4.5) then show that $\gamma_{xy} = \gamma_{yz} = \gamma_{zx} = 0$. *Therefore the principal axes for strains coincide with the principal axes for stresses, in the elastic range.* Because superposition is valid, the above statement is true regardless of the order in which the stresses are applied.

The principal surface strains ϵ_1 and ϵ_2 can be found from strain-gauge measurements (see Sec. 3.3). *It is entirely wrong to convert these strains into stress by multiplying by E.* It is necessary to solve the following equations (from Eqs. 4.2):

$$\epsilon_1 = \frac{1}{E}\left(\sigma_1 - \nu\sigma_2\right)$$

$$\epsilon_2 = \frac{1}{E}\left(-\nu\sigma_1 + \sigma_2\right)$$

The solution is

$$\sigma_1 = E\,\frac{\epsilon_1 + \nu\epsilon_2}{1 - \nu^2} \quad \text{and} \quad \sigma_2 = E\,\frac{\epsilon_2 + \nu\epsilon_1}{1 - \nu^2} \tag{4.6}$$

(The stress σ_3 is zero in the above solution.)

EXAMPLE 4.1. Assume that a 1-in.-diameter steel rod 5 ft long is prevented from contracting lengthwise and that its temperature is changed from 70 to $-40°F$. The coefficient of expansion α for steel is about 6.5×10^{-6} (strain per °F), and E is 29×10^6 psi. The value of ΔT is $-110°F$. If no plastic action occurs, Eq. (4.1) becomes

$$\epsilon = \frac{\sigma}{E} + \alpha(\Delta T) \tag{a}$$

For complete constraint, ϵ must be zero. Equation (a) then becomes

$$\sigma = -E\alpha(\Delta T) \tag{b}$$

Substituting the above values for E, α, and ΔT,

$$\sigma = -(29 \times 10^6)(6.5 \times 10^{-6})(-110)$$
$$\sigma = 20{,}800 \text{ psi} \qquad \text{tension}$$

This answer may now be checked to determine whether conditions actually do remain in the elastic range. If not, a plastic-strain term would have to be included in Eq. (a). If an expression for this term is not available, the procedure would be to calculate the thermal strain $\alpha(\Delta T)$ and enter the stress-strain diagram at this value, to find the corresponding stress.

Note that the dimensions of the rod do not enter into this computation. Also, the relatively small changes of E and α over this temperature range are neglected.

EXAMPLE 4.2.   A circular aluminum alloy plate ($D = 60$ in., $t = 0.040$ in.) is loaded by a radial force of $q = 2{,}000$ lb/in. $E = 10 \times 10^6$ psi, $\nu = \frac{1}{3}$. Find the change in diameter. Also calculate the *apparent* value of E in the radial direction.

The stress along any diameter is

$$\sigma_1 = \sigma_2 = \frac{q}{t} = \frac{2{,}000}{0.040} = 50{,}000 \text{ psi}$$

$$\sigma_3 = 0 \qquad \text{across thickness}$$

From Eqs. (4.2),

$$\epsilon_1 = \frac{1}{E}(\sigma_1 - \nu\sigma_2) = \frac{\sigma_1}{E}(1 - \nu) \tag{a}$$

$$= \frac{50{,}000}{10 \times 10^6}\left(1 - \frac{1}{3}\right) = 3.33 \times 10^{-3}$$

$$\Delta D = \epsilon_1 D_0 = 3.33 \times 10^{-3} \times 60 = 0.20 \text{ in.}$$

The *apparent* modulus is defined as

$$E_{\text{app}} = \frac{\sigma_1}{\epsilon_1}$$

Substituting the value of ϵ_1 from Eq. (a),

$$E_{\text{app}} = \frac{E}{1 - \nu} = \frac{3}{2}E = 15 \times 10^6 \text{ psi}$$

This example shows that large errors can result from treating multiaxial loading conditions as if they are uniaxial. The general elastic equations should always be used.

EXAMPLE 4.3.   Two resistance gauges are bonded on the outside surface of a large pipe fitting with an internal tapered thread. After the joint is tightened, the longitudinal gauge reads $\epsilon_z = -0.0010$, and the circumferential gauge reads

$\epsilon_y = +0.0004$. The material is steel ($E = 29 \times 10^6$ psi; $\nu = \frac{1}{3}$). Calculate the circumferential stress, working directly with Eqs. (4.2).

$$\epsilon_x = -0.0010 = \frac{1}{E}(\sigma_x - \nu\sigma_y)$$

$$= \frac{1}{29 \times 10^6}\left(\sigma_x - \frac{1}{3}\sigma_y\right)$$

$$\sigma_x - 0.333\sigma_y = -29 \times 10^3 \text{ psi} \qquad (a)$$

$$\epsilon_y = +0.0004 = \frac{1}{E}(-\nu\sigma_x + \sigma_y)$$

$$= \frac{1}{29 \times 10^6}\left(-\frac{1}{3}\sigma_x + \sigma_y\right)$$

$$-0.333\sigma_x + \sigma_y = +11.6 \times 10^3 \text{ psi} \qquad (b)$$

Solve (a) and (b) simultaneously. The result is

$$\sigma_x = -28,200 \text{ psi} \qquad \text{axial}$$
$$\sigma_y = +2,180 \text{ psi} \qquad \text{circumferential}$$

The error that would be made in using $\sigma_y = \epsilon_y E$ is over 500 percent.

EXAMPLE 4.4. Find the apparent modulus of elasticity in the x direction for a symmetrical state of combined loading ($\sigma_y = \sigma_z = K\sigma_x$). By definition

$$E_{\text{app}} = \frac{\sigma_x}{\epsilon_x}$$

From Eqs. (4.5)

$$\epsilon_x = \frac{1}{E}(\sigma_x - \nu\sigma_y - \nu\sigma_z) = \frac{1}{E}(\sigma_x - \nu K\sigma_x - \nu K\sigma_x)$$

$$= \frac{\sigma_x(1 - 2\nu K)}{E}$$

Substituting this for ϵ_x, above, we obtain

$$E_{\text{app}} = \frac{E}{1 - 2\nu K}$$

For example, let $K = 1$, which represents equal triaxial tension. Then, with $\nu = \frac{1}{3}$,

$$E_{\text{app}} = 3E$$

This result also holds for equal triaxial (hydrostatic) compression.

When the element is simultaneously pulled and laterally compressed in such a way that $K = -1$, the value of E_{app} becomes $0.6E$.

Note: The apparent modulus of elasticity is used only to emphasize that the stiffness of components depends on the state of loading. E_{app} *is not a material property.*

4.4 Volumetric strains

A small cube which has the original dimension L_0 will undergo a change of
volume when subjected to strains ϵ_x, ϵ_y, and ϵ_z. The strained volume will be

$$
\begin{aligned}
V &= L_x L_y L_z \\
&= L_0{}^3 (1 + \epsilon_x)(1 + \epsilon_y)(1 + \epsilon_z)
\end{aligned}
\tag{a}
$$

Since $L_0{}^3 = V_0$, we can obtain the *volumetric strain* from the above equation as

$$
\frac{\Delta V}{V_0} = \epsilon_x + \epsilon_y + \epsilon_z + \epsilon_x \epsilon_y + \epsilon_y \epsilon_z + \epsilon_z \epsilon_x + \epsilon_x \epsilon_y \epsilon_z
\tag{4.7}
$$

The elastic strains developed in structures are usually on the order of
0.001 to 0.005, so the products of strain will be omitted, giving

$$
\frac{\Delta V}{V_0} = \epsilon_x + \epsilon_y + \epsilon_z
\tag{4.8}
$$

When $\sigma_x = \sigma_y = \sigma_z$ ("hydrostatic" stress) the strains become, from Eqs.
(4.5),

$$
\epsilon_x = \epsilon_y = \epsilon_z = \frac{\sigma}{E}(1 - 2\nu)
\tag{b}
$$

Then
$$
\frac{\Delta V}{V_0} = \frac{3\sigma}{E}(1 - 2\nu)
\tag{c}
$$

The *volumetric modulus of elasticity* β (also called *modulus of dilatation,*
or *modulus of compressibility*) is defined as the ratio of stress to volumetric
strain, for equal triaxial stress ("hydrostatic").

$$
\beta = \frac{\sigma}{\Delta V / V_0}
\tag{4.9}
$$

Substituting from (c),

$$
\boxed{\beta = \frac{E}{3(1 - 2\nu)}}
\tag{4.10}
$$

Then
$$
\frac{\Delta V}{V_0} = \frac{\sigma}{\beta}
\tag{4.11}
$$

Note: When $\nu = \frac{1}{3}$, $\beta = E$.

The change of volume caused by shear strains is zero (if higher-order terms are
neglected). This is evident from the fact that a small change of angle γ_{xy} does
not have any appreciable affect on an element of area in the xy plane, and the
strain ϵ_z was found to be zero in pure plane shear. Therefore Eq. (4.8) can be
used in the general case when all three axial stresses are not equal and shear

stresses are present. Then

$$\frac{\Delta V}{V_0} = \frac{\sigma_x + \sigma_y + \sigma_z}{E}(1 - 2\nu) \tag{d}$$

This can be put in the form of Eq. (4.11) by using the average normal stress.

$$\sigma_{av} = \frac{\sigma_x + \sigma_y + \sigma_z}{3} \tag{e}$$

Then

$$\frac{\Delta V}{V_0} = \frac{3\sigma_{av}}{E}(1 - 2\nu) \tag{4.12}$$

and

$$\frac{\Delta V}{V_0} = \frac{\sigma_{av}}{\beta} \tag{4.13}$$

The average normal stress is an *invariant* (does not vary in magnitude under rotation of axes). When it is subtracted from each of the three axial stresses there remain three stresses that *cause no change in volume* (their sum is zero). These stress differences, called the *stress deviators*, are

$$\sigma'_x = \sigma_x - \sigma_{av} \qquad \sigma'_y = \sigma_y - \sigma_{av} \qquad \sigma'_z = \sigma_z - \sigma_{av}$$

A state of stress can therefore be represented by the *average stress* σ_{av}, which causes *only* a change of volume, and the *stress deviators*, which cause *only* distortion. This system is widely used in advanced studies of plastic deformation.

4.5 Elastic strain energy

The elastic strain energy per unit volume can be expressed in terms of the stresses and elastic strains. On the force-deflection level the elastic energy is

$$U = \tfrac{1}{2}P\delta \tag{a}$$

For a cubic element of dimensions L_0 we have, for *pure tension*,

$$P = \sigma A = \sigma L_0^2$$
$$\delta = \epsilon L_0$$

Substituting in (a), $U = \tfrac{1}{2}\sigma\epsilon L_0^3$. Dividing by the volume, to obtain energy per unit volume (u),

$$u = \frac{U}{\text{volume}} = \frac{1}{2}\sigma\epsilon \tag{4.14}$$

When *three principal stresses* are acting

$$u = \tfrac{1}{2}(\sigma_1\epsilon_1 + \sigma_2\epsilon_2 + \sigma_3\epsilon_3) \tag{4.15}$$

For *pure shear* (only) on all faces of the element

$$u = \tfrac{1}{2}(\tau_{xy}\gamma_{xy} + \tau_{yz}\gamma_{yz} + \tau_{zx}\gamma_{zx}) \tag{4.16}$$

For the *general state of stress*

$$u = \tfrac{1}{2}(\sigma_x\epsilon_x + \sigma_y\epsilon_y + \sigma_z\epsilon_z + \tau_{xy}\gamma_{xy} + \tau_{yz}\gamma_{yz} + \tau_{zx}\gamma_{zx}) \qquad (4.17)$$

The values of σ_x, ϵ_x, γ_{xy}, and so on, can be calculated from the foregoing equations and substituted in the above formulas to obtain energy per unit volume as a function of either stress or strain. In the general case, Young's modulus and Poisson's ratio will be involved, either directly or through the use of G.

The *modulus of resilience* is a property which is a measure of the ability of a material to absorb energy in uniaxial loading without undergoing permanent deformation. It is found by substituting in Eq. (4.14) the values of the proportional limit (σ_p) and Young's modulus, giving

$$\text{Modulus of resilience} = \frac{1}{2}\sigma_p\epsilon_p = \frac{1}{2}\frac{\sigma_p{}^2}{E} \qquad (4.18)$$

This quantity is represented by the area under the straight (elastic) portion of the stress-strain diagram, to the proper scale.

PROBLEMS

4.1. For the cylindrical pressure vessel of Prob. 2.4, use steel as a material ($E = 29 \times 10^6$ psi, $\nu = \tfrac{1}{3}$) and perform the following analysis for an assigned set of parameters in the table. Action is to be assumed to be purely elastic.

(a) Calculate the principal strains in the cylindrical wall and draw Mohr's circle for strain.

(b) Find the increase in mean diameter.

(c) Calculate the normal and shear strains for an element oriented at the prescribed angle θ.

(d) Calculate the strain energy stored in the cylinder wall (omit end closures and local effects at the ends of the cylinder).

(e) Calculate $\Delta V/V_0$ for an element of the cylinder wall, by adding the normal strains algebraically. Do this for orientations of $\theta = 0$ and for θ designated in Table P2.4. Repeat by using Eq. (4.12).

4.2. In the preliminary design of a titanium-alloy spherical pressure vessel, it is established that the mean diameter must be 20 in., and the maximum expected pressure difference is 1,000 psi. A factor of safety of 2.0 is required with respect to yielding, which is assumed to occur when the maximum shear stress in the material reaches a value of 80,000 psi.

(a) Find the required wall thickness.

(b) Calculate the increase in diameter when the pressure difference actually reaches 1,000 psi ($E = 16 \times 10^6$ psi, $\nu = \tfrac{1}{3}$).

4.3. For a designated set of measured *principal* strains in the following table calculate the corresponding stresses, with $E = 16 \times 10^6$ psi, $\nu = \frac{1}{3}$. Calculations are to be done by simultaneous solution of Eqs. (4.2), not by Eqs. (4.6), which may be used as a check. Note that the measured strains are *surface* strains, i.e., a state of plane stress is involved ($\sigma_3 = 0$). Sketch Mohr's circles for both stress and strain, approximately to scale.

TABLE P4.3

	1	2	3	4	5	6	7
ϵ_1	+0.008	+0.006	−0.007	−0.005	+0.009	+0.004	−0.003
ϵ_2	−0.002	+0.002	−0.003	+0.004	−0.004	+0.004	+0.009

4.4. A thin flat plate, before loading, has a 2 in. × 2 in. square accurately drawn on it. After loading, the square has the dimensions indicated by the dashed line of Fig. P4.4 (deformations exaggerated for clarity).

(a) Calculate the principal strains and their directions. Check by Mohr's strain circle.

(b) For $E = 10 \times 10^6$ and $\nu = \frac{1}{3}$, find the principal stresses, assuming elastic action. (If stresses appear to be high this may indicate that plastic action has taken place, but this possibility is to be omitted in this problem.)

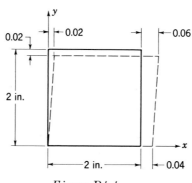

Figure P4.4

4.5. In estimating the frequencies of vibration of a circular flat drumhead at a given radial tension q, a strip of the material was tested in pure tension and E was determined. Assume that Poisson's ratio for the material is 0.40 and find the correction factor by which E must be multiplied to find the apparent modulus of elasticity of the drumhead.

4.6. Derive the following equation for the energy per unit volume under biaxial loading ($\sigma_z = 0$):

$$\frac{U}{\text{volume}} = \frac{1}{2E} \left(\sigma_x^2 - 2\nu\sigma_x\sigma_y + \sigma_y^2 \right)$$

4.7. A circular steel plate, 0.050 in. thick, is subjected to a radial tensile force field of 15,000 lb/in. By what fraction does the diameter increase? ($E = 30 \times 10^6$ psi, $\nu = \frac{1}{3}$.)

4.8. Prove that the elastic energy per unit volume is the same under pure axial loading ($\sigma_1,0,0$) and equal triaxial loading ($\sigma_1 = \sigma_2 = \sigma_3$) when $\nu = \frac{1}{3}$.

4.9. The so-called "Kelvin effect" is demonstrated when a rubber band is suddenly stretched and is observed to undergo an appreciable increase in temperature. Explain, by using Eqs. (4.2) and (4.8), what this tells us about the approximate value of ν for the material.

4.10. A solid sphere of 20 in. diameter is submerged in the ocean at a depth of 10,000 ft. The value of E is 8×10^5 psi and $\nu = 0.35$. (The density of sea water is 64.0 lb/ft³.) Calculate (a) the volumetric modulus of elasticity, β; (b) the fractional decrease in volume, using β; (c) the decrease in diameter in inches; and (d) the elastic energy stored in the material. (e) Check the accuracy of part c by including terms involving ϵ^2 and ϵ^3 in the equation for $\Delta V/V_0$.

4.11. (Refer to appendix for material properties.) In a certain building design, relatively thin-sheet panels of steel are used to form the outer surface. They are riveted along their edges to a massive substructure which transmits the primary structural loads. On a hot day the panels may reach a temperature of 120°F, while the steel substructure remains at 60°F.

(a) Consider the panels to be rigidly constrained against expansion in the x direction but not in y or z directions (z is normal to sheet). What stress σ_x is developed?

(b) If panels are rigidly constrained against expansion in both x and y directions, find stresses σ_x and σ_y. [*Note:* Such panels will buckle if the ratio of width to thickness exceeds a certain value (Sec. 11.7).]

Chapter 5

Plastic Stress-Strain Relationships

5.1 Nature of plastic strain

Plastic deformation of a polycrystalline metal or alloy is the result of *slip* along certain planes within the individual crystals (see Fig. 4.10). The crystals tend to have a random distribution of orientation. Slip within a crystal is a complex phenomenon in which the primary action is that of *dislocation movement*. Dislocations are defects that can be described roughly as the presence of an "extra" plane of atoms ending within a crystal, as indicated by the model of Fig. 5.1. Under the action of shear stress, the extra plane tends to move to a more stable position (to the right in Fig. 5.1), while the plane immediately to its right becomes the extra plane. This goes on until the dislocation (*not* the original plane itself) reaches the edge of the crystal, as indicated in (*b*), or encounters an internal obstruction.

Because slip occurs progressively by a wavelike motion, it can be produced by shear stresses that are relatively small and the degree of slip can be large.* Materials which, in a tension test, exhibit large plastic strain (relative to the elastic strain) are called *ductile*. Those which have very little or no plastic deformation are called *brittle*. Plastic deformation is strongly influenced by the *state of stress* and by *temperature*. Experiments show that for metals the relationship between plastic strain and shear stress is usually highly nonlinear. It is more or less sensitive to the rate of loading.

Slip in a single crystal can be thought of as analogous to that in a

---

* The normal stresses acting across the slip plane have little effect on plastic strain, for most structural materials, unless very high pressures are involved (see Bridgman, Ref. 5).

pack of cards, as shown in Fig. 5.2. In the pure metal, the "cards" (planes of atoms) slide easily. If a small amount of sand is introduced between the cards, there will be less slip under the same shear stress. It may be found that there is no measurable slip up to some critical value of the shear stress, after which slip increases with increasing stress. When slip does occur, the work done thereby is converted into heat; the action is *irreversible.*

A pure metal (iron or aluminum for example) usually begins to slip at a relatively low shear stress; that is, the tensile stress-strain diagram

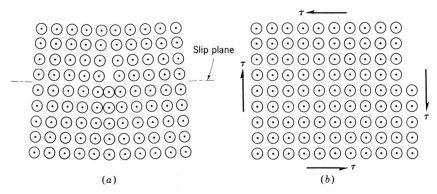

Slip plane

(a)   *(b)*

Figure 5.1. Movement of an edge dislocation.

(a) Pure metal   *(b)* Alloy

Figure 5.2. Slip-plane analogy.

departs from the elastic line at low values of tensile stress. To make the metal "stronger," alloying constituents are introduced, usually accompanied by special heat-treatment or cold-working processes. The effects are shown in Figs. 5.3 and 5.4 for aluminum and iron.

The plastic strain that can be developed before the ultimate tensile stress is reached tends to decrease with increasing ultimate tensile strength. This decrease represents a loss of ductility (see Sec. 1.5).

The relative amount of alloying material needed to inhibit slip is usually very small. Consequently, alloying does not appreciably affect the modulus of elasticity, as indicated by Figs. 5.3 and 5.4, for typical alloys.

5.2 Three-dimensional plastic strain (multiaxial loading)

In Chap. 4 it was shown how the values of E and ν determined from a tension test (uniaxial loading) can be used to predict the complete elastic behavior of an element in a general (multiaxial) state of stress. This is accomplished by the linear equations (4.2). In contrast, the plastic

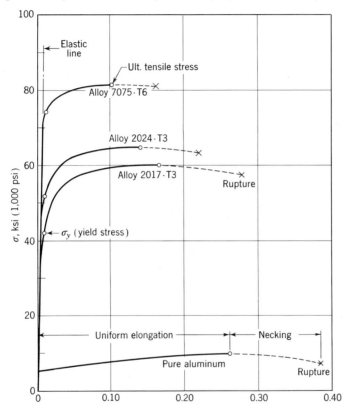

Figure 5.3. Effects of alloying and heat-treating on aluminum (typical data).

strain in uniaxial loading does not vary linearly with stress and, as previously noted, the plastic strains are caused primarily by shear stresses. In view of the complexity thereby introduced, one cannot expect to derive a simple set of equations by which plastic strains can be accurately calculated for any state of stress, as was done for elastic strains. Nevertheless, it is possible to develop a theory that can be expressed by the same type of equations as those used for elastic strains [Eqs. (4.2)]. Such "pseudoelastic" equations* are written below in terms

---

* Equations of this type were introduced by Nadai, Ref. 9. See also Ref. 66, Chap. 1.

of principal stresses and plastic strains (this type of theory is classed as *deformational*).

$$\epsilon_1{}^P = \frac{1}{E_P} (\sigma_1 - \nu_P\sigma_2 - \nu_P\sigma_3)$$

$$\epsilon_2{}^P = \frac{1}{E_P} (-\nu_P\sigma_1 + \sigma_2 - \nu_P\sigma_3) \qquad (5.1)$$

$$\epsilon_3{}^P = \frac{1}{E_P} (-\nu_P\sigma_1 - \nu_P\sigma_2 + \sigma_3)$$

where ϵ^P = plastic strain (superscript used for clarity)

E_P = "modulus of plasticity" (or "secant modulus") a function of the state of stress

ν_P = Poisson's ratio for plastic strains

In this type of theory the following postulates are made:

1. *Plastic deformation is caused by shear stresses only.*
2. *The three principal stresses (therefore all stresses) remain in proportion during loading.*

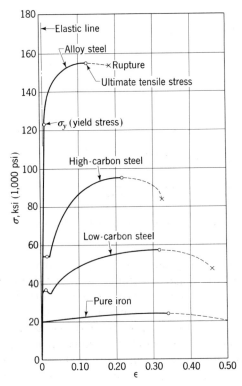

Figure 5.4. Stress-strain diagrams for iron and steel.

3. *For a given state of stress the principal plastic (normal) strains are proportional to the principal stresses.*
4. *The principal axes for strains coincide with those for stress.*
5. *Volume remains constant.*
6. *Plastic strain is irreversible.*

The pseudoelastic aspects of this theory are contained in postulate 3. The nonlinear relationship between stress and plastic strain is provided by making E_P a function of the state of stress such that the quantity $1/E_P$ represents a measure of the magnitude of plastic action.

First we determine a suitable value for ν_P, Poisson's ratio for pure plastic action. This is found by using postulate 5. From Eq. (4.8) we have (neglecting higher-order terms),

$$\frac{\Delta V}{V_0} = 0 = \epsilon_1 + \epsilon_2 + \epsilon_3$$

If the values from Eqs. (5.1) are substituted in this equation, we find that ν_P must have the value of *one-half* (assume $\sigma_1 + \sigma_2 + \sigma_3 \neq 0$).

$$\boxed{\nu_P = \tfrac{1}{2}} \tag{5.2}$$

The next step is to find a method of determining E_P as a function of the state of stress. One requirement is that the method must give results that agree with the tensile stress-strain diagram when the state of stress is pure tension.

First we plot the tensile (uniaxial) stress-strain diagram for *plastic strains only*, as in Fig. 5.5. At any point on this diagram the ratio σ/ϵ^P represents the secant modulus for plastic strain. We shall use this value as the pseudoelastic modulus for an element subjected to combined stresses. The essential problem is to derive an expression for an *effective stress* $\bar{\sigma}$ at which we can enter the stress-strain diagram to determine E_P.

Various theories for accomplishing this are available. Only two will be presented here. They are the *maximum shear-stress theory* and the *octahedral shear-stress theory*.

MAXIMUM SHEAR-STRESS THEORY (Tresca). Because plastic strains are caused by shear stresses, it would appear logical to use the maximum value of the shear stress as a basis for determining E_P.

For pure tension $(\sigma, 0, 0)$,

$$\tau_{\max} = \frac{\sigma}{2} \tag{a}$$

For the general state $(\sigma'_1, \sigma'_2, \sigma'_3)$,

$$\tau'_{\max} = \frac{\sigma'_1 - \sigma'_3}{2} \tag{b}$$

where $\sigma'_1 > \sigma'_2 > \sigma'_3$. (Primes indicate general state.)

In this theory, *the effective stress $\bar{\sigma}$ is defined as that value of stress which in pure tension will produce the same maximum shear stress as that which occurs in the general state of stress.*

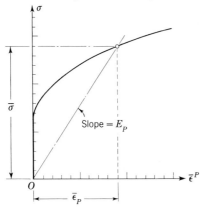

Figure 5.5. Determination of E_p for combined loading (plastic strains only).   *Figure 5.6. Octahedral plane.*

To find $\bar{\sigma}$, we let $\tau_{\max \text{ (tension)}} = \tau'_{\max \text{ (general)}}$. Then, from Eqs. (a) and (b),

$$\frac{\bar{\sigma}}{2} = \frac{\sigma'_1 - \sigma'_3}{2}$$

which gives the effective stress for the *maximum shear-stress theory*:

$$\boxed{\bar{\sigma} = \sigma'_1 - \sigma'_3} \tag{5.3}$$

where $\sigma'_1 > \sigma'_2 > \sigma'_3$.

To determine E_P enter the plastic stress-strain diagram for pure tension (Fig. 5.5) at the computed value of $\bar{\sigma}$ and read $\bar{\epsilon}^P$. Then

$$E_P = \frac{\bar{\sigma}}{\bar{\epsilon}^P} \tag{5.4}$$

OCTAHEDRAL SHEAR-STRESS THEORY (von Mises).   In this theory we use the octahedral shear stress instead of the maximum shear stress, in the manner described above. This value (τ_{oct}) is the maximum value that occurs on the octahedral plane. This plane can be visualized by laying off equal lengths on the σ_1, σ_2, σ_3 axes and passing a plane through the resulting points, as indicated in Fig. 5.6. An *octahedron* (octahedral element) is obtained by doing this for each octant, giving a picture such as that of Fig. 5.7.

It can be proved that the maximum shear stresses on faces of the octahedral element are equal.* (This should be suspected intuitively, because each face is acted upon, at the same angles, by all three principal stresses.)

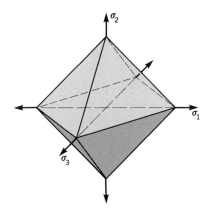

Figure 5.7. Octahedral element (octahedron).

Therefore we need only to work with one face, as shown in Fig. 5.6. The octahedral shear stress† is given, in terms of principal stresses, by

$$\tau'_{oct} = \tfrac{1}{3} \sqrt{(\sigma'_1 - \sigma'_2)^2 + (\sigma'_2 - \sigma'_3)^2 + (\sigma'_3 - \sigma'_1)^2} \qquad (5.5)$$

For simple tension $(\sigma, 0, 0)$,

$$\tau_{oct} = \frac{\sqrt{2}}{3}\,\sigma$$

To find the value of $\bar{\sigma}$ we equate the above values of τ_{oct} giving, for the *octahedral shear-stress theory:*

$$\bar{\sigma} = \frac{1}{\sqrt{2}} \sqrt{(\sigma'_1 - \sigma'_2)^2 + (\sigma'_2 - \sigma'_3)^2 + (\sigma'_3 - \sigma'_1)^2} \qquad (5.6)$$

The (plastic) tensile stress-strain diagram (Fig. 5.5) is entered at this value of $\bar{\sigma}$, to find E_P.

When the reference axes are *not* principal axes, the octahedral shear stress (see Ref. 9) is (dropping primes)

$$\tau_{oct} = \tfrac{1}{3} \sqrt{(\sigma_x - \sigma_y)^2 + (\sigma_y - \sigma_z)^2 + (\sigma_z - \sigma_x)^2 + 6(\tau_{xy}{}^2 + \tau_{yz}{}^2 + \tau_{zx}{}^2)} \qquad (5.7)$$

---

* The normal stress on any octahedral plane is equal to the average of the principal stresses.

† For derivation see Ref. 9, Sec. 10.3.

Equation (5.6) is then modified accordingly:

$$\bar{\sigma} = \frac{1}{\sqrt{2}} \sqrt{(\sigma_x - \sigma_y)^2 + (\sigma_y - \sigma_z)^2 + (\sigma_z - \sigma_x)^2 + 6(\tau_{xy}^2 + \tau_{yz}^2 + \tau_{zz}^2)}$$

$$(5.8)$$

This equation reveals a practical advantage of τ_{oct} over τ_{max} as a basis for plastic-strain analysis. It is easier to find τ_{oct} than τ_{max}, for the general state of stress referred to nonprincipal axes.

When the reference axes are *not* principal axes, shear deformation of the element will occur. The plastic-shear strains are found by extending the "pseudoelastic" equations as follows.

The relationship between G and E, from Eq. (4.4), becomes

$$G_P = \frac{E_P}{2(1 + \nu_P)} \qquad (a)$$

Substituting $\nu_P = \frac{1}{2}$,

$$G_P = \frac{E_P}{3} \qquad (5.9)$$

Equations (5.1) can now be extended to the set of axes, x, y, z, as follows:

$$
\begin{aligned}
\epsilon_x{}^P &= \frac{1}{E_P}\left(\sigma_x - \frac{1}{2}\sigma_y - \frac{1}{2}\sigma_z\right) & \gamma_{xy}{}^P &= 3\frac{\tau_{xy}}{E_P} \\
\epsilon_y{}^P &= \frac{1}{E_P}\left(-\frac{1}{2}\sigma_x + \sigma_y - \frac{1}{2}\sigma_z\right) & \gamma_{yz}{}^P &= 3\frac{\tau_{yz}}{E_P} \\
\epsilon_z{}^P &= \frac{1}{E_P}\left(-\frac{1}{2}\sigma_x - \frac{1}{2}\sigma_y + \sigma_z\right) & \gamma_{zz}{}^P &= 3\frac{\tau_{zz}}{E_P}
\end{aligned}
\qquad (5.10)
$$

The above equations have been found to give good results when the material is polycrystalline and, in bulk, homogeneous and isotropic; the theory does not apply to single crystals.

For symmetrical states of stress (two principal stresses equal), the octahedral shear-stress and the maximum shear-stress theories give identical results. The greatest difference occurs in the state of pure (plane) shear.

The *total* strain is found by adding elastic and plastic strains. The stress-strain history is assumed to be governed by postulate 2 (all stresses remain in proportion). To provide for situations where this is not true the *incremental* (or *flow*) theory of plasticity has been developed. In this theory the pseudoelastic equations are written in terms of plastic-strain increments $(d\epsilon^P)$. The degree of plastic action during an incremental change of state of stress is assumed to be proportional to the increment of effective stress $(d\bar{\sigma})$. For example, a pure tensile stress σ_x might be applied and then held constant while applying a shear stress τ_{xy}.

It has been found that for many practical cases (such as inelastic buckling) the deformation type of theory predicts behavior better than the incremental type. For this reason the incremental theory is not presented in detail (see Ref. 6 for additional information).

Theories of plasticity are used in various ways to predict behavior of a material under a state of combined stress. Such behavior is revealed by the modified stress-strain diagram.

EXAMPLE 5.1 Symmetrical state of stress. In a symmetrical state of stress, two of the three principal stresses are equal. Let $\sigma_2 = \sigma_3$. Then the two different theories of plasticity give the following results:

MAXIMUM SHEAR-STRESS THEORY.

$$\bar{\sigma} = \sigma_1 - \sigma_3$$

OCTAHEDRAL SHEAR-STRESS THEORY. Substitute σ_3 for σ_2 in Eq. (5.6):

$$\bar{\sigma} = \frac{1}{\sqrt{2}} \sqrt{(\sigma_1 - \sigma_3)^2 + (\sigma_3 - \sigma_3)^2 + (\sigma_3 - \sigma_1)^2}$$
$$= \sigma_1 - \sigma_3$$

This means that both theories give the same values of E_P in this case, and therefore the same plastic strains.

EXAMPLE 5.2. To show the effect of state of stress on the stress-strain relationship, it is convenient to work with a symmetrical state of stress in which

$$\sigma_2 = \sigma_3 = K\sigma_1 \tag{a}$$

where K is a constant.

The apparent modulus of elasticity was found in Example 4.4 to be

$$E_{\text{app}} = \frac{E}{1 - 2\nu K} \tag{b}$$

Because of symmetry we may use either of the two theories of plasticity; the same results will be obtained.

$$\bar{\sigma} = \sigma_1 - \sigma_3 = \sigma_1 - K\sigma_1 = \sigma_1(1 - K) \tag{c}$$

The plastic strain at stress σ_1 is

$$\epsilon_1{}^P = \frac{1}{E_P}\left(\sigma_1 - \frac{1}{2}K\sigma_1 - \frac{1}{2}K\sigma_1\right) = \frac{\sigma_1}{E_P}(1 - K) \tag{d}$$

But $E_P = \bar{\sigma}/\bar{\epsilon}^P$ (on plastic stress-strain diagram for pure tension). Substituting this in (d),

$$\epsilon_1{}^P = \frac{\sigma_1}{\bar{\sigma}}\bar{\epsilon}^P(1 - K) \tag{e}$$

where $\epsilon_1{}^P$ is plastic strain at σ_1. Substituting the value of $\bar{\sigma}$ from (c),

$$\epsilon_1{}^P = \bar{\epsilon}^P$$

This means that we merely transfer the plastic strain $\bar{\epsilon}^P$ to the stress level σ_1, plotting it to the right of the E_{app} line to best obtain the "apparent" σ-ϵ diagram.

In setting up a computation table it is best to start with values of $\bar{\sigma}$ and convert them to σ_1 by the formula

$$\sigma_1 = \frac{\bar{\sigma}}{1 - K} \qquad\qquad (f)$$

Figure E5.2 shows several diagrams obtained in this manner. Note that when $K = +1$, the value of σ_1 becomes infinite. This means that there is no plastic strain. When $K = -1$, the diagram is much lower than for pure tension.

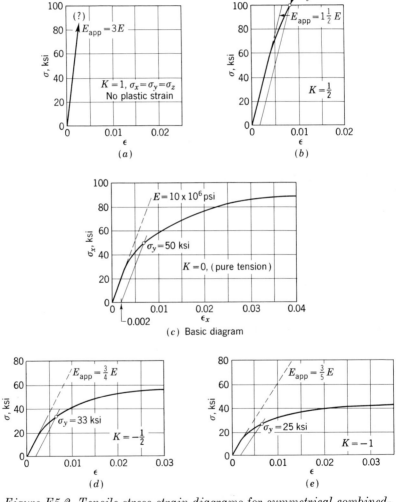

Figure E5.2. Tensile stress-strain diagrams for symmetrical combined-stress conditions.

If the *apparent yield stress* for combined loading is defined as that value of σ_1 (maximum principal stress) at which the plastic strain $\epsilon_1{}^P = 0.002$, Eq. (*f*) gives the conversion directly. (Let $\bar{\sigma} = \sigma_y$.) For example, if a lateral pressure equal to $-0.5\sigma_1$ acts simultaneously with σ_1 in a test, we can expect the yield stress to be modified by the multiplying factor

$$\frac{\sigma'_y}{\sigma_y} = \frac{1}{1-K} = \frac{1}{1-(-0.5)} = \frac{2}{3}$$

If it were possible to apply a "hydraulic tension" of the same degree ($K = +0.5$) the apparent yield stress would be doubled.

EXAMPLE 5.3. Convert the tensile stress-strain diagram to a shear stress-strain diagram by two different methods: the *maximum shear-stress theory*, and the *octahedral shear-stress theory*.

ELASTIC STRAIN. For pure shear, with $\nu = \frac{1}{3}$,

$$G = \frac{E}{2(1+\nu)} = \frac{3}{8}E$$

PLASTIC STRAIN, MAXIMUM SHEAR-STRESS THEORY.

$$\bar{\sigma} = \sigma_1 - \sigma_3 = \tau - (-\tau) = 2\tau$$

Then $\tau = \bar{\sigma}/2$:

$$\gamma^P = \frac{\tau}{G_P} = 3\frac{\tau}{E_P} = 3\frac{\bar{\sigma}/2}{\bar{\sigma}/\bar{\epsilon}^P} = \frac{3}{2}\bar{\epsilon}^P$$

Select a value for $\bar{\sigma}$ and find the corresponding $\bar{\epsilon}^P$ from the tensile diagram. Then use $\tau = 0.5\bar{\sigma}$ and $\gamma^P = 1.5\bar{\epsilon}^P$ for a point on the shear diagram (to right of G line).

PLASTIC STRAIN, OCTAHEDRAL SHEAR-STRESS THEORY.

$$\bar{\sigma} = \frac{1}{\sqrt{2}}\sqrt{(\sigma_1 - \sigma_2)^2 + (\sigma_2 - \sigma_3)^2 + (\sigma_3 - \sigma_1)^2}$$

For pure shear,

$$\sigma_1 = \tau, \quad \sigma_2 = 0, \quad \sigma_3 = -\tau$$

then

$$\bar{\sigma} = \frac{1}{\sqrt{2}}\sqrt{(\tau - 0)^2 + (0 + \tau)^2 + (-\tau - \tau)^2}$$

$$= \frac{1}{\sqrt{2}}\sqrt{6\tau^2} = \sqrt{3}\,\tau$$

Therefore $\tau = \bar{\sigma}/\sqrt{3} = 0.577\bar{\sigma}$, and

$$\gamma^P = 3\frac{\tau}{E_P} = 3\frac{\bar{\sigma}/\sqrt{3}}{\bar{\sigma}/\bar{\epsilon}^P} = \sqrt{3}\,\bar{\epsilon}^P = 1.732\bar{\epsilon}^P$$

Computations for a typical stress-strain diagram are shown in Table E5.3 (octahedral shear-stress theory only). Note that the elastic strains have been calculated and added to the plastic strains.

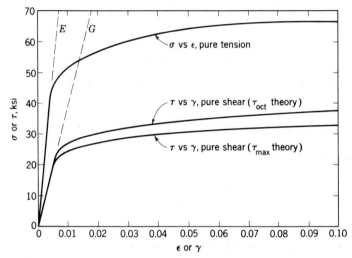

Figure E5.3. Reduction of tensile-stress-strain diagram to pure-shear diagram (two theories illustrated).

Figure E5.3 shows the results for both methods. The maximum shear-stress theory predicts a greater plastic shear strain than that obtained with the octahedral shear-stress theory.

TABLE E5.3

Computations for shear-stress-strain diagram

(Octahedral shear-stress theory)

$\bar{\sigma}$, ksi	$\bar{\epsilon}^P$	$\tau = 0.577\bar{\sigma}$	$\gamma^P = 1.732\bar{\epsilon}^P$	$\gamma^E = \dfrac{\tau}{G}$	$\gamma_{tot} = \gamma^P + \gamma^E$
40	0	23.1	0	.0062	.0062
45	.0010	26.0	.0017	.0069	.0086
50	.0040	28.8	.0069	.0077	.0146
55	.0110	31.7	.0191	.0085	.0276
60	.0250	34.6	.0442	.0093	.0535
62.5	.0330	36.0	.0571	.0096	.0667
65	.0530	37.5	.0918	.0100	.1018
66	.0800	38.0	.1385	.0102	.1487

Notes: 1. $E = 10 \times 10^6$ psi; $G = 3.75 \times 10^6$ psi.
      2. Values of $\bar{\sigma}$ and $\bar{\epsilon}^P$ are taken from tensile stress-strain diagram.
      3. Values of $\bar{\sigma}$ are selected so as to obtain several points in plastic range.

EXAMPLE 5.4. In a cylindrical, thin-walled pressure vessel of circular cross section the principal stresses have the relationship $\sigma_2 = \sigma_1/2$, where σ_1 is the circumferential stress, and σ_2 the longitudinal stress. The stress σ_3 is neglected. The tensile stress-strain diagram of Example 5.3 will be modified to show the effect of this state of stress on the stress-strain relationship in the circumferential direction.

ELASTIC STRAIN $(E = 10 \times 10^6; \nu = \frac{1}{3})$.

$$\epsilon_1 = \frac{1}{E}(\sigma_1 - \nu_E\sigma_2 - \nu_E\sigma_3) = \frac{1}{E}\left(\sigma_1 - \frac{1}{3}\frac{\sigma_1}{2} - 0\right) = \frac{5}{6}\frac{\sigma_1}{E}$$

$$E_{\mathrm{app}} = \frac{\sigma_1}{\epsilon_1} = \frac{6}{5}E = 12 \times 10^6 \text{ psi}$$

PLASTIC STRAIN, MAXIMUM SHEAR-STRESS THEORY $(\nu_P = \frac{1}{2})$.

$$\bar{\sigma} = \sigma_1 - \sigma_3 = \sigma_1 - 0 = \sigma_1$$

$$\epsilon_1{}^P = \frac{1}{E_P}(\sigma_1 - \nu_P\sigma_2 - \nu_P\sigma_3)$$

$$= \frac{1}{E_P}\left(\sigma_1 - \frac{1}{2}\frac{\sigma_1}{2} - 0\right) = \frac{3}{4}\frac{\sigma_1}{E_P}$$

Substituting $\bar{\sigma} = \sigma_1$,

$$\epsilon_1{}^P = \frac{3}{4}\frac{\sigma_1}{\bar{\sigma}/\bar{\epsilon}^P} = \frac{3}{4}\bar{\epsilon}^P$$

PLASTIC STRAIN, OCTAHEDRAL SHEAR-STRESS THEORY.

$$\bar{\sigma} = \frac{1}{\sqrt{2}}\sqrt{\left(\sigma_1 - \frac{\sigma_1}{2}\right)^2 + \left(\frac{\sigma_1}{2} - 0\right)^2 + \left(0 - \sigma_1\right)^2}$$

$$= \frac{1}{\sqrt{2}}\sqrt{\frac{3}{2}\sigma_1{}^2} = \frac{\sqrt{3}}{2}\sigma_1 = 0.866\sigma_1$$

$$\sigma_1 = \frac{\bar{\sigma}}{0.866} = 1.155\bar{\sigma}$$

Following the same steps as in the maximum shear-stress theory, above, we have

$$\epsilon_1{}^P = \frac{3}{4}\frac{\sigma_1}{E_P} = \frac{3}{4}\frac{\sigma_1}{\bar{\sigma}/\bar{\epsilon}^P} = \frac{3}{4}\frac{\sigma_1\bar{\epsilon}^P}{0.866\sigma_1} = 0.866\bar{\epsilon}^P$$

The results are plotted in Fig. E5.4. For ductile materials, experimental results tend to agree with the octahedral shear-stress theory.

5.3 Creep (time-dependent plastic strain)

For most structural materials at room temperature, time effects are so small that they can be neglected. In general, however, the slip which causes plastic strain is more or less time dependent. For example, a metal wire carrying a steady tension load at a relatively high stress over a long period of time may *creep*. The rate of creep is strongly affected by the intensity of the stress and by the temperature. As the temperature approaches the melting point of the material, the rate of creep increases greatly. It is usually necessary to consider creep in the design of components that operate at high temperature.

For engineering purposes, the situation can be greatly simplified by assuming that the total plastic strain is composed of two parts, a *time-independent part* (slip) and a *time-dependent part* (creep). As already

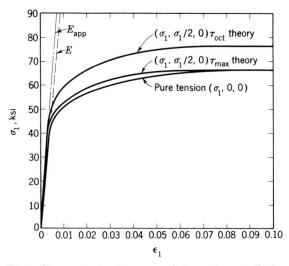

Figure E5.4. Stress-strain diagrams (circumferential) for cylindrical thin-walled pressure vessel (two theories illustrated).

shown, the time-independent plastic strain can be expressed as a function of the stress. For simple tension this relationship can be approximated by a power function.

The time-dependent portion of the plastic strain for simple tension can be determined experimentally by applying a constant tension load to a specimen and measuring the extension continuously or at regular intervals. The results may be plotted as a curve of plastic strain against time, as shown in Fig. 5.8a. Such a curve represents a single test at *constant load* and *constant temperature*. The stress is obtained by dividing the load by the original cross-sectional area and is therefore constant. (The "true" stress is, of course, not constant but increases as the cross-sectional area decreases.)

Figure 5.8a also includes the time-independent plastic strain (slip). This is represented by ϵ_{P_o}, at $t = 0$. The time-dependent strain usually starts out at a fairly rapid rate, which falls off quickly and settles down to a virtually constant rate. These two stages are shown on the graph by an initial curved portion (*transient creep*), followed by a straight portion (*steady creep*). Then a stage is reached in which the strain rate increases markedly. This increased rate is shown by the curved portion at the right side of Fig. 5.8a.* The specimen finally fails completely, usually after necking down, at a stress considerably less than the ultimate

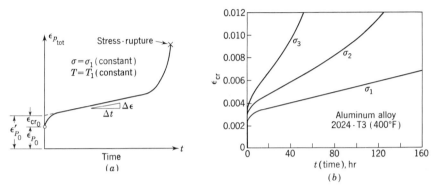

Figure 5.8. Creep curves.

tensile stress developed in the usual (short-time) tension test. This type of failure is called *stress rupture* (or *creep rupture*).

Figure 5.8b shows a number of creep curves, each obtained from a test at a different loading. For the higher loadings the curves are steeper (higher creep rate), and the time to rupture is less. Various other ways of plotting and using creep data are employed (see Ref. 19).

The steady creep rate is greatly affected by both the stress level and the temperature. This is shown in Fig. 5.9. At a temperature of 800°F, for example, there is very little creep up to a stress of about 4,000 psi. At high stresses the rate increases very rapidly with increasing stress.

For a constant stress, the creep rate increases with temperature in a highly nonlinear manner (see Refs. 15, 66).

To represent creep data mathematically various empirical formulas have been used. At a constant temperature any one of the curves of Fig. 5.9 can be approximated by the power function

$$\frac{d\epsilon}{dt} = C_2 \sigma^{n_2} \tag{5.11}$$

where $d\epsilon/dt$ is the creep rate, and C_2 and n_2 are constants determined by curve fitting.

---

* The three stages are sometimes called *primary, secondary,* and *tertiary* creep, respectively.

The *exponential* function and the *hyperbolic sine* function have also been extensively used for creep rate.

For a *constant creep rate*, Eq. (5.11) can be converted to *creep strain* by integration (multiplying by t). For example, Eq. (5.11) becomes

$$\epsilon_{\text{creep}} = C_2 \sigma^{n_2} t \tag{5.12}$$

When only large strains are of interest, the transient stage can be provided for merely by extrapolating the constant creep line to zero time, as indicated in Fig. 5.8a. The intercept value can then be given by a separate formula. It is also possible to include this in the equation for time-independent strain (which

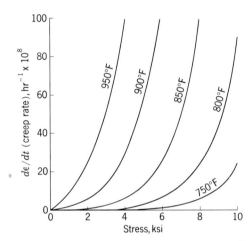

Figure 5.9. Steady creep rate as affected by stress and temperature.

amounts to a redefinition of the slip strain). In that case, the *total plastic strain*, including time effects, can be given by a simple equation, such as

$$\epsilon_P = C_1 \sigma^{n_1} + C_2 \sigma^{n_2} t \tag{5.13}$$

At relatively low temperatures the second right-hand term may be negligible (as for structural materials at room temperature). The equation then reduces to Eq. (1.15). At high temperatures or for soft materials loaded for long periods, the second right-hand term may represent the larger portion of the strain.

EXAMPLE 5.5.   A cable having a cross-sectional area of 2.5 sq in. supports a centrally located transverse load of 6,600 lb over a span of 15 ft. Initial sag of the midpoint is 1.0 ft. It is desired to find the deflection of the load after the system is subjected to a constant temperature of 800°F for a period of 7 years. The solution will consider steady creep only, and will utilize the data of Fig. 5.9. Time-independent strain will be neglected.

This is a "large-deflection" problem in which deflections cause a considerable change in geometry. This change tends to decrease the load in the cables. The solution will be obtained first by neglecting the effects of geometrical changes, and then by accounting for the effects of deflection.

SMALL-DEFLECTION THEORY.

$$L_0 = \sqrt{7.5^2 + 1^2} = 7.57 \text{ ft}$$

Tension in cable:

$$P = \frac{6,600}{2} \times \frac{L}{\delta} = 3,300 \times \frac{7.57}{1.0} = 24,980 \text{ lb} \qquad (a)$$

Stress in cable:

$$\sigma = \frac{24,980}{2.5} = 10,000 \text{ psi}$$

From Fig. 5.9:

$$\frac{d\epsilon}{dt} = 90 \times 10^{-8} \text{ hr}^{-1} = 78.8 \times 10^{-4} \text{ yr}^{-1} \qquad (b)$$

When the effects of geometrical changes are omitted, the creep rate given by (b) is assumed constant over the entire 7-year period (since it is assumed that stress remains unchanged). Therefore, after 7 years

$$\epsilon = 78.8 \times 10^{-4} \times 7 = 551.6 \times 10^{-4} = 0.05516$$
$$\Delta L = 0.05516 \times 7.57 = 0.418 \text{ ft}$$
$$L = 7.57 + 0.42 = 7.99 \text{ ft}$$

and
$$\delta = \sqrt{L^2 - 7.5^2} = \sqrt{7.99^2 - 7.5^2} = 2.75 \text{ ft} \qquad (c)$$

LARGE-DEFLECTION THEORY. From the above solution, at the calculated value of deflection the tension force in the cable would be, from Eq. (a), 9,600 lb. This corresponds to a stress of 3,840 psi, and is considerably less than the value of

TABLE E5.5

t (yr)	$\Delta\epsilon$ $\times 10^4$	$\Delta L_i^* =$ $L_0 \times \Delta\epsilon$ ft	$L_i =$ $L_{i-1} + \Delta L_i$ ft	δ ft	σ ksi	$\Delta\epsilon/\Delta t$ yr$^{-1} \times 10^4$
0	. . . .	. . . . . .	7.57	1.0	10.00	78.8
0.25	19.7	0.0149	7.58	1.07	9.20	42.1
0.5	10.5	0.0080	7.59	1.12	8.95	35.9
1.0	17.9	0.0136	7.60	1.25	8.06	22.8
2.0	22.8	0.0172	7.62	1.36	7.39	15.3
4.0	30.6	0.0232	7.64	1.47	6.86	9.6
7.0	28.9	0.0219	7.66	1.57	4.93	. . . .

* Engineering strain, rather than true strain, is used. This corresponds to the usual method of presentation of creep data.

10,000 psi which was assumed constant. Obviously, then, the value of creep rate cannot be constant.

A method of solution similar to that of the previous case may be utilized provided that a sequence of small time increments is chosen such that the error produced by assuming constant stress (and therefore constant creep rate) over the interval is not unreasonably large. (An "exact" mathematical solution could be obtained if the relationships of Fig. 5.9 were to be expressed as functions of stress. However, a step-by-step procedure is employed here to emphasize the physical behavior.) The change in geometry at the end of each time interval is used to determine a new stress and creep rate and the process is repeated. Table E5.5 shows the calculations. The results for both small and large-deflection theories are compared graphically in Fig. E5.5b. In the latter case the creep rate is found to approach zero as the geometry of the system changes.

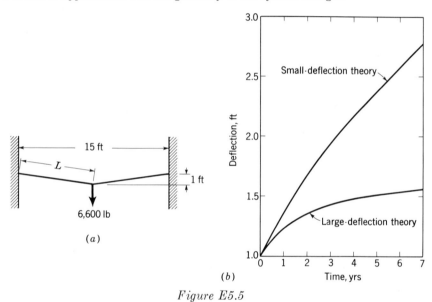

Figure E5.5

5.4 General equations for strain, including creep

The total strain in uniaxial loading may be expressed as

$$\epsilon = \epsilon_E + \epsilon_P + \epsilon_T$$

We now write expressions for each of these strains, as follows:

$$\epsilon_E = \frac{\sigma}{E}$$

$$\epsilon_P = C_1\sigma^{n_1} + C_2\sigma^{n_2}t$$

$$\epsilon_T = \alpha\,\Delta T$$

By combining all types of strain, we obtain a general equation of the following form:

$$\epsilon = \frac{\sigma}{E} + C_1 \sigma^{n_1} + C_2 \sigma^{n_2} t + \alpha \, \Delta T \tag{5.14}$$

In the above equation, the various constants depend on the temperature. The equation therefore actually represents constant-temperature conditions and is inconsistent to the extent that ΔT represents a change in temperature. However, if ΔT is not large, the values of the other constants will not be seriously affected. A more serious limitation is the fact that the third right-hand term is based on *constant-stress* conditions. The equation therefore cannot be applied directly to situations in which the stress varies with time. Although the theory of creep under variable loading is not well established, mathematical methods can be developed that will give satisfactory results for most engineering purposes. (For example, see Ref. 14.)

As previously explained, the first and last terms of Eq. (5.14) (elastic and thermal) may be treated as *reversible*. The second term (time-independent plastic strain) may be considered to be *irreversible;* that is, a reduction in the applied stress will have no effect on this term: the plastic strain will remain constant. The third term (time-dependent strain) may be considered *irreversible.**

For *creep under combined stress* (any state of stress) the methods presented in Sec. 5.2 may be applied. It is necessary only to change from plastic strain to *plastic-strain rate*. The effective stress $\bar{\sigma}$ is found as in Sec. 5.2 (the octahedral shear stress is usually used as a basis). This is used with a diagram in which the applied uniaxial stress is plotted against the corresponding creep rate. The value of $\bar{\sigma}$ determines a *secant modulus for time-dependent plastic strain*, defined as

$$E_{P_t} = \frac{\bar{\sigma}}{\dot{\epsilon}_P} \tag{5.15}$$

where $\dot{\epsilon}_P = d\epsilon_P/dt$. Equations (5.10) are now rewritten in terms of plastic strain rate:

$$
\begin{array}{ll}
\dot{\epsilon}_x^P = \dfrac{1}{E_{P_t}}\left(\sigma_x - \dfrac{1}{2}\sigma_y - \dfrac{1}{2}\sigma_z\right) & \dot{\gamma}_{xy}^P = 3\dfrac{\tau_{xy}}{E_{P_t}} \\[2mm]
\dot{\epsilon}_y^P = \dfrac{1}{E_{P_t}}\left(-\dfrac{1}{2}\sigma_x + \sigma_y - \dfrac{1}{2}\sigma_z\right) & \dot{\gamma}_{yz}^P = 3\dfrac{\tau_{yz}}{E_{P_t}} \\[2mm]
\dot{\epsilon}_z^P = \dfrac{1}{E_{P_t}}\left(-\dfrac{1}{2}\sigma_x - \dfrac{1}{2}\sigma_y + \sigma_z\right) & \dot{\gamma}_{zz}^P = 3\dfrac{\tau_{zz}}{E_{P_t}}
\end{array} \tag{5.16}
$$

See Eqs. (5.2) for other terms.

* A small amount of "recovery" of plastic strain has been observed in tests.

PROBLEMS

(Same basic stress-strain diagram may be used in Probs. 5.1 to 5.3.)

5.1. *Symmetrical loading.* Using a specified uniaxial stress-strain diagram from Appendix A, determine and plot a new diagram (for σ_1 and ϵ_1) for each of the following cases of combined loading. (Use $\nu = 1/3$.)

    (a) $\sigma_2 = \sigma_3 = +\frac{1}{3}\sigma_1$

    (b) $\sigma_2 = \sigma_3 = -\frac{1}{3}\sigma_1$

    (c) $\sigma_2 = \sigma_3 = \sigma_1$

Calculate the apparent modulus of elasticity for each case.

5.2. *Pure shear.* For the material specified in Prob. 5.1 determine the stress-strain (τ-γ) diagram for pure shear. (Use $\nu = 1/3$.)

5.3. *Unsymmetrical state of stress.* For a specified stress-strain diagram from Appendix A, determine and plot *two* stress-strain diagrams (σ_1-ϵ_1), one based on the maximum shear-stress theory, the other on the octahedral shear-stress theory, for an assigned set of ratios from Table P5.3. (Use $\nu = 1/3$.)

TABLE P5.3

	1	2	3	4	5	6	7
σ_2/σ_1	0.5	−0.4	0.6	0.5	−0.2	0.4	−0.3
σ_3/σ_1	0.2	−0.6	−0.2	−0.5	−0.4	0.3	−0.5

5.4. A tube having a mean diameter of 4 in. and a wall thickness of 0.010 in. is subjected to an internal pressure p (gauge) which is always proportional to an applied axial load P (positive axial load is tension). The ends of the tube are closed. The pressure is supplied by a hydraulic pump. Neglect the stress in a direction normal to the tube wall. Predict the stress σ_1, in the circumferential direction, at which the material will develop a plastic strain of $\epsilon_1 = 0.002$, using two different theories of plasticity (maximum shear stress and octahedral shear stress). Use an assigned material from Table A1, Appendix A, which gives the yield stress σ_y (for uniaxial load) corresponding to a plastic strain of 0.002. Use an assigned value of P/p from Table P5.4.

TABLE P5.4

	1	2	3	4	5	6
$\dfrac{P}{p}$, in.^{2}	5	8	12	2.5	−5	−12

5.5. A thin-walled tube of assigned cross-sectional dimensions D_{av} and t (see Table P5.5) serves as a cylinder in which a "frictionless" piston produces an internal pressure p. For a small square element cut from the side of the tube let σ_x, σ_y, and σ_z represent the normal stresses in the axial, circumferential, and thickness directions, respectively. While under pressure the tube also transmits a torsional moment which is proportional to the pressure p and which causes a shear stress τ_{xy} which is always equal to one-half the circumferential stress σ_y. Using a designated material from Appendix A, convert the specified tensile stress-strain diagram to one which describes the behavior of the tube in the circumferential (y) direction. [*Note:* Use octahedral shear-stress theory and membrane theory; let $\sigma_z = 0$ (across thickness).] (Use $\nu = 1/3$.)

Also determine the pressure at which a *permanent* circumferential strain of 0.002 would be developed.

TABLE P5.5

	1	2	3	4	5	6	7
D_{av}, in.	9	4	12	6	5	8	7
t, in.	0.25	0.10	0.375	0.30	0.125	0.120	0.25

5.6. A certain steel, in pure tension, has a "sharp" yield stress of 33,000 psi, below which no plastic strain occurs. In a state of plane stress ($\sigma_3 = 0$) let $\sigma_2 = K\sigma_1$, where $\sigma_1 \geq \sigma_2$.

(*a*) Derive a factor by which the yield stress in simple tension is multiplied to find the apparent yield stress in the plane state of stress (formula to be in terms of K).

(*b*) Calculate the apparent yield stresses (psi) for the following states of stress:

$$K = 1.0 \qquad K = \tfrac{1}{2} \qquad K = -\tfrac{1}{2} \qquad K = -1$$

5.7. A small cubic element of metal is subjected to a state of stress described by the following tensor (quantities in ksi), where the x, y, z system is used.

$$\begin{bmatrix} 20 & 15 & 12 \\ 15 & 10 & 8 \\ 12 & 8 & -30 \end{bmatrix}$$

(*a*) Calculate the octahedral shear stress using Eq. (5.7).

(*b*) Calculate the principal stresses σ_1, σ_2, and σ_3, and use Eq. (5.5) to calculate the octahedral shear stress, which should be equal to that calculated in (*a*).

5.8. Fig. P5.8 represents a common way of depicting a state of "plane stress," in which $\sigma_3 = 0$. For a material with a sharp yield stress σ_y, envelopes can be drawn showing the state of stress (σ_1, σ_2) at which yielding will occur. The family of curves thus obtained for different values of σ_y has been condensed in Fig. P5.8 by normalizing with respect to σ_y.

(a) Prove that the maximum shear-stress theory and the octahedral shear-stress theory predict the two different "yield envelopes" shown. Derive equations and also indicate which theory applies to each envelope.

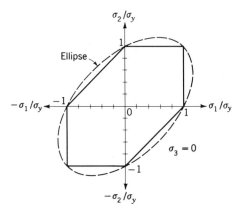

Figure P5.8

(b) Draw on Fig. P5.8 an axis representing all states of pure shear and calculate the percentage difference between the two theories when used for predicting the yield stress in this state. (Answer can be checked from diagram.)

(c) Indicate how the failure envelope would look if it is postulated that the critical stress for material failure is independent of actual shear stress and is governed only by the attainment of a *normal* tensile stress equal to σ_y. (*Note:* σ_y is used here as a fracture stress to avoid changing the drawing.) Assume that no failure occurs in compression.

(d) Assume that in pure compression a transverse tensile stress of σ_1 is generated at internal voids or flaws. Draw the complete envelope. (Such envelopes are typical of the behavior of some brittle materials.)

5.9. *Creep relaxation.* A steel bolt ($E = 29 \times 10^6$ psi) is used to clamp two rigid plates together. These plates are in an environment where the ambient temperature is kept at a constant value of 1,000°F. The bolt is initially tightened to such a degree that the tensile stress is 10,000 psi. Previous tests of this material at this same temperature indicate that the steady creep rate is given by Eq. (5.11) with $n_2 = 3.0$ and $C_2 = 4.37 \times 10^{-19}$. (*Note:* For these coefficients $d\epsilon/dt$ will have dimensions of strain/hr.) Assume that the bolt is tightened at ambient temperature.

(a) Neglecting any deformation of the plates and considering steady creep only, calculate the length of time after which the tensile stress in the bolt will have been reduced to one-half its initial value. [*Note:* An equation for solving this problem is to be developed based on the conceptual model implied by the statement that the total strain in the bolt (elastic plus creep) remains constant.]

(*b*) Using the equation developed in part *a*, determine the stress in the bolt after one year has elapsed.

5.10. *Design problem; large-deflection.* Find the minimum required cross-sectional area of a cable which is to transmit a centrally located 2,000 lb vertical load over a horizontal span of 20 ft. Figure P5.10 shows the initial position the cable and load are to have when installed. The cable must

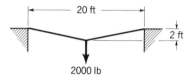

2000 lb

Figure P5.10

operate at a constant temperature of 850°F. It is required that the point of load application must not sag more than 1.0 ft during a "life" of 10 years. The material is to be low-carbon steel (see Fig. 5.9) or any other material for which creep data are available. For low-carbon steel the maximum allowable stress may be assumed to be 20,000 psi.

It may be found convenient to estimate first an initial cross-sectional area, then assume increments of deflection and calculate the elapsed time to the occurrence of that deflection. The process may be repeated until a minimum cross-sectional area is established. Neglect elastic deflections and consider steady creep only. (Use a computation table.)

Chapter 6

Shear and Bending Moment

6.1 Definitions and conventions

In Sec. 1.2 the structural function was described in terms of four different states of loading which may occur simultaneously, but which are usually analyzed separately. Uniaxial loading was treated in Chap. 1, biaxial and triaxial loading in Chaps. 2 to 5. In many structures, such as buildings and bridges, there are components which perform primarily the function of transmitting transverse forces (*shear*) and transverse moments (*bending*). Such members, if relatively slender, are usually called *beams*.

In analyzing the behavior of beams it is convenient to start with a state of *pure bending*. Several examples are shown in Fig. 6.1. In this figure, sketches *d* and *e* represent the shear and moment diagrams for a beam in which only the center portion is subjected to pure bending (this type of loading is often used in testing specimens).

From the force-transmission viewpoint, shear and moment diagrams represent plots of the resultant transverse force and bending moment being transmitted at every cross section along the beam. In Fig. 6.2*c*, the general loading condition at station *z* is represented by three resultants: an axial force *P*, a transverse force (shear) *V*, and a resultant moment *M*. This sketch implies that there are no force components acting normal to the *zy* plane. There are also no torsional moments. This beam is classed as a *cantilever;* the direction of force transmission is "one-way."

In Fig. 6.2*d* the *reacting* forces and moments are shown. By Newton's third law, they must be equal and opposite to the resultants shown in sketch *c*. When a structure, component, or element is in static equilibrium, any isolated ("cut") portion must remain in equilibrium under the action of all forces and moments acting on it. Sketch *d* represents a *free-body diagram*, for which the laws of static equilibrium must be satisfied. For the two-dimensional abstraction represented by Fig. 6.2, only three

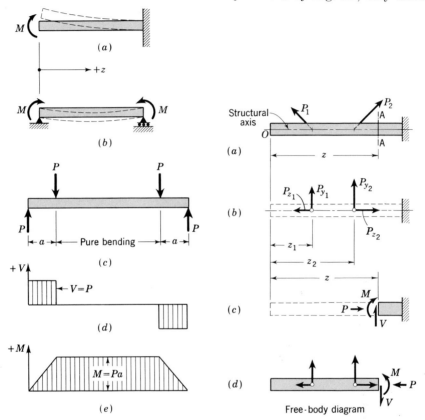

Figure 6.1. Examples of pure bending.

Figure 6.2. Cantilever beam with concentrated loads.

equilibrium equations are meaningful. They are $\Sigma P_y = 0$, $\Sigma P_z = 0$, $\Sigma M_x = 0$, where the summation includes all external loads, as well as the reacting forces and moments at any "cut" surface or supports.

Figure 6.3 shows a beam with various types of loading. The ends are "pinned" (or "hinged"). The free-body diagram is shown in sketch *b*. The *reactions must be shown in the free-body diagram*, even though their values are not initially known. A roller is is shown at one end of the beam. This convention indicates that the support is incapable of resisting a force parallel with the surface on which the roller bears.

Figure 6.4 shows two examples of *statically indeterminate* beams (Sec. 9.3). The end conditions shown represent the conditions of *constraint* used in the conceptual model.

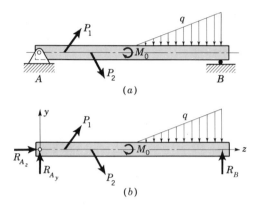

(a)

(b)

Figure 6.3. Simply supported beam with various loadings.

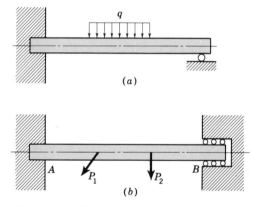

(a)

(b)

Figure 6.4. Statically indeterminate beams.

In the calculation of shear and bending moment at any point, certain conventions about signs and state of loading must be adopted. Those usually used in beam analysis are shown in Fig. 6.5. These sketches represent positive *states* of shear and bending. In applying the laws of equilibrium, positive conventions with respect to *sense* must be used.

The shear convention of Fig. 6.5 does not agree with that used for "state of stress" (see Fig. 2.5). Furthermore, the conventions are ambiguous for vertical or curved beams, or for gravity-free structures in outer space (where there is no way to distinguish "up" or "down").

A typical generalized engineering system, which is independent of gravity, is indicated below:

1. Select a positive direction of transmission along the structural axis. (For curved beams use s; for straight beams use z.)
2. Work with the shear and bending moment acting on the portion of the beam toward which they are transmitted.
3. Positive bending moments act clockwise.
4. Positive shear acts in a direction such that a positive increment of moment is produced over a distance ds (or dz) in the positive direction of transmission.

For a curved beam the above conventions are illustrated in Fig. 6.6. (The structural axis lies in the plane of the paper.) For a horizontal

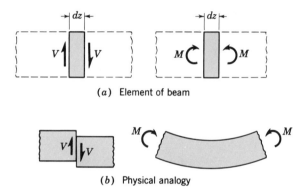

(a) Element of beam

(b) Physical analogy

Figure 6.5. Positive states of shear and bending (structural engineering system).

straight beam with force transmission from left to right, the conventions agree with those of Fig. 6.5.

With these conventions a positive state of shear is represented either by a positive shear force transmitted in a positive direction or a negative shear force transmitted in a negative direction. A similar rule applies for a positive state of bending.

6.2 Relationships between loading, shear, and bending moment

Figure 6.7 shows a narrow slice through a beam with distributed loading. The local loading at station s is given by the value of line force q, which is a function of s. At an incremental distance Δs to the right, the loading is $q + \Delta q$. Over the distance Δs the loading is shown as varying linearly. The increment of shear is

$$\Delta V = q\,\Delta s + \tfrac{1}{2}\Delta q\,\Delta s$$

The rate of change of shear is found by dividing by Δs:

$$\frac{\Delta V}{\Delta s} = q + \frac{1}{2}\Delta q$$

Now let Δs approach zero as a limit. The value of Δq also approaches zero, giving, in the limit,

$$\boxed{\frac{dV}{ds} = q} \qquad\qquad (6.1)$$

The increment of moment is

$$\Delta M = V\,\Delta s + (q\,\Delta s)(\tfrac{1}{2}\Delta s) + (\tfrac{1}{2}\Delta q\,\Delta s)(\tfrac{1}{3}\Delta s)$$

Dividing by Δs,

$$\frac{\Delta M}{\Delta s} = V + \frac{1}{2}q\,\Delta s + \frac{1}{6}\Delta q\,\Delta s$$

Let Δs approach zero as a limit; then

$$\boxed{\frac{dM}{ds} = V} \qquad\qquad (6.2)$$

These important equations, (6.1) and (6.2), completely represent the relationships between distributed loading, shear, and bending moment. It will be shown later how these equations can also be used for concentrated forces, moments, and discontinuous distributions.

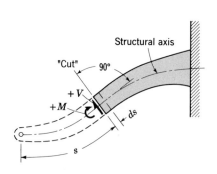
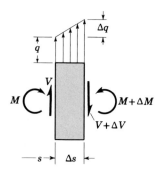

Figure 6.6. Structural conventions for positive shear and bending in a curved beam.

Figure 6.7. Incremental relationships between loading, shear, and bending moment.

Stated in words:

1. The rate of change of shear at a point is equal to the value of the distributed loading at that point.
2. The rate of change of bending moment at a point is equal to the value of the shear at that point.

As a corollary, Eq. (6.2) tells us that *a relative maximum or minimum value of M will occur wherever* $V = 0$. In the above statements, "point" refers to a point on the structural axis.

Either of two different procedures may be used to evaluate reactions, shears, and moments.

DEFINITE INTEGRAL METHOD. Calculate reactions R_A and R_B in advance by applying the equations of equilibrium. These reactions are then treated as external loads on the free body and are applied in the proper directions.

INDEFINITE INTEGRAL METHOD. Integrate Eqs. (6.1) and (6.2) successively, retaining the constants of integration. The latter are then evaluated by applying the known boundary conditions at the two ends. The shears at a support determine the reacting force R (see Example 6.2).

All terms in the equations for shear and bending moment must refer to forces and moments acting on that portion of the beam in the direction of transmission.

The *principle of superposition* may be used; that is, a beam having several different types of loading may be analyzed for each type independently and the shears (or moments) at any point may be added algebraically to obtain the final result. This method is valid when the shear and moment are linear functions of the intensity of loading; for example, when deflections are relatively small and no axial forces are being transmitted.

EXAMPLE 6.1. For the beam shown in Fig. E6.1, the loading function is

$$q = -10 \text{ lb/in.}$$

The reactions can be calculated by treating the entire beam as a free body, replacing the distributed loading by its resultant, which is equal to $10 \times 180 = 1,800$ lb, acting at a distance $z = 90$ in., or 70 in. to the right of A.

For $\Sigma M = 0$ about A,

$$1,800 \times 70 - 120R_B = 0 \qquad R_B = +1,050 \text{ lb} \quad \text{(up)}$$

For $\Sigma M = 0$ about B,

$$-1,800 \times 20 + 120R_A = 0 \qquad R_A = +750 \text{ lb} \quad \text{(up)}$$

FOR SECTIONS TO THE LEFT OF A.

$$V = \int q\,dz + C_1 = \int -10dz + C_1 = -10z + C_1$$

At $z = 0$, $V = 0$; therefore $C_1 = 0$, $V = -10z$,

$$M = \int V\,dz + C_2 = \int -10z\,dz + C_2 = -5z^2 + C_2$$

At $z = 0$, $M = 0$; therefore $C_2 = 0$,

$$M = -5z^2$$

FOR SECTIONS BETWEEN A AND B. The reaction R_A must be included in the loading. C_1 and C_2 remain zero:

$$V = 750 - 10z$$
$$M = \int V\,dz = 750(z - 20) - 5z^2$$

FOR SECTIONS TO THE RIGHT OF B. Both R_A and R_B must be included:

$$V = 750 + 1,050 - 10z = 1,800 - 10z$$
$$M = \int V\,dz = 750(z - 20) + 1,050(z - 140) - 5z^2$$

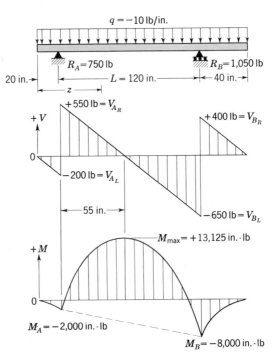

Figure E6.1

Applying these equations to sections respectively to the left and right of A,

$$V_{A_L} = -10z = -10 \times 20 = -200 \text{ lb}$$
$$V_{A_R} = 750 - 10 \times 20 = +550 \text{ lb}$$
$$M_{A_L} = -5 \times 20^2 = -2,000 \text{ in.-lb}$$
$$M_{A_R} = 1,800(20 - 20) - 5 \times 20^2 = -2,000 \text{ in.-lb}$$

(This result confirms the fact that no bending moment can be resisted by the support at A.)

FOR STATIONS TO THE LEFT AND RIGHT OF B.

$$V_{B_L} = 750 - 10 \times 140 = -650 \text{ lb}$$
$$V_{B_R} = 1,800 - 10 \times 140 = +400 \text{ lb}$$
$$M_{B_L} = 750(140 - 20) - 5 \times 140^2 = -8,000 \text{ in.-lb}$$
$$M_{B_R} = 750(140 - 20) + 1,050 \times (140 - 140) - 5 \times 140^2$$
$$= -8,000 \text{ in.-lb (check)}$$

These values are shown in Fig. E6.1.

To find the maximum bending moment in the central span, let $V = 0$. Using the proper equations for V and M,

$$0 = 750 - 10z$$
$$z = \tfrac{750}{10} = 75 \text{ in. (55 in. to right of } A)$$
$$M_{\max} = 750(75 - 20) - 5 \times 75^2 = +13,125 \text{ in.-lb}$$

EXAMPLE 6.2. The central span of the beam of Example 6.1 will be analyzed by treating it as a simple beam with known moments applied at each end, using the indefinite integral method. The overhang shears V_{A_L} and V_{B_R} are resisted at the supporting points and are not transmitted across the central span: therefore they do not appear in the equations. The distance z is measured from station A.

$$V = \int q \, dz + C_1 = -10z + C_1$$
$$M = \int V \, dz + C_2 = -5z^2 + C_1z + C_2$$

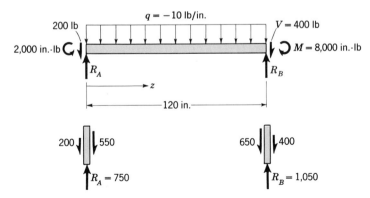

Figure E6.2

Boundary conditions are as follows: at A, $(z = 0)$; $M_A = -2,000$ in.-lb. Substituting in the moment equation gives

$$-2,000 = 0 + 0 + C_2 \quad \text{and} \quad C_2 = -2,000$$

therefore $M = -5z^2 + C_1 z - 2,000$. At B, $(z = 120)$; $M_B = -8,000$ in.-lb.
Note: Since the equation for M gives the moment on the portion *to the right* of the station, we must treat M_B as negative in using this method of solution.

Substituting in the above moment equation gives

$$-8,000 = -5 \times 120^2 + C_1 \times 120 - 2,000$$
$$C_1 = \frac{-8,000 + 72,000 + 2,000}{120} = +550 \text{ lb}$$

therefore,
$$V = -10z + 550$$

To find the reaction at A we evaluate the shear to the right of A:

$$V_{A_R} = V_{(z=0)} = +550 \text{ lb}$$

Isolating a small element just above the reacting force (see figure) we show this shear as negative because it is being transmitted in a negative direction (to the left).

Applying the equation of equilibrium for the small isolated body (forces positive upward) we have

$$R_A - 200 - 550 = 0$$
$$R_A = +750 \text{ lb} \quad \text{(up)}$$

Similarly, at B,

$$R_B - 650 - 400 = 0$$
$$R_B = +1,050 \text{ lb} \quad \text{(up)}$$

6.3 Local and discontinuous loadings (singularity functions)

The two basic equations (6.1) and (6.2), giving the relationship between shear, bending moments, and applied loading, were derived in Sec. 6.2. For a straight beam they are

$$\frac{dV}{dz} = q \quad \text{and} \quad \frac{dM}{dz} = V$$

It has been shown that the determination of shear and bending moments consists of the successive integration of these equations, together with evaluation of the constants of integration. But the loading on the beam may include concentrated forces (F or P) and concentrated moments (M). The loading function q is in terms of *line force* and therefore cannot provide for such localized loadings. However, by the introduction of special integration rules, q can be made to provide for local forces and moments. At the same time the complications involved in integrating discontinuous functions can be conveniently bypassed by introducing certain operational rules, described below.

Following the presentation of Ref. 6, the *singularity function* is written as

$$q(z) = \langle z - a \rangle^n \qquad (6.3)$$

where z is any distance along the beam, and a is the particular value of z at which the discontinuity or singularity occurs.

The operational rules are as follows:

1. When the quantity within the angle brackets is *negative* ($z < a$), the entire bracketed quantity is *zero*.
2. When the quantity within the angle brackets is *positive* ($z > a$), the angle brackets behave as ordinary brackets; that is, $\langle z - a \rangle$ is replaced by $(z - a)$.

Simply stated, nothing happens at values of z less than a. From that point on, the quantity being treated is a function of $(z - a)$.

Singularities of different degrees are indicated by the value of n, as shown in Table 6.1.

These functions obey the following integration law:

$$\int_{-\infty}^{z} \langle z - a \rangle^n \, dz = \frac{\langle z - a \rangle^{n+1}}{n + 1} \qquad \text{for } n \geq 0 \qquad (6.4)$$

The first two functions of Table 6.1 ("doublet" and "impulse") are defined so as to obey the following special integration rules:

$$\int_{-\infty}^{z} \langle z - a \rangle_{-2} \, dz = \langle z - a \rangle_{-1} \qquad (6.4a)$$

$$\int_{-\infty}^{z} \langle z - a \rangle_{-1} \, dz = \langle z - a \rangle^0 = \begin{cases} 0 & \text{when } z < a \\ 1 & \text{when } z > a \end{cases} \qquad (6.4b)$$

Two other functions of Table 6.1 are summarized below:

$$\int_{-\infty}^{z} \langle z - a \rangle^0 \, dz = \langle z - a \rangle^1 = \begin{cases} 0 & \text{when } z < a \\ (z - a) & \text{when } z > a \end{cases} \qquad (6.4c)$$

$$\int_{-\infty}^{z} \langle z - a \rangle^1 \, dz = \frac{\langle z - a \rangle^2}{2} = \begin{cases} 0 & \text{when } z < a \\ \dfrac{(z - a)^2}{2} & \text{when } z > a \end{cases} \qquad (6.4d)$$

The singularity functions are active from $z = a$ to $z = \infty$. To "stop" the loading at $z = b$, it is necessary to apply a supplementary loading of the same type (but of opposite sense) at $z = b$.

The special integration rules represented by Eqs. (6.4a) and (6.4b) can be interpreted as withholding the loading functions (F or M) from the successive integration process until the proper level of abstraction has been reached.

TABLE 6.1

Singularity functions

Type of loading	Designation	Physical picture
Concentrated moment (doublet function)	$q(z) = M_0\langle z - a \rangle_{-2}$	
Concentrated force (impulse, or Dirac function)	$q(z) = F_0\langle z - a \rangle_{-1}$	
Line force (step function)	$q(z) = q_0\langle z - a \rangle^0$	
Linearly varying force (ramp function)	$q(z) = S_0(z - a)^1$	
Quadratically varying force	$q(z) = C_0 \dfrac{\langle z - a \rangle^2}{2}$	

EXAMPLE 6.3. In this example the loading function is

$$q = -10\langle z - 20 \rangle^0 + 10\langle z - 70 \rangle^0 \text{ lb/in.} \tag{a}$$

$$V = \int q \, dz + C_1 = -10[\langle z - 20 \rangle^1 - \langle z - 70 \rangle^1] + C_1 \tag{b}$$

$$M = \int V \, dz + C_2 = -10\left[\frac{\langle z - 20 \rangle^2}{2} - \frac{\langle z - 70 \rangle^2}{2}\right] + C_1 z + C_2 \tag{c}$$

The boundary conditions are as follows: At $z = 0$, $M = 0$; therefore $C_2 = 0$. At $z = 100$, $M = 0$, thus

$$0 = -5[(100 - 20)^2 - (100 - 70)^2] + 100C_1$$
$$C_1 = \tfrac{5}{100}(5{,}500) = +275$$
$$R_A = V_A = 275 \text{ lb}$$
$$R_B = 10 \times 50 - 275 = 225 \text{ lb}$$

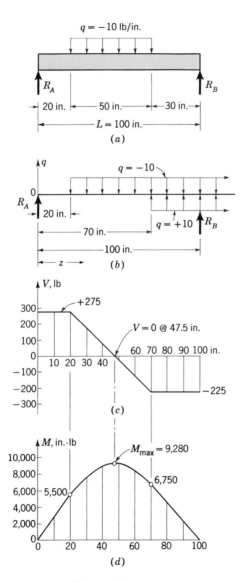

Figure E6.3

Substituting in (*b*) and (*c*),

$$V = 275 - 10[\langle z - 20 \rangle^1 - \langle z - 70 \rangle^1] \qquad (d)$$
$$M = 275z - 5[\langle z - 20 \rangle^2 - \langle z - 70 \rangle^2] \qquad (e)$$

To find z at which $V = 0$ and $M = M_{max}$, assume that z is less than 70 in. but greater than 20 in. Then

$$0 = 275 - 10(z - 20) = 275 - 10z + 200$$
$$z_{(V=0)} = 47.5 \text{ in.}$$
$$M_{max} = 275 \times 47.5 - 5(47.5 - 20)^2$$
$$= 13,060 - 3,780 = 9,280 \text{ in.-lb}$$
$$M_{20} = 275 \times 20 = 5,500$$
$$M_{70} = 275 \times 70 - 5(70 - 20)^2 = 6,750$$

The shear and bending-moment curves are shown in Fig. E6.3*c–d*.

6.4 Area-moment method

By definition, the centroidal distance $\bar{x}$ of an area is obtained by finding the moment of the area about some point and dividing this moment by

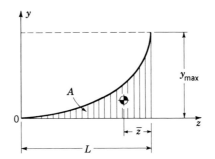

Figure 6.8. Area-moment relationships.

the area. Therefore the moment of the area may be found by reversing the procedure, giving (see Fig. 6.8)

$$M_{area} = \bar{z}A$$

where M is the moment about a point on the z axis where $z = L$. Thus, if the area and centroidal distance of a diagram are both known, it is unnecessary to perform the integrations.

The area-moment method is most useful in dealing with power functions. By integration, the following relationships will be found:

Function	Area factor	Moment-arm factor
$y = C_1$	1.0	$\frac{1}{2}$
$y = C_2 z$	$\frac{1}{2}$	$\frac{1}{3}$
$y = C_3 z^2$	$\frac{1}{3}$	$\frac{1}{4}$
$y = Cz^n$	$\dfrac{1}{n+1}$	$\dfrac{1}{n+2}$

where (see Fig. 6.8)

$$\text{Area factor} = \frac{\text{actual area}}{\text{area of rectangle}} = \frac{A}{y_{max} L}$$

$$\text{Moment-arm factor} = \frac{\text{centroidal distance}}{\text{base length}} = \frac{\bar{z}}{L}$$

EXAMPLE 6.4. Find the maximum shear and bending moment for a cantilever beam with linearly varying loading (Fig. E6.4)

$$q = Cz \qquad \text{and} \qquad q_{max} = CL$$

The area of the loading triangle, to the proper scale, gives the shear at point z,

$$V = \tfrac{1}{2}Cz^2$$
$$V_{max} = \tfrac{1}{2}CL^2 = \tfrac{1}{2}q_{max}L$$

To find M multiply this area by the distance from the centroid to the point z.

$$M = \left(\frac{1}{2}Cz^2\right) \times \frac{z}{3} = \frac{1}{6}Cz^3$$
$$M_{max} = \tfrac{1}{6}CL^3 = \tfrac{1}{6}q_{max}L^2$$

EXAMPLE 6.5. Find the reactions for the simple beam of Fig. E6.5. The resultant force is

$$R_q = \tfrac{1}{2}q_{max}L \qquad \text{and} \qquad \bar{z} = \frac{L}{3}$$

For moment equilibrium with respect to the right end,

$$R_A L - R_q \bar{z} = 0$$
$$R_A = \frac{1}{2}\frac{q_{max}L\bar{z}}{L} = \frac{1}{2}q_{max}\frac{L}{3} = \frac{1}{6}q_{max}L$$

Repeating for the left end,

$$-R_B L + R_q(L - \bar{z}) = 0$$
$$R_B = \frac{\tfrac{1}{2}q_{max}L(2L/3)}{L} = \frac{1}{3}q_{max}L$$

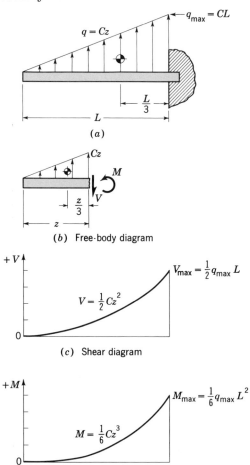

$$q = Cz$$

$$q_{max} = CL$$

(a)

(b) Free-body diagram

$$V = \frac{1}{2}Cz^2$$

$$V_{max} = \frac{1}{2}q_{max}L$$

(c) Shear diagram

$$M = \frac{1}{6}Cz^3$$

$$M_{max} = \frac{1}{6}q_{max}L^2$$

(d) Moment diagram

Figure E6.4

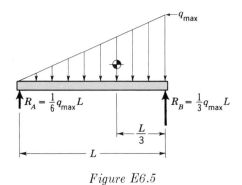

$$q_{max}$$

$$R_A = \frac{1}{6}q_{max}L$$

$$R_B = \frac{1}{3}q_{max}L$$

Figure E6.5

Check for $\Sigma P_y = 0$:

$$\tfrac{1}{6}q_{max}L + \tfrac{1}{3}q_{max}L - \tfrac{1}{2}q_{max}L = 0$$

Replacing distributed loadings by their resultants gives the correct answer for the reactions. *This method must be used with caution in dealing with the internal shear and bending moment.* For example, the V and M diagrams for beams actually loaded with the resultant force *only* would be quite different from the diagrams for Fig. E6.5.

6.5 Shear and bending in curved beams

For a curved beam lying in a plane, it is convenient to establish two orthogonal axes and to determine the shear with respect to each of these axes separately. The bending moment about the axis normal to the plane is determined by integrating the shear along each axis and adding the results algebraically.

Applied concentrated forces must first be resolved into components along each axis. For a parallel line force q, the effect of q in a given direction is obtained by multiplying q by the projected length of the portion of the structural axis involved.

The following equations apply when the conventions of Fig. 6.9 are used:

$$V_z = \sum_{i=1}^{n} P_{z_i}$$

$$V_y = \sum_{i=1}^{n} P_{y_i}$$

$$M = \sum_{i=1}^{n} P_{y_i}(z - z_i) - \sum_{i=1}^{n} P_{z_i}(y - y_i)$$

$$V_s = V_y \cos \theta - V_z \sin \theta$$

$$P_a = V_y \sin \theta + V_z \cos \theta$$

In the last equation V has been replaced by P_a, because this component of the forces is actually an axial force (V usually implies a transverse force). Figure 6.9c shows P_a as compression.

A beam having a different type of curvature from that shown in Fig. 6.9 may require a new set of conventions to be established; this may change some of the signs in the equations.

It should be noted that no change of the moment is required in going from Fig. 6.9b to c. (This follows from the fact that the axis for moments does not change direction. This axis is normal to the zy plane.) Furthermore, it would be wrong to use the shear components V_z and V_y (Fig. 6.9b) in analyzing the beam for stresses and deflections.

Curved simple beams may be analyzed in the same general manner as straight simple beams. The reactions are found by writing the equations of equilibrium for the beam as a free body. The shear and moment values are then found, treating the reactions as applied loads.

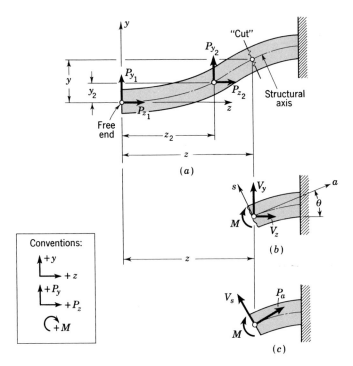

(a)

(b)

(c)

Figure 6.9. Forces and moments in a curved cantilever beam.

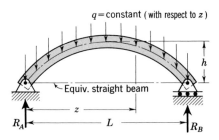

Figure 6.10. Simple curved beam under uniform loading.

The special case of uniform loading is shown in Fig. 6.10, where q is assumed to be constant with respect to the horizontal distance z. The *vertical* shear and bending-moment curves will be identical with those for a straight beam between the two points of support, provided that the reactions are vertical, as shown.

Figure 6.11 shows a curved beam for which one of the reactions is compelled to occur in a direction other than vertical (by angular placement of rollers). The required value of the *vertical component of R_A* is found from the free-body diagram.

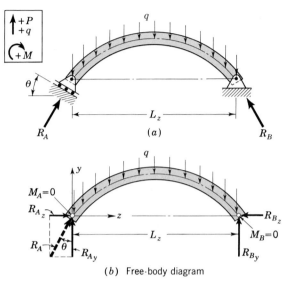

(b) Free-body diagram

Figure 6.11. Curved beam with slanted reactions.

Taking moments about pin B and applying $\Sigma M = 0$,

$$R_{A_y} L_z - \frac{(qL_z)L_z}{2} = 0$$

$$R_{A_y} = \frac{qL_z}{2}$$

Since R_A must lie at the angle θ,

$$R_A = \frac{R_{A_y}}{\cos \theta} \quad \text{and} \quad R_{A_z} = R_{A_y} \tan \theta$$

Applying $\Sigma P_z = 0$,

$$R_{A_z} - R_{B_z} = 0$$
$$R_{B_z} = R_{A_z}$$

Applying $\Sigma P_y = 0$,

$$R_{A_y} - qL_z + R_{B_y} = 0$$
$$R_{B_y} = qL_z - R_{A_y} = \frac{qL_z}{2}$$

When the two components of the reactions at A have been found, the shear and bending-moment values at any point along the beam can be determined by applying the method developed for the curved cantilever beam (the known reactions must be treated as applied loads).

When the beam is uniformly loaded over the span and the shape is parabolic, the angle θ may be chosen so as to make the reaction R_A coincide with the direction of the structural axis at point A. The bending moment at any point along the beam will then be found to be zero (neglecting any effects of change in shape of beam under loading; see Prob. 6.14).

PROBLEMS*

6.1. Sketch shear and bending moment diagrams for assigned beams in Fig. P6.1, roughly to scale. Show expressions for the maximum (absolute) values of V and M in terms of parameters shown (L,a,b,P,q_0).

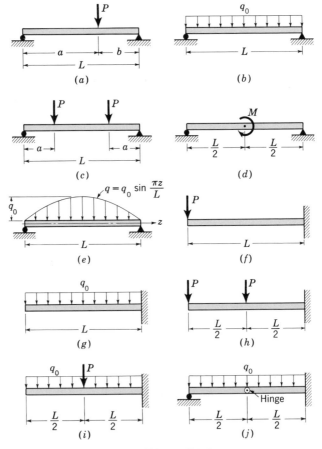

Figure P6.1

---

* Probs. 6.1 and 6.2 may be omitted if the student has had adequate training on this subject in statics.

6.2. Draw shear and bending moment diagrams (to scale) for assigned beams in Fig. P6.2 (dimensions are in inches, and loads are in kips or kips per inch). Calculate and state actual values of V_{max} and M_{max}.

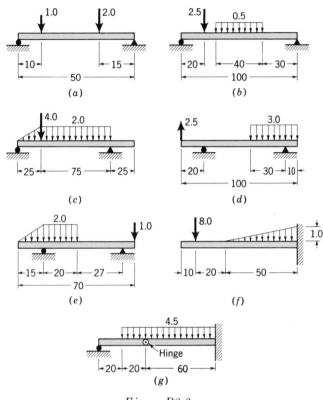

Figure P6.2

6.3. A uniformly loaded beam is supported as shown. Determine the distance a to support points if the maximum absolute value of bending moment is to be as small as possible. Also find a when loading q_0 acts partially over *any* portion of beam.

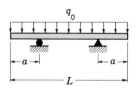

Figure P6.3

6.4. Derive expressions for the axial force, shear, and bending moment in one arm of the structure shown in Fig. P6.4.

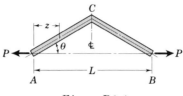

Figure P6.4

6.5. Draw shear, bending moment, and axial load diagrams for the beam of Prob. 1.1 (Chap. 1). Assume that the structural axis is defined by the equation $y = 87.5 + 62.5 \cos (\pi x/240)$. Adjust coordinates of points C and D to be (300, 43.3) in. and (140, 71.3) in., respectively. Omit the z component of F_2; that is, let $F_2 = (-400, -100, 0)$ lb. The diagrams may be drawn with reference to the horizontal axis. (Note that the axis system used in Prob. 1.1 is not the same as that used in this chapter.)

6.6. Draw shear, bending moment, and axial load diagrams for the beam of Prob. 1.2. Plot values normal to curved centerline of beam in this case.

6.7. A truck having a front axle load of 5 kips, a rear axle load of 10 kips, and a wheelbase of 10 ft crosses a bridge of 50-ft span. What is the value of the maximum bending moment in the span? Neglect dynamic effects. (*Note:* Two possible approaches to the solution are as follows: 1. Bending moment diagrams may be found for various truck locations and the maximum moment determined by this trial-and-error procedure. 2. An exact value may be determined mathematically for the location of the resultant of the two axle loads which will lead to maximum moment under the larger of the two loads. Start by computing reactions, using resultant truck weight. Then write an expression for M under the rear axle in terms of distance from the beam end to the load resultant, and distance from the resultant to the rear axle. Differentiate this expression with respect to z, and set equal to zero to find the desired truck location.)

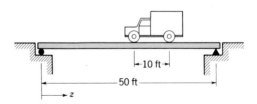

Figure P6.7

6.8. Shear and moment diagrams for a beam are shown in Fig. P6.8.

(*a*) Draw the free-body sketch and indicate all forces and moments acting on the beam, including reactions. Perform statical checks to insure that the loading system is in equilibrium.

(*b*) Express the loading on the beam in terms of singularity and related functions.

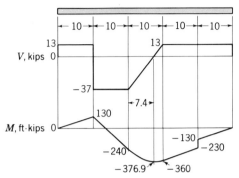

Figure P6.8

6.9. Given the shear diagram of Fig. P6.9, construct the loading picture, showing values of loads and reactions. Also compute the maximum values of the positive and negative bending moments. (*Note:* There are no concentrated moments acting on the beam.)

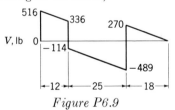

Figure P6.9

6.10. Compute the state of loading (*M* and *P*) at a point on the curved member (Fig. P6.10) at which the bending moment is a maximum. Also

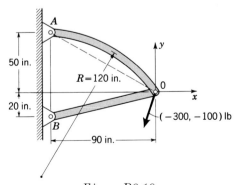

Figure P6.10

find the compressive load in the lower member. (*Hint:* Analyze by using the "phantom" member indicated by dashed line. Omit changes of geometry due to deflections.)

6.11. The structure shown in Fig. P6.11 is elliptical, that is, $z = a \cos \theta$, $y = b \sin \theta$. Let $k = b/a$, and derive equations for V and M in terms of P, a, k, and θ. Calculate values for 30° intervals for $P = 1,000$ lb, $a = 60$ in., and $b = 40$ in.

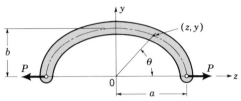

Figure P6.11

6.12. Sketch a parabolic arch having a value of $h/L = 0.20$ (see below). The arch is attached to a rigid foundation by pins at each end. Write an equation for the centerline in terms of y (height), z (horizontal distance from left end), h (maximum value of y), and L (span). Let the arch be loaded by uniformly spaced vertical cables, each carrying the same load, such that the loading can be approximated by a constant value of q acting over the span. (This load must include weight of arch, in actual design.) Prove that the horizontal component (H) of the reacting force at a pin must equal M_{max}/h, if the assumption is made that *no bending moments exist in the arch member.* Then show that this assumption will be fulfilled for the above value of H.

Notes: (*a*) M_{max} refers to the maximum bending moment for a substitute horizontal beam.

(*b*) Calculate H by drawing the free-body diagram for a half arch, with no moment in the arch at its midpoint.

(*c*) This structure is statically indeterminate. It can be made statically determinate by inserting a third pin (or hinge) at any point (usually at the apex).

(*d*) The "two-hinged" (statically indeterminate) arch actually behaves in the manner described except for relatively small moments that are the result of deformations.

(*e*) This problem illustrates the basic principle involved in masonry arches, in which it is necessary that bending moments be small, relative to the axial loads.

Chapter 7

Analysis of Bending

7.1 Historical development of the bending theory

A member which transmits transverse loads was probably one of the earliest structures used by man. It was also one of the first for which a stress analysis was attempted. The following passage is quoted from Galileo's famous book "Two New Sciences" (Ref. 7). Figure 7.1 has been copied from the original publication of 1638.

Proposition I

A prism or solid cylinder of glass, steel, wood or other breakable material which is capable of sustaining a very heavy weight when applied longitudinally is, as previously remarked, easily broken by the transverse application of a weight which may be much smaller in proportion as the length of the cylinder exceeds its thickness.

Let us imagine a solid prism $ABCD$ fastened into a wall at the end AB, and supporting a weight E at the other end; understand also that the wall is vertical and that the prism or cylinder is fastened at right angles to the wall. It is clear that, if the cylinder breaks, fracture will occur at the point B where the edge of the mortise acts as a fulcrum for the lever BC, to which the force is applied; the thickness of the solid BA is the other arm of

the lever along which is located the resistance. This resistance opposes the separation of the part BD, lying outside the wall, from that portion lying inside. From the preceding, it follows that the magnitude (*momento*) of the force applied at C bears to the magnitude (*momento*) of the resistance, found in the thickness of the prism, that is, in the attachment of the base BA to .its contiguous parts, the same ratio which the length CB bears to half the length BA; if now we define absolute resistance to fracture as that offered to a longitudinal pull (in which case the stretching force acts in the same direction as that through which the body is moved), then it follows that the absolute resistance of the prism BD is to the breaking load placed at the end of the lever BC in the same ratio as the length *BC* is to the half of *AB* in the case of a prism, or the semidiameter in the case of a cylinder. This is our first proposition. Observe that in what has here been said the weight of the solid *BD* itself has been left out of consideration, or rather, the prism has been assumed to be devoid of weight.

Galileo's hypothesis implies that the axial stresses resisting bending are uniformly distributed over the cross section and that the axis of rotation of the cross section is at the edge, as shown in Fig. 7.2*a*. Although this is now known to be incorrect, the general principles used by Galileo were correct, and he developed from them many other useful propositions.

Figure 7.1. Illustration used by Galileo. (From Ref. 7.)

The next major step was taken by J. Bernoulli, as indicated in Fig. 7.2*b*. He used the concept that plane cross sections remain plane and also applied Hooke's law, thereby obtaining a linearly varying stress distribution.

Both Galileo and Bernoulli apparently failed to realize that, when there is no axial (horizontal) force applied externally, there can be no resultant axial resisting force within the beam or at the point of support. Figures 7.2*a* and *b* clearly show this discrepancy. These theories fail to satisfy the law of equilibrium, $\Sigma P = 0$, although they do satisfy the law $\Sigma M = 0$.

The correct stress distribution was independently discovered by Parent and Coulomb, as indicated in Fig. 7.2c. They introduced the concept of a *neutral axis*, about which both laws of equilibrium must be satisfied.

The values of the maximum (elastic) stress for a rectangular cross section are shown in Fig. 7.2. Galileo's theory gives a stress of one-third

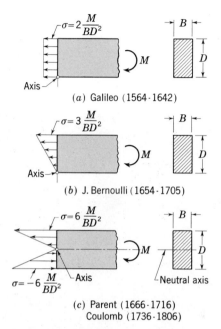

(a) Galileo (1564-1642)

(b) J. Bernoulli (1654-1705)

(c) Parent (1666-1716)
Coulomb (1736-1806)

Figure 7.2. Historical development of bending theory.

of the correct value; Bernoulli's gives one-half. (For additional historical background, see Ref. 1.)

Galileo: $\qquad\qquad \sigma_{\max} = 2\dfrac{M}{BD^2} \qquad$ wrong

J. Bernoulli: $\qquad\quad \sigma_{\max} = 3\dfrac{M}{BD^2} \qquad$ wrong

Parent-Coulomb: $\qquad \sigma_{\max} = 6\dfrac{M}{BD^2} \qquad$ correct

where B is the width, and D is the depth, of a rectangular cross section. Note that all three theories are identical except for the constant factor. They can be written in the following form:

$$\sigma_{\max} = \frac{M}{Z}$$

where Z is the *section modulus*. For a rectangular cross section,

$$Z = \frac{BD^2}{6}$$

7.2 Theory of pure bending (symmetrical)

Although bending moments are usually the result of transverse force transmission (shear), the theory of bending is best developed first for *pure bending moment* (no axial load, no shear, no torsion). Such a loading condition can be obtained in a test in which the center portion of the

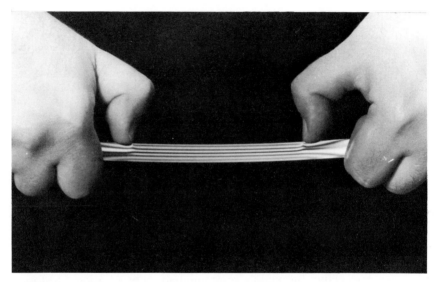

Figure 7.3. Photoelastic demonstration of a beam under pure bending.

specimen is subjected to pure bending (see Fig. 6.1). However, there is a small region adjacent to the points of load application where the internal stress distribution is complex. In accordance with Saint-Venant's principle (Sec. 1.3), the local effects will disappear in a distance roughly on the order of the depth of the beam. (For this reason, the length of the center portion of a test specimen should be at least three times the depth, and measurements should not be made close to the points of load application.)

Figure 7.3 shows a classroom demonstration specimen made of a transparent plastic material through which a beam of polarized light is passed. The alternate bands are called *isochromatics*. Their number and spacing is a function of the difference in principal stresses. Proper interpretation of the photograph shows that the normal stress distribution varies linearly over the depth. (For additional information on photoelasticity see Refs.

4, 8, 11, or similar texts.) Such experimental evidence supports the basic postulate that, in pure bending, initially plane cross sections remain plane (except near areas of local loading or rapidly changing cross section).

The conceptual model which we shall analyze is *initially straight*, with *constant cross section*. The material is isotropic and homogeneous. The cross section is *symmetrical* about a centerline lying in the plane of bending (that is, the plane of symmetry is normal to the moment vector). In Fig. 7.4 a negative state of bending is used in order to obtain positive (tensile) stresses in the positive quadrant of the cross section.

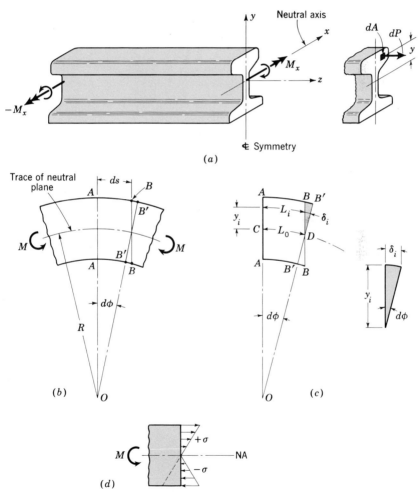

Figure 7.4. Pure bending of a straight beam (symmetrical cross section).

The analysis is started by bending the beam to a known curvature $(1/R)$. The originally straight z axis then becomes an arc of radius R (see Fig. 7.4b).

The *curvature* of a line (lying in a plane) is defined as

$$\boxed{\frac{1}{R} \equiv \frac{d\phi}{ds}} \qquad (7.1)$$

where R = radius of curvature

   $1/R$ = curvature, a vector normal to the plane in which the curved line lies*

   $d\phi$ = infinitesimal change in angle of tangent over length ds

   ds = infinitesimal length along curved line

To reduce the number of derivative symbols we shall replace ds by a small, finite length L_0, representing the distance between two parallel planes through the initially straight beam. These planes are normal to the z axis (see Fig. 7.4c).

We now apply the basic postulate:

Initially plane cross sections remain plane.

(*Note*: Compare with the postulate used for pure axial loading, Sec. 1.10, in which the planes not only remain plane but also remain parallel.)

In Fig. 7.4c this postulate permits us to draw the line $B'B'$ as a straight line. It has rotated through the angle $d\phi$, (with respect to the original position BB) about some axis lying in the cross section. This axis is called the *neutral axis*, NA (axis of zero strain). Its location is not yet determined. The x–z plane containing the neutral axes of adjacent cross sections is called the *neutral plane*. It is the plane of zero strain.

As shown in Fig. 7.4c, a "fiber" of original length L_i undergoes a change in length. The increase in length δ_i of a fiber located at a distance y_i from the neutral axis can be found by equating the values of $d\phi$ for the small shaded triangle and the large triangle COD:

$$d\phi = \frac{\delta_i}{y_i} = \frac{L_0}{R} \qquad (a)$$

from which $$\delta_i = \frac{y_i L_0}{R} \qquad (b)$$

The normal strain in the fiber at y_i is defined as δ_i/L_i. Dividing Eq. (b) by L_i gives

$$\epsilon_i = \frac{y_i}{R}\left(\frac{L_0}{L_i}\right) \qquad (c)$$

* *Curvature* is a vector quantity but *rotation* (finite change of angle) is not.

For an initially straight beam, all fibers L_i have the same initial length L_0, and L_0/L_i is unity. Therefore, dropping subscripts, we obtain the following important equation for the (engineering) *normal strain in pure bending*:

$$\epsilon = \frac{y}{R} \qquad (7.2)$$

Stated in words:

When an initially straight beam is given a curvature $1/R$, the normal strain at a distance y from the neutral plane is equal to y times the curvature.

Equation (7.2) is not limited to the elastic range.

The normal stress at a point located at a distance y from the neutral plane can be found from the relationship between strain and stress. For a "narrow" beam (width not much greater than depth) it is satisfactory to use the stress-strain diagram for uniaxial loading.

In the elastic range, the stress is found by multiplying the strain from Eq. (7.2) by Young's modulus, giving

$$\sigma = \frac{Ey}{R} \qquad (7.3)$$

The total axial force is found by multiplying every element of area dA by the normal stress acting on dA, to give dP, and integrating dP over the entire cross-sectional area. This gives the internal resultant axial force

$$P = \int_A \sigma \, dA = \frac{E}{R} \int_A y \, dA \qquad (7.4)$$

The second integral term represents the *first (static) moment of area* of the cross section. If this moment is not equal to zero, an axial force P is required (in addition to M) to bend the beam about the chosen axis (axis of zero strain). But for pure bending, P must equal zero. (Note mistakes made by Galileo and Bernoulli, Fig. 7.2.) Therefore Eq. (7.4) shows that, for pure bending, the first moment of area about the neutral axis must equal zero. This means that *the neutral axis must pass through the centroid of cross-sectional area, for pure bending (elastic).*

To find the resultant moment M of the internal stress distribution, each elemental force dP is multiplied by its distance y from the neutral axis, to obtain dM. Integration over the cross section gives

$$M_x = \int_A y \, dP = \int_A y\sigma \, dA = \frac{E}{R} \int_A y^2 \, dA \qquad (7.5)$$

The last integral is defined as the *moment of inertia* (or *second moment of area*) of the cross section (about an x axis). That is,

$$I_x \equiv \int_A y^2 \, dA \qquad (7.6)$$

Substituting in Eq. (7.6) gives

$$M_x = \frac{EI_x}{R} \qquad (7.7)$$

This is the moment required to produce the curvature $(1/R)_x$ when stresses remain in the elastic range. Equation (7.7) can be written in the following general form:

$$\frac{d\phi}{ds} = \frac{M}{EI} \qquad (7.8)$$

where $d\phi/ds \equiv 1/R$ and the quantity EI represents the elastic resistance of a beam against curvature.

Equation (7.8) forms the basis for the theory of elastic bending deflection of beams.

The normal stress at any point on the cross section is found by substituting the above value of $1/R$ in Eq. (7.3), giving

$$\sigma = \frac{My}{I} \qquad (7.9)$$

This is the general form of the equation used to compute the stresses[*] in a beam of symmetrical cross section subjected to a pure bending moment, when stresses remain in the elastic range (that is, stress distribution is linear) as shown in Fig. 7.4.

Equation (7.9) depends only on the linearity of stress distribution over the cross section. For example, let

$$\sigma = By \qquad (a)$$

where B is an unknown constant.

For internal moment equilibrium,

$$M = \int_A \sigma y \, dA = B \int_A y^2 \, dA = BI \qquad (b)$$

Therefore
$$B = \frac{M}{I} \qquad (c)$$

---

[*] A normal stress caused by pure bending is often called a *bending stress*.

Substitute (*c*) in (*a*) to obtain

$$\sigma = \frac{My}{I} \qquad (d)$$

This derivation shows that the bending-stress equation is independent of the value of *E*, *provided that the material has a linear stress-strain relationship.*

Equation (7.9) shows that, for a given cross section, the maximum bending stress occurs where *y* has a maximum value. For pure bending, there will always be a maximum tensile and a maximum compressive stress. If the sense of the moment is known, the locations of these maxima can be determined by inspection.

The maximum value of *y* is often denoted by *c*. Then

$$\sigma_{max} = \frac{Mc}{I} \qquad (7.10a)$$

This may be written as

$$\sigma_{max} = \frac{M}{Z} \qquad (7.10b)$$

where the *section modulus Z* is defined as

$$Z = \frac{I}{c}$$

The section modulus is a property of the cross section which represents resistance to the development of bending stress. For a given "allowable" stress, the section modulus is a measure of relative bending strength. Since the cross-sectional area *A* is a measure of relative weight, the section having the highest value of *Z/A* will be the most efficient, for pure bending.*

Although the foregoing analysis is based on a conceptual model of a beam of constant cross section, the results can be used for beams of moderate taper, without introducing appreciable errors.

EXAMPLE 7.1 Comparison of beam sections. Given a certain allowable bending stress and a moment to be transmitted, compare the efficiency of several cross sections.

For the same bending moment to be developed at the given value of stress, each cross section must have the same value of *Z*. For a solid rectangular section of width *b* and height *h*,

$$Z = \frac{I}{c} = \frac{bh^3/12}{h/2} = \frac{bh^2}{6} \qquad (a)$$
$$A = bh$$

* The quantity *Z/A* represents also the *core radius* (Sec. 7.6).

Now select a wide-flange beam from Appendix Table B4, say, 10 in. by 8 in. by 45 lb/ft. For bending about the x axis, $Z_x = 49.1$ in.³ and $A = 13.24$ in.² Compare this with a rectangular section for which $h = 2b$. The section modulus is

$$Z = \frac{bh^2}{6} = \frac{b(2b)^2}{6} = \frac{2b^3}{3}$$

Equating section modulii we obtain, for the rectangular section,

$$b_{\text{req'd}} = 4.19 \text{ in.} \qquad h_{\text{req'd}} = 2b = 8.38 \text{ in.} \qquad A = bh = 35.0 \text{ in.}^2$$

The relative efficiency is given by the ratio of cross-sectional areas:

$$\frac{13.24}{35.0} = 0.38$$

Therefore this particular wide-flange section requires only 38 percent of the volume of material of an equivalent rectangular section having $h = 2b$.

Note that the above comparison was made on a *constant-strength* basis. Comparisons are often erroneously made on a constant-weight basis.

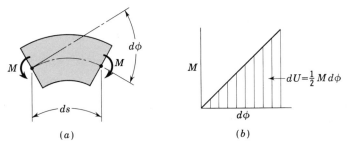

Figure 7.5. Bending energy (elastic).

The *elastic energy of bending* can be found by working with an elemental length ds, as shown in Fig. 7.5. We know that as M increases, $d\phi$ increases linearly. Therefore the work done is

$$dU = \tfrac{1}{2}M\,d\phi \qquad (a)$$

To find the work per unit length, divide by ds;

$$\frac{dU}{ds} = \frac{1}{2}M\frac{d\phi}{ds} \qquad (b)$$

But from Eq. (7.8), for a symmetrical cross section,

$$\frac{d\phi}{ds} = \frac{M}{EI}$$

Therefore

$$\boxed{\frac{dU}{ds} = \frac{1}{2}\frac{M^2}{EI}}$$ (7.11a)

and

$$U = \frac{1}{2}\int \frac{M^2}{EI}\,ds$$ (7.11b)

Note that M and I may each be a function of s. For initially straight beams s may be replaced by z.

7.3 Unsymmetrical bending (principal-axis method)

In Sec. 7.1 the bending theory was developed by causing the beam to bend about a particular axis (the neutral axis) and calculating the

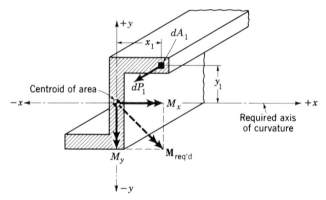

Figure 7.6. Bending of a beam having an unsymmetrical cross section.

required bending moment. Because the section was symmetrical, there was no need to calculate the internal moment about an axis normal to the axis of bending; it was obviously zero.

In Fig. 7.6 we require the beam to be bent to a curvature $(1/R)_x$ about the x axis, which passes through the centroid of the section. The strain at an element of area dA is given by Eq. (7.2),

$$\epsilon = y\left(\frac{1}{R}\right)_x$$ (a)

Proceeding exactly as before, we find that the stress (in the elastic range) is

$$\sigma = \epsilon E = Ey\left(\frac{1}{R}\right)_x$$ (b)

The elemental force is

$$dP = \sigma\,dA = Ey\left(\frac{1}{R}\right)_x dA$$ (c)

The moment about the x axis is

$$M_x = \int_A y \, dP = E \left(\frac{1}{R}\right)_x \int_A y^2 \, dA = E \left(\frac{1}{R}\right)_x I_x \qquad (d)$$

where I_x is the second moment of area about the x axis ("moment of inertia"). But we must also calculate the internal moment about the y axis. This moment is (for tension in element dA)

$$M_y = - \int_A x \, dP = - \left(\frac{1}{R}\right)_x E \int_A xy \, dA \qquad (e)$$

The *product of inertia* is defined as follows:

$$\boxed{I_{xy} \equiv \int_A xy \, dA} \qquad (7.12)$$

Therefore we can write Eq. (e) as

$$M_y = - \left(\frac{1}{R}\right)_x EI_{xy} \qquad (f)$$

In order to bend the unsymmetrical beam about the x axis (that is, to have the beam bend in a plane normal to this axis), it is necessary to apply not only M_x from Eq. (d) but also M_y from Eq. (f). The resultant bending moment has the magnitude

$$|\mathbf{M}| = \sqrt{M_x^2 + M_y^2} \qquad (g)$$

Its angle with the x axis is given by

$$\tan \theta = \frac{M_y}{M_x} \qquad (h)$$

The resultant moment is indicated by the dashed vector in Fig. 7.6.

When $\mathbf{M}$ is applied as shown, the neutral axis does not coincide with the $\mathbf{M}$ axis. Therefore Eqs. (7.8) and (7.9) can be used for unsymmetrical beams *only* when the axes are chosen such that $I_{xy} = 0$. For any cross section there are two such axes, called the *principal axes*. One method of analysis for the unsymmetrical cross section is to determine the principal axes and to resolve the applied bending moment into components along these axes.

An axis of symmetry is a principal axis (the other principal axis is normal to it). Figure 7.7 shows a situation of this type. The applied moment $\mathbf{M}$ is resolved into components, giving the following curvature equations (note that curvature is a vector quantity).

$$\left(\frac{1}{R}\right)_x = \frac{M_x}{EI_x}$$

$$\left(\frac{1}{R}\right)_y = \frac{M_y}{EI_y}$$

The magnitude of the resultant curvature is

$$\left| \frac{1}{R} \right| = \sqrt{\left(\frac{1}{R}\right)_x^2 + \left(\frac{1}{R}\right)_y^2} \qquad (7.13)$$

The location of the neutral axis is given by

$$\tan \beta = \frac{(1/R)_y}{(1/R)_x} = \frac{M_y}{M_x}\frac{I_x}{I_y} \qquad (7.14)$$

The plane of bending deflection is normal to the resultant curvature vector. Figure 7.7b indicates how the cross section would be displaced, due to bending. The beam does *not* deflect in the plane normal to **M**.

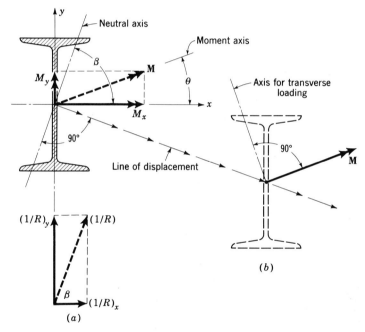

Figure 7.7. Symmetrical beam in unsymmetrical bending.

The stress at a point (x, y) is given by

$$\boxed{\sigma = \frac{M_x y}{I_x} - \frac{M_y x}{I_y}} \qquad (7.15)$$

The negative sign indicates that a positive moment M_y, applied *to* the cross section, causes a compressive stress. (Use the right-hand rule in Fig. 7.7. Fingers point *toward* cross section, indicating compression.)

EXAMPLE 7.2. A steel I beam (8 in. by 23 lb/ft) is installed (by accident) so that its y axis makes an angle of 20° with the vertical. It is loaded by gravity loads. The analysis, based on vertical installation, indicated that the maximum compressive stress would be 18,000 psi for the loading condition used. What would the maximum stress be for the beam installed at 20°?

Appendix Table B.5 gives the properties:

$$\text{Depth} = 8 \text{ in.} \qquad I_x = 64.2 \text{ in.}^4$$
$$\text{Width} = 4.17 \text{ in.} \qquad I_y = 4.4 \text{ in.}^4$$

For the *correct* installation,

$$\sigma = 18,000 = \frac{My_{max}}{I_x} = \frac{M_x \times 4}{64.2}$$

$$M_x = \frac{18,000 \times 64.2}{4} = 289,000 \text{ in.-lb}$$

$$M_y = 0$$

For the *incorrect* installation,

$$M'_x = M_x \cos 20° = 289,000 \times 0.9397 = 271,000 \text{ in.-lb}$$
$$M'_y = M_x \sin 20° = 289,000 \times 0.3420 = 99,000 \text{ in.-lb}$$

$$\sigma_{max} = \frac{M'_x y_{max}}{I_x} - \frac{M'_y x_{max}}{I_y}$$

Select a corner where stresses add, that is, upper left ($x_{max} = -2.09$). Then

$$\sigma_{max} = \frac{271,000 \times 4}{64.2} + \frac{99,000 \times 2.09}{4.4}$$
$$= 16,900 + 4,700 = 21,600 \text{ psi}$$

This represents an increase of 20 percent, as compared with the correct installation.

The sensitivity to this type of misalignment is influenced by the ratio I_y/I_x. Note that this ratio is quite low for standard I beams, but is considerably higher for wide-flange beams. The latter shape is therefore less sensitive to angular misalignment.

EXAMPLE 7.3. Calculate the values of I_x, I_y, and I_{xy} for the Z section shown in Fig. E7.3. Also determine the location of the centroid and the principal moments of inertia.

The first step is to divide the cross section into elements for which the areas and centroids can be conveniently determined. Note that in this problem the upper flange is thicker than the lower flange; consequently it is necessary to calculate the location of the centroid. The procedure is to establish an arbitrary axis system (x, y), preferably outside the cross section (to avoid negative numbers). The remaining steps are shown in the accompanying computation table (values are in the *inch* system). Note that the terms I_{x_0} and I_{y_0} represent the individual moments of inertia of each element about its own principal axes.

Location of centroid: $\bar{x} = \dfrac{Q_y}{A} = 0.678$ in.

$$\bar{y} = \dfrac{Q_x}{A} = 0.522 \text{ in.}$$

Moments of inertia about the x, y axes *through centroid* (from the parallel-axis theorem, Appendix B):

$$I'_y = I_y - A\bar{x}^2 = 0.2113 - 0.170 = 0.0413 \text{ in.}^4$$
$$I'_x = I_x - A\bar{y}^2 = 0.1507 - 0.1008 = 0.0499 \text{ in.}^4$$
$$I'_{xy} = I_{xy} - A\bar{x}\bar{y} = 0.1673 - 0.131 = 0.0363 \text{ in.}^4$$

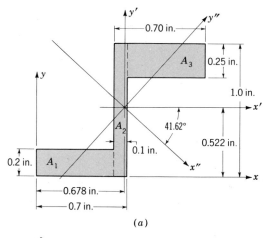

(a)

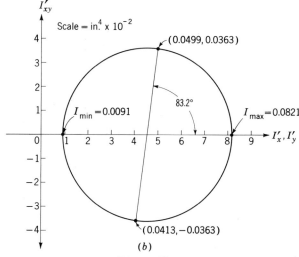

(b)

Figure E7.3

TABLE E7.3

Element no. (i)	x	y	A_i	Q		I_x		I_y		I_{xy}
				$A_i x =$ (2) × (4)	$A_i y =$ (3) × (4)	$A_i y^2 =$ (3) × (6)	$I_{x_0} = \dfrac{bh^3}{12}$	$A_i x^2 =$ (2) × (5)	$I_{y_0} = \dfrac{hb^3}{12}$	$A_i xy =$ (3) × (5)
(1)	(2)	(3)	(4)	(5)	(6)	(7)	(8)	(9)	(10)	(11)
1	0.30	0.10	0.12	0.036	0.012	0.0012	0.0004	0.0108	0.0036	0.0036
2	0.65	0.50	0.10	0.065	0.050	0.0250	0.0083	0.0423	0.0001	0.0325
3	1.0	0.875	0.15	0.150	0.131	0.1150	0.0008	0.1500	0.0045	0.1312
$\sum \rightarrow$			0.37	0.251	0.193	0.1412	0.0095	0.2031	0.0082	0.1673
			A, in.^{2}	Q_y, in.^{3}	Q_x, in.^{3}	$I_x = 0.1507$ in.^{4}		$I_y = 0.2113$ in.^{4}		$I_{xy} = 0.1673$ in.^{4}

LOCATION OF PRINCIPAL AXIS. It can be proved that the moment of inertia (or second moment of area) is, like stress, a tensor quantity.* Therefore the procedure developed for analyzing a state of stress in Sec. 2.5 can be used. To find the location of the principal axis, use Eqs. (2.11) and (2.12) for plane stress, with stress symbols replaced by I. From Eq. (2.11),

$$\tan 2\theta = \frac{2I'_{xy}}{I'_x - I'_y} = \frac{2(0.0363)}{0.0499 - 0.0413} = 8.44$$
$$\theta = 41.62 \text{ degrees}$$

From Eq. (2.12),

$$I''_x = I_{max} = \frac{I'_x + I'_y}{2} + \sqrt{\left(\frac{I'_x - I'_y}{2}\right)^2 + I'^2_{xy}}$$
$$= 0.0456 + 0.0365 = 0.0821 \text{ in.}^4$$

$$I''_y = I_{min} = \frac{I'_x + I'_y}{2} - \sqrt{\left(\frac{I'_x - I'_y}{2}\right)^2 + I'^2_{xy}}$$
$$= 0.0456 - 0.0365 = 0.0091 \text{ in.}^4$$

Mohr's circle for moments of inertia is also drawn, as a check (see Sec. 2.6).

Note: An alternative procedure involves changing the values of x and y to x' and y' after column 6 by subtracting $\bar{x}$ and $\bar{y}$. The transfer formula is then not needed.

7.4 Unsymmetrical bending (general method)

The method used in Sec. 7.2 for symmetrical bending will now be applied to an unsymmetrical cross section.

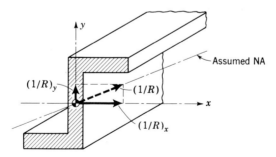

Figure 7.8. General method for unsymmetrical bending.

In Fig. 7.8 assume an arbitrary curvature indicated by the vector $(1/R)$. The strain at a point (x, y) is found by algebraic addition of the

* See Ref. 73.

strains produced by the two curvature components:

$$\epsilon = \left(\frac{1}{R}\right)_x y - \left(\frac{1}{R}\right)_y x \qquad (a)$$

Multiplying this by E gives the stress. Multiplying again by dA gives dP. (The x and y axes pass through the centroid, so $P = 0$.)

$$dP = E\epsilon\, dA = E\left[\left(\frac{1}{R}\right)_x y - \left(\frac{1}{R}\right)_y x\right] dA \qquad (b)$$

To obtain the elemental moments about each axis, multiply dP by the moment arms, giving

$$dM_x = y\, dP = E\left[y^2\left(\frac{1}{R}\right)_x - xy\left(\frac{1}{R}\right)_y\right] dA \qquad (c)$$

$$dM_y = -x\, dP = E\left[-xy\left(\frac{1}{R}\right)_x + x^2\left(\frac{1}{R}\right)_y\right] dA \qquad (d)$$

The total moments are found by integration over the cross section, giving

$$M_x = E\left[I_x\left(\frac{1}{R}\right)_x - I_{xy}\left(\frac{1}{R}\right)_y\right] \qquad (e)$$

$$M_y = E\left[-I_{xy}\left(\frac{1}{R}\right)_x + I_y\left(\frac{1}{R}\right)_y\right] \qquad (f)$$

Usually we wish to find the curvature resulting from a given bending moment **M**. Therefore Eqs. (e) and (f) are solved simultaneously for the curvature components, giving

$$\boxed{\begin{aligned}\left(\frac{1}{R}\right)_x &= \frac{1}{E}\frac{M_x I_y + M_y I_{xy}}{I_x I_y - I_{xy}{}^2} \\ \left(\frac{1}{R}\right)_y &= \frac{1}{E}\frac{M_y I_x + M_x I_{xy}}{I_x I_y - I_{xy}{}^2}\end{aligned}} \qquad (7.16)$$

Equation (7.2) is used to find the strains, which are then multiplied by E to obtain stresses, giving

$$\sigma = \left[\left(\frac{1}{R}\right)_x y - \left(\frac{1}{R}\right)_y x\right] E$$

Substituting the values from Eq. (7.16),

$$\boxed{\sigma = \left(\frac{M_x I_y + M_y I_{xy}}{I_x I_y - I_{xy}{}^2}\right) y - \left(\frac{M_y I_x + M_x I_{xy}}{I_x I_y - I_{xy}{}^2}\right) x} \qquad (7.17)$$

Note that when $I_{xy} = 0$, Eq. (7.17) reduces to Eq. (7.15) for symmetrical cross sections.

The general method outlined above eliminates the necessity for calculating the principal moments of inertia, the angle of principal axis, and the transformed coordinates of a point.

Equation (7.17) can be put in a more convenient form by introducing the concept of *equivalent bending moments*. Such moments (M'_x and M'_y) are defined as those values which, if used in the equations for symmetrical cross sections, would produce the correct results. The resulting stress equation is

$$\sigma = \frac{M'_x y}{I_x} - \frac{M'_y x}{I_y} \qquad (7.18)$$

where
$$M'_x = \frac{M_x + k_y M_y}{1 - k_x k_y} \qquad M'_y = \frac{M_y + k_x M_x}{1 - k_x k_y}$$

and
$$k_x = \frac{I_{xy}}{I_x} \qquad k_y = \frac{I_{xy}}{I_y}$$

The constants k_x and k_y represent the degree of antisymmetry of a given cross section. Equation (7.18) is convenient when a beam must be analyzed for various combinations of M_x and M_y.

The *elastic energy per unit length* is

$$\frac{dU}{ds} = \frac{1}{2}\left[M_x \left(\frac{d\phi}{ds}\right)_x + M_y \left(\frac{d\phi}{ds}\right)_y \right] \qquad (7.19)$$

But
$$\left(\frac{d\phi}{ds}\right)_x \equiv \left(\frac{1}{R}\right)_x \qquad \text{and} \qquad \left(\frac{d\phi}{ds}\right)_y \equiv \left(\frac{1}{R}\right)_y$$

Therefore the values of curvature given by Eq. (7.16) can be substituted in the above equation to give the unit energy in terms of bending moments, moments of inertia, and Young's modulus. The equation for dU/ds can also be expressed in terms of real and effective moments. The formulas have not been worked out here, since they are seldom used in this form. (For initially straight beams use dz in place of ds.)

7.5 Combined bending and axial loading

Any case of combined axial loading and bending can be reduced to the situation shown in Fig. 7.9. The axial force P acts at the centroid of cross-sectional area; the bending moments have been resolved into components along the principal axes. When this is done, the combined axial stress at any point on the cross section (x, y) is found by adding the individual values algebraically:

$$\sigma = \frac{P}{A} + \frac{M_x y}{I_x} - \frac{M_y x}{I_y} \qquad (7.20a)$$

For unsymmetrical sections, use Eq. (7.18):

$$\sigma = \frac{P}{A} + \frac{M'_x y}{I_x} - \frac{M'_y x}{I_y} \qquad (7.20b)$$

where M' is the effective moment.

In the foregoing development of the beam theory, the general loading condition was broken down into two separate cases, pure axial loading and pure bending, and the principle of superposition was used. It is possible to develop a general theory which treats both types of loading simultaneously.

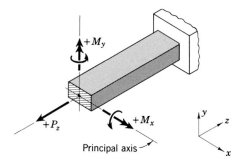

Figure 7.9. Combined axial and bending loads.

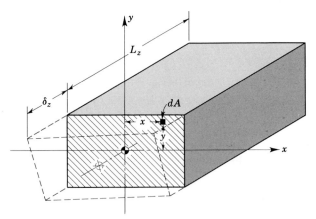

Figure 7.10. General displacement of plane cross section.

Figure 7.10 shows a plane cross section which has been given a displacement from its original position. This consists of a translation along the z axis, a rotation about the x axis, and a rotation about the y axis. *The cross section remains plane.* The displacement δ_z at any point on the cross section will therefore be a linear function of the coordinates x and y. If the member is originally straight, the original lengths of all axial elements (L_z) will be the same. Since the strain ϵ_z is obtained by dividing δ_z by L_z, a constant, the strain is also a linear function of x and y. This can be written (dropping subscript z),

$$\epsilon = ax + by + c \tag{a}$$

where $a = -(1/R)_y$
$\qquad b = (1/R)_x$
$\qquad c = \epsilon_{\text{axial}}$

In the elastic range, the stress σ is equal to $E\epsilon$. Therefore, at a point (x, y),

$$\sigma = E(ax + by + c) \tag{b}$$

The elemental force acting on an element of cross-sectional area is given by

$$dP = \sigma \, dA$$

The moments of this force about the x and y axes, respectively, are

$$dM_x = y \, dP = y\sigma \, dA$$
$$-dM_y = x \, dP = x\sigma \, dA$$

The total force and moments acting on the cross section are found by integrating these expressions over the entire cross section, giving

$$\int \sigma \, dA = P$$
$$\int y\sigma \, dA = M_x$$
$$\int x\sigma \, dA = -M_y$$

Substituting for σ from Eq. (*b*) gives, for equilibrium,

$$a\int Ex \, dA + b\int Ey \, dA + c\int E \, dA = P \tag{7.21a}$$
$$a\int Exy \, dA + b\int Ey^2 \, dA + c\int Ey \, dA = M_x \tag{7.21b}$$
$$a\int Ex^2 \, dA + b\int Exy \, dA + c\int Ex \, dA = -M_y \tag{7.21c}$$

These three linear equations with three unknown constants (a, b, c) represent the *general elastic case of combined axial loading and bending in an initially straight beam*. Given the shape of the cross section and the value of E at each point, together with the loading (P, M_x, and M_y), it is possible to evaluate the integrals and solve the equations for the constants a, b, and c. The values thus obtained are then substituted in Eq. (*b*), giving an expression for the stress at any point on the cross section.

For composite (heterogeneous) beams the integrals must include the individual values of E for each different material.

The effects of thermal strains can be included by adding to Eq. (*a*) a term for thermal strain [Eq. (1.22)]. For nonuniform temperature, T is a function of x and y.

EXAMPLE 7.4.   In the case of *pure axial loading* it was found that the stress is equal to P/A when the load P is applied at the centroid of the cross section. To illustrate the use of the general equations, this elementary case will be analyzed.

By definition of the centroid, $\int x\, dA$ and $\int y\, dA$ are both zero. For a member made from a single material, E is the same for all elements of area, and $\int E\, dA$ becomes EA. Equation (7.21a) then reduces to

$$c = \frac{P}{EA}$$

Since M_x and M_y are both zero for pure axial loading, the constants b and c must be zero in Eqs. (7.21b) and (7.21c). Equation (b) then becomes

$$\sigma = \frac{P}{A}$$

Equation (a) gives the strain as

$$\epsilon = \frac{P}{EA}$$

EXAMPLE 7.5.   Let us use the general Eqs. (7.21) for pure bending. For *pure bending about the x axis*, $P = 0$, $M_y = 0$. If the x and y axes are principal axes, the term $\int xy\, dA$ (product of inertia) is zero. From Eq. (7.21a), the constant c is found to be zero. Equation (7.21b) gives the result

$$b\int Ey^2\, dA = M_x$$

which may be written

$$b = \frac{M_x}{EI_x}$$

Then, from Eqs. (b) and (a), respectively,

$$\sigma = \frac{M_x y}{I_x}$$

$$\epsilon = \frac{M_x y}{EI_x}$$

Since $\epsilon/y = 1/R$, the latter equation may be written

$$\frac{1}{R} = \frac{M_x}{EI_x}$$

These agree with expressions obtained in Sec. 7.2. Similarly, the equation for combined axial loading and bending [Eq. (7.16)] can be derived.

7.6 Eccentric axial loading

Figure 7.11 shows how the effect of an *eccentric axial load* can be analyzed. If the cross section being analyzed is some distance away from the point of application of the load, the postulate that plane cross sections remain plane is applicable (Saint-Venant's principle). The normal stress at any point (x, y) on the cross section is then found from Eq. (7.20). By substituting the values for bending moment (from Fig. 7.11), the normal stress is found to be

$$\sigma = \frac{P}{A} + \frac{Pe_y y}{I_x} + \frac{Pe_x x}{I_y} \tag{a}$$

From the definition of the *radius of gyration*,

$$\rho_y{}^2 \equiv \frac{I_x}{A} \tag{b}$$

$$\rho_x{}^2 \equiv \frac{I_y}{A} \tag{c}$$

where ρ_y is measured along the y axis, ρ_x along the x axis.

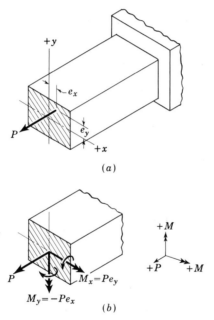

Figure 7.11. Eccentric axial loading.

Equation (a) can now be written

$$\sigma = \frac{P}{A}\left(1 + \frac{e_y y}{\rho_y{}^2} + \frac{e_x x}{\rho_x{}^2}\right) \tag{7.22}$$

The term in parentheses may be thought of as a factor by which the *concentric* normal stress is multiplied to account for eccentricity.

When the eccentricity occurs only along one of the principal axes, either e_x or e_y will be zero. Assume that e_x is zero and that $y = c$, the maximum distance from the x axis to the edge of the cross section. Dropping subscripts,

$$\sigma_{\max} = \frac{P}{A}\left(1 + \frac{ec}{\rho^2}\right) \qquad (d)$$

The term ρ^2/c is defined as the *core radius*. Equation (d) may therefore be written

$$\sigma_{\max} = \frac{P}{A}\left(1 + \frac{e}{r_c}\right) \qquad (7.23)$$

where $r_c \equiv \rho^2/c$ = core radius.

The parenthetical term is a multiplying factor which shows the effect of eccentricity on the maximum stress in the section. The expression e/r_c may be thought of as a *reduced eccentricity*, or eccentricity ratio. For example, any member which has an eccentricity ratio of 0.5 will be subjected to a 50 percent increase in maximum normal stress, as compared with a noneccentric member.

The *core* (sometimes called *kern*) is defined as *that portion of the cross section within which an axial force can be applied without causing a stress of opposite sign at any point*. It has a practical application in masonry construction, where it is desirable to avoid tensile stresses in the material.

The core radius is the value of eccentricity, along a principal axis, at which the stress on the opposite edge becomes zero. The core radius for a rectangular cross section is illustrated in Fig. 7.12.

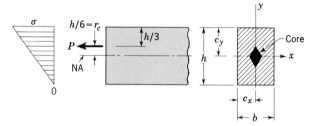

Figure 7.12. Core radius.

To find an expression for core radius, Eq. (d) can be modified to give the minimum stress:

$$\sigma_{\min} = \frac{P}{A}\left(1 - \frac{ec}{\rho^2}\right) \qquad (e)$$

where c is the distance to the edge, in a direction *opposite* to e. The value of e at which $\sigma_{\min}$ becomes zero is found by letting $\sigma_{\min} = 0$ and solving this equation, giving the *core radius:*

$$e = r_c = \frac{\rho^2}{c} \qquad (7.24)$$

(Note that r_c is measured opposite to the direction of c; this will apply to unbalanced sections.)

The value of the core radius for a rectangular cross section ($b \times h$) is

$$r_c = \frac{\rho^2}{c} = \frac{I}{A(h/2)} = \frac{bh^3}{12bh(h/2)} = \frac{h}{6}$$

The core therefore intersects the principal axes at the third points, as shown in Fig. 7.12.

An alternative expression for the core radius can be obtained by using the *section modulus* Z in the equation for minimum stress:

$$\sigma_{\min} = \frac{P}{A} - \frac{Pe}{Z} = \frac{P}{A}\left(1 - \frac{eA}{Z}\right)$$

By definition of the core radius, $\sigma_{\min}$ must equal zero. Making this substitution and solving for e gives

$$r_c = \frac{Z}{A}$$

This is a convenient form of the equation because the values of A and Z are specified in tables for section properties.

To determine the shape of the core for a *rectangular section* (Fig. 7.12) the most highly stressed point is first selected by observation. When the force P is in the upper right quadrant, the stress will be a maximum in the upper right corner and a minimum in the lower left corner. Let c_x and c_y represent the distances to this corner ($c_x = -b/2$; $c_y = -h/2$). These are substituted in Eq. (7.22) for x and y, and σ is set equal to zero, giving

$$0 = 1 - \frac{e_y c_y}{\rho_y{}^2} - \frac{e_x c_x}{\rho_x{}^2}$$

Substituting the symbols for core radius,

$$\frac{e_y}{r_{c_y}} + \frac{e_x}{r_{c_x}} = 1 \tag{f}$$

This is the equation of a straight line between the two values of core radius, giving the shaded area shown in Fig. 7.12.

The core radius for the *solid circular section* of radius R is

$$r_c = \frac{R}{4}$$

For a *thin-walled circular section* of average radius R and thickness t,

$$r_c = \frac{R^2}{2(R + t/2)} \approx \frac{R}{2}$$

7.7 Inelastic bending

When stress is not proportional to strain, the postulate that plane cross sections remain plane may still be employed, giving a linear strain distribution over the cross section (for initially straight beams).

For an assumed location of the neutral axis and a value of curvature $(1/R)$, the strain at any point on the cross section is given by Eq. (7.2),

$$\epsilon = y\left(\frac{1}{R}\right)$$

where y is the distance from the neutral axis.

Let the stress be related to strain by a function $\sigma = f(\epsilon)$, such as that represented by the tension stress-strain diagram. (Note that for bending this function or diagram must include both the tension and compression range.) The normal stress distribution over the cross section is thereby determined. The resultant axial force is

$$P = \int_A \sigma \, dA$$

For pure bending, $P = 0$; therefore the neutral axis must be located so that the above integral is zero. Assuming that the neutral axis is so located and that it coincides with the x axis, the resultant components of the bending moment are given by

$$M_x = \int_A y\sigma \, dA \tag{7.25}$$

$$M_y = \int_A x\sigma \, dA \tag{7.26}$$

By performing the above integrations for various values of curvature $(1/R)$ the relationship between bending moment and curvature may be determined. If the cross section is symmetrical about the y axis, the value of M_y will be zero. If the cross section is also symmetrical about the x axis and the stress-strain diagram is antisymmetrical, the neutral axis will pass through the centroid of area, as for elastic bending.

Figure 7.13 shows typical strain and stress distributions for a beam having a rectangular cross section. Figure 7.14 illustrates two simplified stress distributions for inelastic bending.

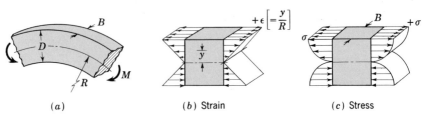

(a)　　　　　　　　　(b) Strain　　　　　　　(c) Stress

Figure 7.13. Strains and stresses in inelastic bending.

When the *ideally plastic* stress distribution is used for a beam of rectangular cross section, the bending moment calculated by Eq. (7.25) becomes

$$M = \frac{BD^2}{4} \sigma_{max}$$

For the *elastic* stress distribution, the corresponding moment is

$$M = \frac{I}{c} \sigma_{max} = \frac{BD^2}{6} \sigma_{max}$$

In this case the use of the ideally plastic theory results in an increase of 50 percent in the bending moment required to produce the same maximum value of stress, as compared with elastic theory.

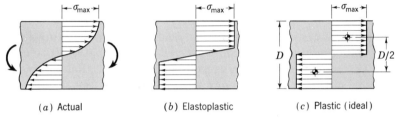

(*a*) Actual   (*b*) Elastoplastic   (*c*) Plastic (ideal)

Figure 7.14. Simplified stress distributions for inelastic bending.

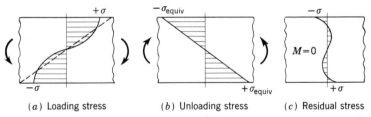

(*a*) Loading stress   (*b*) Unloading stress   (*c*) Residual stress

Figure 7.15. Determination of residual stresses in bending (rectangular cross section).

The fact that plastic strain is irreversible has important consequences in bending beyond the elastic range. When the bending moment is removed, *residual stresses* will remain in the beam. These stresses are "self-equilibrating"; that is, when integrated over the cross section, they satisfy $\Sigma P = 0$ and $\Sigma M = 0$ internally.

The residual stresses may be calculated by postulating that plane cross sections remain plane during unloading and that the stress-strain relationship during unloading is elastic. As shown in Fig. 7.15, the residual stresses are found by subtracting from the actual inelastic stress distribution an equivalent elastic stress distribution representing the value of the applied bending moment. (This obviously reduces the external moment to zero.)

For ideal plasticity in which the maximum stress is represented by a yield stress σ_y, the maximum *equivalent elastic stress* for a rectangular cross section is found by equating M_{plastic} and M_{elastic} previously determined, giving $\sigma_{\text{equiv}} = 1.5\sigma_y$, as shown in Fig. 7.16. The residual stress at

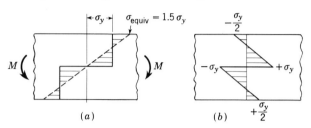

Figure 7.16. Residual stresses in a rectangular member, for ideal plasticity.

the surface is found to be one-half the yield stress. At the neutral plane the calculated residual stress equals the yield stress; this result is unrealistic (high) because elastic strains were omitted. Note that the residual stress at a surface will be of opposite sign to that of the stress applied during actual bending.

The *modulus of rupture* in bending is defined as the maximum equivalent elastic stress at the ultimate bending moment developed in a test. For the rectangular cross section with ideal plasticity, the modulus of rupture is 50 percent greater than the yield stress. As shown in the following example, the apparent increase in bending strength depends strongly on the shape of the cross section, becoming less as the section becomes more efficient (as it approaches the idealized "two-flange" beam).

Springback is a phenomenon encountered in the cold-forming of materials. The springback angle can be estimated by calculating the strain corresponding to the equivalent elastic stress (see Ref. 19 for details).

EXAMPLE 7.6. The elastic and ideally plastic theories of bending will be compared for a cross section of I shape, having dimensions shown in Fig. E7.6. The

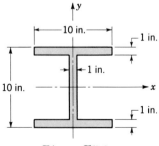

Figure E7.6

bending moments required to produce the same maximum stress σ_y will be computed.

ELASTIC (linear stress distribution).

$$I_x = 2(10 \times 4.5^2) + 2\left(\frac{10 \times 1^3}{12}\right) + \frac{1 \times 8^3}{12}$$
$$= 449.4 \text{ in.}^4$$
$$M_E = \frac{I}{c}\sigma_y = \frac{449.4}{5}\sigma_y = 89.88\sigma_y$$

PLASTIC (constant stress distribution). The bending moment will be equal to the stress times twice the static moment of half the cross section about the neutral axis:

$$M_P = 2(10 \times 4.5 + 4 \times 2)\sigma_y$$
$$= 106\sigma_y$$
$$\frac{M_P}{M_E} = \frac{106}{89.88} = 1.18$$
$$\text{Modulus of rupture} = 1.18\sigma_y$$

7.8 *Summary of the theory of pure bending*

Table 7.1 represents the most important features of the conceptual model used in deriving Eqs. (7.8) and (7.9). The conditions under which the various statements are correct are listed on the right side of the table. Limitations of the theory appear on the left side.

TABLE 7.1

Summary of the theory of pure bending

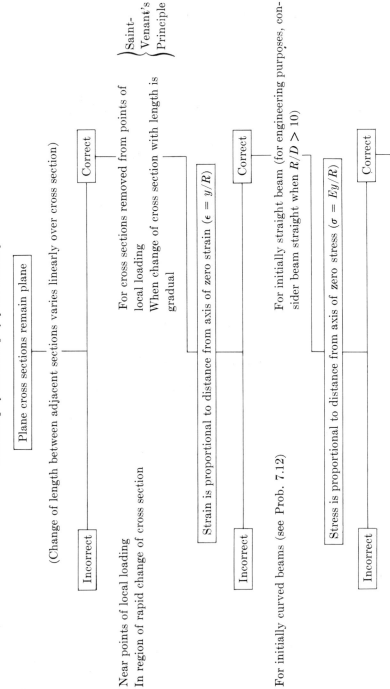

Plane cross sections remain plane

Correct

(Change of length between adjacent sections varies linearly over cross section)

Incorrect

Near points of local loading
In region of rapid change of cross section

For cross sections removed from points of local loading
When change of cross section with length is gradual

$\Big\}$ Saint-Venant's Principle

Strain is proportional to distance from axis of zero strain ($\epsilon = y/R$)

Correct

Incorrect

For initially curved beams (see Prob. 7.12)

For initially straight beam (for engineering purposes, consider beam straight when $R/D > 10$)

Stress is proportional to distance from axis of zero stress ($\sigma = Ey/R$)

Correct

Incorrect

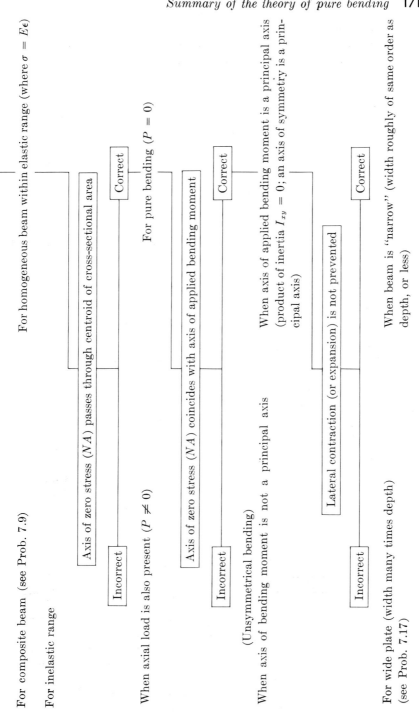

For composite beam (see Prob. 7.9)

For inelastic range

For homogeneous beam within elastic range (where $\sigma = E\epsilon$)

Axis of zero stress (NA) passes through centroid of cross-sectional area

Correct

Incorrect

When axial load is also present ($P \neq 0$)

For pure bending ($P = 0$)

Axis of zero stress (NA) coincides with axis of applied bending moment

Correct

Incorrect

(Unsymmetrical bending)

When axis of bending moment is not a principal axis

When axis of applied bending moment is a principal axis (product of inertia $I_{xy} = 0$; an axis of symmetry is a principal axis)

Correct

Lateral contraction (or expansion) is not prevented

Incorrect

For wide plate (width many times depth) (see Prob. 7.17)

When beam is "narrow" (width roughly of same order as depth, or less)

Correct

PROBLEMS

7.1. (*a*) Find the maximum absolute value of the elastic bending stress in the beams having cross sections shown in Fig. P7.1. Let $M_x = 10,000$

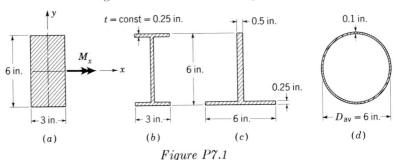

Figure P7.1

in.-lb. (*Note:* Actual stresses for other values of M_x can be found by proportion.)

(*b*) Repeat with cross sections rotated 90° from the orientations shown. (Principal axes rotate to new orientation x'–y'. Vector M_x remains in original position.)

(*c*) Repeat with cross sections rotated 45° from the orientations shown.

7.2. For one or more of the thin-walled cross sections shown in Fig. P7.2, all of which have constant wall thickness t, derive the approximate formulas shown in Table P7.2. (*Note:* Large dimensions are mean values measured to mid-plane of walls.)

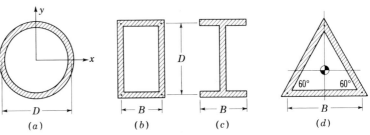

Figure P7.2

TABLE P7.2

Section	A	z_x	I_x	ρ_x
(*a*) Circle	$2\pi Rt$	$\pi R^2 t$	$\pi R^3 t$	$\dfrac{2}{\sqrt{2}}$
(*b*) Rectangle	$2(B + D)t$	$\dfrac{tD(3B + D)}{3}$	$\dfrac{tD^2(3B + D)}{6}$	$\dfrac{D}{2\sqrt{3}}\left(\dfrac{3B + D}{B + D}\right)^{\frac{1}{2}}$
(*c*) I beam	$(2B + D)t$	$\dfrac{tD(6B + D)}{6}$	$\dfrac{tD^2(6B + D)}{12}$	$\dfrac{D}{2\sqrt{3}}\left(\dfrac{6B + D}{2B + D}\right)^{\frac{1}{2}}$
(*d*) Triangle	$3Bt$	$\dfrac{\sqrt{3}\,tB^2}{4}$	$\dfrac{tB^3}{4}$	$\dfrac{B}{2\sqrt{3}}$

7.3. (*a*) For the dimensions given in an assigned column of Table P7.3, draw an accurate full-sized sketch of the cross section shown in Fig. P7.3.

TABLE P7.3

(*Dimensions in inches*)

D	2.70	2.50	2.00	2.50	2.25
b	1.30	1.60	1.10	1.00	1.50
t	0.250	0.230	0.240	0.220	0.210

(*b*) Calculate section properties, values of maximum and minimum moments of inertia, and directions of principal axes; indicate them on the sketch.

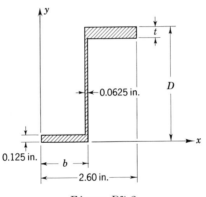

Figure P7.3

(*c*) Apply a pure bending moment $M_x = 10,000$ in.-lb, and calculate the magnitude of the resultant curvature vector $1/R$ and the location of the axis about which it occurs ($E = 29 \times 10^6$ psi). Also find the curvatures about the x and y axes. [*Note:* Calculate components of curvature $(1/R)_x$ and $(1/R)_y$ separately, then add vectorially, as in Fig. 7.8.]

(*d*) Calculate the maximum normal strain in the cross section. This may be done in either of two ways: first, maximum strain will occur at the point farthest from the neutral axis, and will be a function of resultant curvature; second, strain at various corners of the section will be a function of curvature *components* (either about the principal axes, or about the x and y axes). Values of strain at different corners may be compared to find the maximum.

(*e*) Calculate the stress at the two corners of the section farthest removed from the centroid, using the moment components about the principal axes. Check by the general method, using either Eq. (7.17) or Eq. (7.18).

(*f*) Calculate the elastic energy per unit length of the member.

7.4. Arbitrary numerical values for the beam parameters shown in Fig. P6.1 are given in Table P7.4. For a particular beam assigned by the instructor calculate the cross-sectional dimensions required, assuming shapes dimensionally similar to each of the cross sections shown in Fig. P7.1, such that the maximum bending stress (absolute value) will equal 10,000 psi. (*Note:* Dimensional similarity here implies that all cross-sectional dimensions are multiplied by a constant factor.)

TABLE P7.4

	Beam (Fig. P6.1)									
	a	*b*	*c*	*d*	*e*	*f*	*g*	*h*	*i*	*j*
L, in.	80	70	130	200	170	110	72	96	72	108
a, in.	60	—	30	—	—	—	—	—	—	—
P, lb	800	—	600	—	—	500	—	500	400	—
M, in.-lb	—	—	—	8,000	—	—	—	—	—	—
q_0, lb/in.	—	12	—	—	10	—	8	—	6	9

7.5. Find the maximum stress due to bending for the beam of Fig. P7.5, using an assigned set of values from Table P7.5. Plot variation of stress over span.

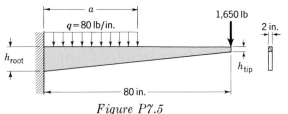

Figure P7.5

TABLE P7.5

	1	2	3	4	5	6	7
a, in.	40	80	40	50	50	60	60
h_{tip}, in.	2	2	1	1	2	1	2
h_{root}, in.	10	10	5	4	5	4	7

7.6. A downward vertical force of 1,200 lb is to be transmitted horizontally to a wall 12 ft away, by means of a cantilever steel beam of *constant* cross section. The maximum design normal stress (due to bending only) is limited to 20,000 psi. (Effects of transverse loading are covered in later problems.) Select from Table B.4 a cross-sectional *shape* corresponding to a wide-flange beam 10 in. by 10 in. by 72 lb/ft (or any other beam section designated by your instructor). For a dimensionally similar cross section, determine the actual cross-sectional dimensions required, and also the area, for the following cases. (*Note:* Section modulus for dimensionally similar cross sections varies as the cube of a dimension.)

(*a*) Neglecting beam weight.

(*b*) Including beam weight.

(*c*) Repeat part *a*, assuming that the beam is installed (by error) so that its median plane makes an angle of 20° with the vertical, while loads continue to act vertically.

7.7. Assuming that the same bending moment M_x is applied to each of the three cross sections of Fig. P7.7, calculate the relative increase in maximum bending stress for cases *b* and *c*, using case *a* as a basis. (Use elastic theory.) Explain why adding material in case *c* causes an *increase* in bending stress.

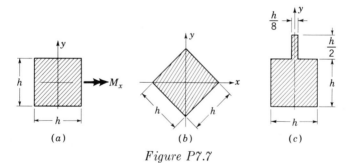

Figure P7.7

7.8. A solid round bar has been designed as a beam, such that an elastic bending stress of 50,000 psi is developed by an applied (pure) bending moment of 39,250 in.-lb.

(*a*) Find the diameter of the bar and its cross-sectional area.

(*b*) To improve the efficiency, design a tubular bar for which the inside diameter R_i is made equal to $0.8R_o$ (where R_o = outside diameter). The new bar must transmit the same bending moment and develop the same maximum stress. Find R_o and the cross-sectional area.

(*c*) Calculate the relative bending stiffnesses and also the relative cross-sectional areas for the two designs.

Note: This "expansion" process can be extended until the tube wall thickness is so small that local buckling occurs (Sec. 11.8).

7.9. *Composite beam.* A beam is constructed from timber and aluminum alloy plates, giving a cross section as shown in Fig. P7.9. Assuming elastic behavior and using assigned values from Table P7.9, find the maximum allowable bending moment M_x if yield stresses are not be be exceeded.

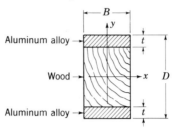

Figure P7.9

Notes: (a) Assume that the beam is initially straight and cross sections remain plane after bending.

(b) Start with Eq. (7.5), noting that E must be placed inside the integral sign and the proper value must be used for each element of area. It is convenient to "transform" the composite section (in the imagination) into an equivalent section of one material (aluminum alloy, in this case). Then each element of area (A_i) is multiplied by a factor $n_i = E_i/E_o$, where E_o = value for base material. The stress in the transformed beam must then be multiplied by n_i to obtain the actual stress.

TABLE P7.9

		1	2	3	4	5	6
Wood	E, psi	2.0×10^6	2.0×10^6	1.6×10^6	1.6×10^6	1.9×10^6	1.9×10^6
	σ_y, psi	6,000	6,000	4,500	4,500	6,500	6,500
Aluminum	E, psi	10×10^6	10×10^6	10×10^6	10×10^6	10×10^6	10×10^6
	σ_y, psi	30,000	30,000	50,000	50,000	70,000	70,000
Dimensions	B, in.	6.0	6.0	6.0	8.0	8.0	8.0
	D, in.	12.0	12.0	12.0	15.0	15.0	15.0
	t, in.	1.0	2.0	2.0	2.0	2.0	3.5

7.10. For an assigned I-beam section from Table B.5, assume that the beam itself is made from aluminum alloy and that steel flange plates are riveted to each flange. Each steel plate has a width equal to that of the beam flange width and a thickness equal to that of the beam web. For $E_{steel} = 29 \times 10^6$ psi, and $E_{alum} = 10 \times 10^6$ psi, calculate:

(a) The "effective EI" for the composite beam

(b) The maximum bending stress in the steel and in the aluminum, when a bending moment M_x is applied which would have produced a maximum stress of 20,000 psi in the unreinforced aluminum-alloy beam

(*Note:* See Prob. 7.9.)

7.11. Find the core radius for each of the following sections:

(*a*) Solid circular section of radius R

(*b*) Thin-walled circular section of average radius R and thickness t

(*c*) Idealized* two-flange beam of depth h (measured between centroids of flanges)

(*d*) Thin-walled square box beam of average dimensions $h \times h \times t$, with $t = h/10$.

The core radius is a measure of efficiency (see Example 7.1) because, for a constant applied moment and constant allowable stress, the value of Z must be constant. Since the core radius can be defined as Z/A, required areas for two different cross-sectional shapes are inversely proportional to their core radii. Using a *solid* square section as a base, calculate the relative area A/A_{square} for each of the above sections.

TABLE P7.12

	1	2	3	4	5	6	7
P, kips	1.5	5.0	3.0	5.0	10.0	10.0	50.0
R, in.	3.0	3.0	2.0	2.0	6.0	8.0	8.0
h, in.	1.0	1.0	1.0	1.0	2.0	2.0	3.0

7.12. An idealized model of a crane hook is shown in Fig. P7.12. A square cross section is used ($h \times h$). Neglecting the effects of curvature on the

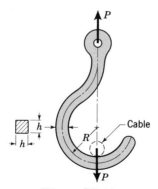

Figure P7.12

beam theory, find the maximum tensile stress in the curved portion of the hook.

Note: The formula $\epsilon = y/R$ is incorrect for initially curved beams. As the ratio h/R increases, the strain on the inner surface becomes increas-

---

* In the idealized two-flange beam, the web is omitted and flange areas are concentrated at their centroids, separated by the distance h.

ingly greater than that given by Eq. (7.2) and the neutral axis moves closer to the inner surface (see Ref. 19 for details). However, the center of resistance for axial loading remains at the centroid (see Sec. 1.11).

7.13. For an assigned stress-strain diagram from Appendix A, plot a curve showing the variation of moment (to ultimate) with curvature, for a rectangular cross section 2 in. by 4 in. Solve this problem for moments about each principal axis (separately).

7.14. Using the concept of "ideal plasticity" (flat-topped stress-strain diagram at $\sigma = \sigma_y$, elastic strains omitted), find the values of ultimate (plastic) bending moment for the three sections shown in Fig. P7.7, letting $h = 1$ in. and $\sigma_y = 30,000$ psi. (*Note:* Be sure $\Sigma P = 0$.)

7.15. *Extension of P7.14.* In Prob. 7.14, let the applied bending moment decrease from M_{ult} to zero and calculate the maximum value of the residual stress at the surface (i.e., neglect residual stresses at internal points). (*Note:* The solutions for Prob. 7.7 can be used to advantage.)

7.16. Sketch a square cross section before and after the beam has been subjected to a large bending moment. Calculate the curvature $(1/R)_z$ about the z axis (*anticlastic* curvature) for the two cases (*a*) elastic ($\nu = \frac{1}{3}$) and (*b*) ideally plastic ($\nu = \frac{1}{2}$), in terms of the bending curvature $(1/R)_x$. (*Suggestion:* bend a rubber eraser and note what happens.)

7.17. Calculate the *apparent* increase in the uniaxial elastic modulus, for bending of a flat plate, using a conceptual model in which lateral strains (across width) are entirely prevented. [*Suggestion:* Use Eqs. (4.2) and (7.2).]

7.18. *Preliminary design.* Imagine that you are a military engineer who must estimate roughly the diameter of a single log required to form the main structure for a footbridge which is to have a span of 40 ft. Assume that the loading (soldiers, planking, rails) has been estimated to be 500 lb/ft, uniformly distributed over the span. (This does not include the weight of the log.) You also know that a test has been made of a small cylindrical specimen of the same wood. The specimen has a 2 in. diameter and a 12 in. span, and broke when a single transverse load of 1,800 lb was applied at mid-span. Using a factor of safety of 3 (by which loads are multiplied), find the required diameter for the log, first neglecting its own weight. Then add the weight of the log to the applied loading (assume that density $= 0.0278$ lb/in.^{3}) and recalculate diameter. (*Note:* For approximate design, the log may be assumed to have constant diameter.)

7.19. Extend Prob. 7.18 to include cases in which logs of smaller diameter must be used. Repeat design calculations for n logs placed side by side (let $n = 2, 3, 4, 5$). Plot the total weight of the logs against n. (*Note:* This problem shows that the single log is most efficient and that efficiency drops off as the number of logs used increases. Explain this.)

7.20. *Wide beam.* A beam is formed by bending a plate of thickness t into a corrugation ("folded-plate" structure) to form one of the cross sections shown in Fig. P7.20. All dimensions between bends have the value b.

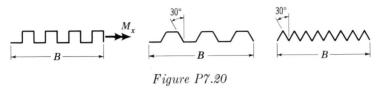

Figure P7.20

(a) Derive formulas for section properties *per unit width*, that is, A/B, Z/B, I/B, ρ_x, in terms of b and t.

(b) Design (determine actual dimensions of) three beams having the cross sections shown, for a situation in which span L is 6 ft (pinned ends), width B is 2 ft, and total load is 1,750 lb (vertical) distributed uniformly over the entire projected area (horizontal) of the beam. The criterion for design is that failure must not occur before the load reaches the above value. Failure is defined here as the attainment of a maximum bending stress of 30,000 psi in the material (neglect shear stresses and omit weight of beam in calculations). Calculate the weights of the beams using a material density of 0.3 lb/in.[3]

Chapter 8

Shear and Bending

8.1 Combined shear and bending

Figure 8.1 shows a shear force V being transmitted over a beam of constant cross section. A bending moment M_x is also shown. At any station along the beam, a small element is isolated by making two transverse "cuts," at a distance Δz apart, together with a horizontal "cut" at distance y_1 from the neutral plane and parallel with it.

The fundamental relationship between shear and bending moment, Eq. (6.2), requires that the moment increase over the length Δz, as indicated in sketch b. The stress distributions on opposite vertical faces of the element are linear (in the elastic range), and are shown in c, the difference being exaggerated for clarity.

The resultants of the normal stresses on the vertical faces of the isolated element are not in equilibrium. The unbalanced force tends to cause the element to slip from right to left. This tendency is resisted by a shear force ΔP acting across the horizontal cut face.

To calculate ΔP we find the axial stress difference, Eq. (7.9):

$$\Delta\sigma = \frac{\Delta My}{I} \tag{a}$$

Integrating this over the cross section of the isolated element, we obtain the total unbalanced axial force

$$\Delta P = \frac{\Delta M}{I} \int_A y \, dA \tag{b}$$

The above integral represents the *static moment* (first moment of area) of the cross section of the isolated element, with respect to the neutral axis. This moment is commonly designated by Q. Since dA can be expressed in terms of dy, we have

$$Q = \int_{y_1}^{y_{max}} y \, dA \tag{8.1}$$

Equation (b) then becomes $\quad \Delta P = \dfrac{\Delta M}{I} Q \tag{c}$

The "horizontal" shear stress over the lower surface of the element is

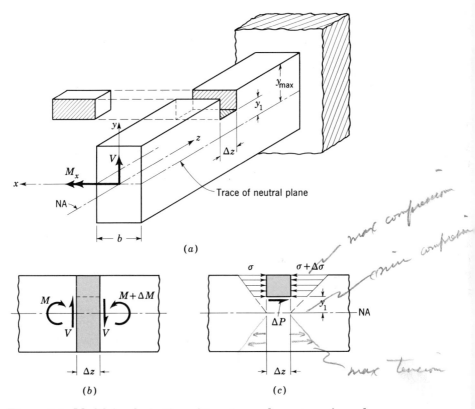

Figure 8.1. Model for derivation of transverse shear-stress formula.

found by dividing ΔP by the area of the horizontal "cut" surface, which is $b \, \Delta z$:

$$\tau = \frac{\Delta P}{b \, \Delta z} = \frac{\Delta M}{\Delta z} \frac{Q}{bI} \tag{d}$$

As Δz approaches zero as a limit we have, from Eq. (6.2),

$$\lim_{\Delta z \to 0} \frac{\Delta M}{\Delta z} = V$$

Substitute this in Eq. (*d*) to derive the equation for "horizontal" shear stress:

$$\tau = \frac{VQ}{bI}$$

(8.2)

where V = shear over entire cross section

Q = static moment of that portion of the cross section between y_1 and y_{max}

b = minimum width of the cross section at y_1

I = moment of inertia of *entire cross section*, about the neutral axis normal to V

The "vertical" shear stress τ_{zy} at any point on a cross section must be equal to the "horizontal" shear stress τ_{yz} at the same point, for rotational

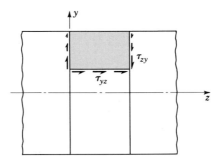

Figure 8.2. Distribution of transverse shear stress.

equilibrium (Fig. 8.2). However, Eq. (8.2) shows that τ_{zy} will decrease as Q decreases (that is, as y_1 approaches y_{max}). At the free surface the "horizontal shear" must be zero; therefore the "vertical" shear must also be zero.

The static moment Q reaches a maximum when $y_1 = 0$; therefore *the maximum shear stress occurs at the neutral axis.* This may not be true for sections that have a smaller width or web thickness at some point other than the neutral axis. Note that the axial stress difference $\Delta\sigma$ changes sign at the neutral axis.

Figure 8.3 shows three special cases in which the dimension b is not measured parallel with the neutral plane. The area for which Q is computed is shaded in each case. Imagine that the solid area is attempting to slip relative to the shaded area (in a direction normal to the paper). The maximum shear stress at a given point is obtained by dividing by the *minimum* width or thickness at that point. In Fig. 8.3*b* the slip is resisted by *both* walls of the tube; therefore $b = 2t$. In Fig. 8.3*c* the area used in computing Q is that for one flange only, as indicated.

In dividing by b in Eq. (8.2), the assumption is being made that the shear stress is uniformly distributed over the width. This assumption will be accurate in some cases but will be only approximately correct for such cross sections as a solid round bar.

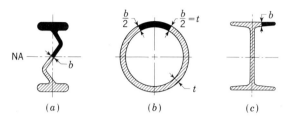

Figure 8.3. Method of cutting cross section for calculation of shear stress.

8.2 Distribution of shear stresses in beams

Figure 8.4 shows how the shear stress (due to transverse forces only) varies over the depth of cross sections of various shapes.

Equations which express this variation will be derived for two cases, the rectangular cross section (Fig. 8.4*b*) and the thin-walled tube (Fig. 8.4*c*).

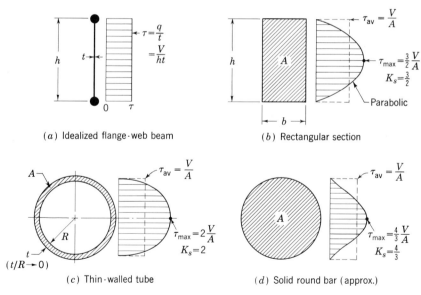

Figure 8.4. Distribution of shear stress for various cross sections.

EXAMPLE 8.1. For the *rectangular cross section* (Fig. E8.1), the value of Q at a distance y from the neutral axis is simply equal to the area above (or below) the

y line, multiplied by the distance from the centroid of this area to the neutral axis:

$$Q = \Delta A \bar{y} = b(c - y)\, \frac{c + y}{2}$$

$$= \frac{b}{2}\,(c^2 - y^2) \qquad\qquad (a)$$

The shear stress is found from Eq. (8.2):

$$\tau = \frac{VQ}{bI} = \frac{V(c^2 - y^2)}{2I} \qquad\qquad (b)$$

At a given station on a beam, all terms in the above equation are constant except y. The value of τ therefore varies parabolically, as shown in Fig. 8.4b.

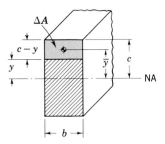

Figure E8.1

To find the maximum shear stress, substitute in Eq. (b), $c = h/2$ and $I = bh^3/12$. This gives

$$\tau = \frac{3}{2}\frac{V}{bh} = \frac{3}{2}\frac{V}{A} \qquad\qquad (c)$$

Therefore

$$\tau_{\max} = \tfrac{3}{2}\tau_{av} \qquad\qquad (d)$$

for a rectangular cross section.

EXAMPLE 8.2.   To determine the variation of shear stress in a *thin-walled tube*, the value of Q is found by integration. In Fig. E8.2 the angle θ will be varied from θ_1 to $(\pi - \theta_1)$, thereby covering the area of the cross section above y_1.

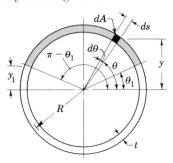

Figure E8.2

The following relationships can be observed from Fig. E8.2:

$$y = R \sin \theta \tag{a}$$
$$ds = R \, d\theta \tag{b}$$
$$dA = t \, ds = Rt \, d\theta \tag{c}$$

From the definition of Q,

$$dQ = y \, dA$$

Substituting from Eqs. (a) and (c),

$$dQ = R \sin \theta \, Rt \, d\theta$$
$$= R^2 t \sin \theta \, d\theta \tag{d}$$

The total value of Q is

$$Q = \int_{\theta_1}^{\pi - \theta_1} dQ = \int_{\theta_1}^{\pi - \theta_1} R^2 t \sin \theta \, d\theta \tag{e}$$

Since R and t are constant,

$$Q = R^2 t [- \cos \theta]_{\theta_1}^{\pi - \theta_1} = 2R^2 t \cos \theta_1 \tag{f}$$

This can be expressed in terms of y by substituting for $\cos \theta_1$ the expression $\sqrt{R^2 - y_1^2}/R$, giving

$$Q = 2R^2 t \sqrt{1 - \left(\frac{y_1}{R}\right)^2} \tag{g}$$

The distribution which corresponds to this equation is shown in Fig. 8.4c. The maximum value of Q occurs at the neutral axis ($y_1 = 0$), where

$$Q_{\max} = 2R^2 t \tag{h}$$

The maximum shear stress is found from Eq. (8.2):

$$\tau_{\max} = \frac{VQ}{2tI} \tag{i}$$

Substituting $I = \pi R^3 t$ (see Appendix Table B.1)

$$\tau_{\max} = \frac{V}{\pi R t} \tag{j}$$

$$\tau_{\mathrm{av}} = \frac{V}{A} = \frac{V}{2\pi R t} \tag{k}$$

Therefore $\qquad \tau_{\max} = 2\tau_{\mathrm{av}} \tag{l}$

It is convenient to express the maximum shear stress in terms of the average shear stress by means of a factor:

$$\tau_{\max} = K_s \tau_{\mathrm{av}} = K_s \frac{V}{A}$$

Values for K_s are shown in Fig. 8.4 for various cross sections. An alternative is to define A_s as A/K_s, as in Table B.3.

EXAMPLE 8.3. Plot the shear-stress distribution over the web of a 10-WF-49 beam (Fig. E8.3) in terms of the average shear stress in the web. From Table B.4,

$$I = 273 \text{ in.}^4$$

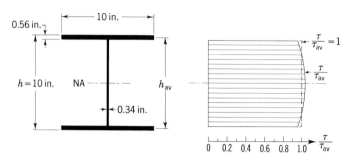

Figure E8.3

Neglecting fillets,

$$Q_{fl} = 10 \times 0.56(5.0 - 0.28)$$
$$= 26.4 \text{ in.}^3$$

At the neutral axis,

$$Q = Q_{fl} + Q_{web} = 26.4 + (5.0 - 0.56) \times 0.34 \times \frac{5.0 - 0.56}{2}$$

$$= 26.4 + 3.35 = 29.75$$

At 2 in. above the neutral axis,

$$Q = Q_{fl} + Q_{web} = 26.4 + (3.0 - 0.56) \times 0.34 \times \left(\frac{3.0 - 0.56}{2} + 2\right)$$

$$= 26.4 + 2.67 = 29.07$$

The shear stress is

$$\tau = \frac{VQ}{bI} = \frac{VQ}{0.34 \times 273} = 0.0108VQ$$
$$\tau_{NA} = 0.0108 \times 29.75 \times V = 0.321V$$
$$\tau_{2 \text{ in.}} = 0.0108 \times 29.07 \times V = 0.314V$$
$$\tau_{\text{at flange}} = 0.0108 \times 26.4 \times V = 0.285V$$

For the idealized web, $h = 10 - 0.56 = 9.44$.

$$t = 0.34$$

$$\tau_{av} = \frac{V}{ht} = \frac{V}{9.44 \times 0.34} = 0.312V$$

The corresponding ratios τ/τ_{av} are 1.029, 1.01, and 0.913. Values of τ/τ_{av} have been plotted opposite the beam in Fig. E8.3. Note that in this case the use of the average stress in the web would be only 2.5 percent on the low side.

The shear stresses in the beam will cause shear strains (see Fig. 4.4). For a rectangular cross section, the shear stress varies over the depth in a parabolic manner. The shear distortion is indicated by Fig. 8.5, which shows that an originally plane cross section does not remain plane. This represents a paradox: we have used a theory, based on plane cross sections' remaining plane, to derive a theory which proves that they do *not* remain plane! For a constant shear V and constant cross section, the

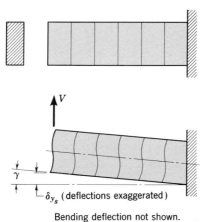

Bending deflection not shown.

Figure 8.5. Effect of shear stress (only) on cross section, for a solid rectangular beam.

shear distortion lines have the same shape; therefore no change of axial lengths occurs because of shear, and the beam theory remains correct. For variable shear an error is introduced, but the effect is usually insignificant.

Figure 8.5 illustrates another phenomenon that causes errors in the calculated bending-stress distribution. If a beam is attached to a "rigid" support (or is continuous and symmetrical over a central support), local normal stresses must be present to insure compatibility (continuity). This is an advanced problem requiring use of the theory of elasticity. The effect is usually small.

8.3 Combined stresses in shear and bending

The transmission of transverse force by means of a straight beam of constant cross section involves both bending stresses and shear stresses. The maximum tension or compression stresses caused by bending alone will occur at the outer fibers. The maximum shear stresses caused by transverse shear alone will usually occur at the neutral axis. In the region between the neutral axis and the outer fibers an element of material will be subjected to combined stresses, which can be calculated from the following equations:

$$\sigma = \frac{My}{I} \quad \text{and} \quad \tau = \frac{VQ}{bI}$$

where Q is the static moment of area "above" y.

In Example 8.1 it was shown that for a *rectangular cross section* the shear stress caused by transverse loading only could be expressed by

$$\tau = \frac{V(c^2 - y^2)}{2I} \tag{a}$$

Substituting $bh^3/12$ for I and $h/2$ for c gives

$$\tau = \frac{V}{A}\left[\frac{3}{2} - 6\left(\frac{y}{h}\right)^2\right] \tag{b}$$

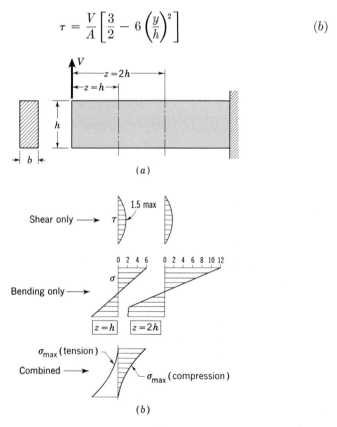

Figure 8.6. Comparison of shear and bending stresses in a rectangular beam.

A similar equation can be derived for the axial stress caused by the bending moment. For a single concentrated force V, at a free end, the equation is

$$\sigma = \pm 12 \frac{V}{A} \frac{y}{h} \frac{z}{h} \qquad (c)$$

where z is the distance from the free end of the beam.

These equations are useful in obtaining an idea of the relationship between shear stresses and normal stresses. In Fig. 8.6 the stress distributions have been plotted to the same scale for a unit average shear stress $V/A = 1$. This figure shows that, for any rectangular beam having a length considerably greater than its depth, the stresses due to transverse shear are relatively small as compared with the normal stresses caused by bending.

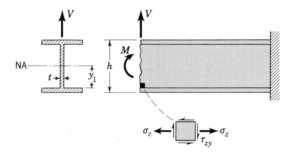

Figure 8.7. Calculation of maximum combined stresses in an I beam.

Also shown in Fig. 8.6 are the maximum tensile and compressive stresses determined by combining the stresses caused by shear and bending. [Equation (2.13) or Mohr's circle is used to obtain these.] For the beam of rectangular cross section, the effect of the transverse shear stresses does not cause the maximum normal stress to exceed the bending stress at the outer fiber.

This example shows that transverse shear stresses can be neglected in the design of beams of rectangular cross section, except for materials having relatively low shear strength, such as wood. The effect of shear stresses on deflection will also be negligible, as compared with the effects of bending stresses.

For conventional I beams or wide-flange beams, the shear-stress distribution in the web is nearly constant (see Example 8.3). Consequently, an element near the juncture of flange to web can develop shear and normal stresses that are higher than those at the neutral axis and outer fiber, respectively.

Figure 8.7 shows a small element located at the lower edge of the web (where $y = y_1$). The bending and shear stresses are

$$\sigma_z = \frac{My_1}{I} \quad \text{and} \quad \tau_{zy} = \frac{VQ_1}{tI}$$

The maximum stresses at this point are

$$\tau_{max} = \sqrt{\left(\frac{\sigma_z}{2}\right)^2 + \tau_{zy}^2} \quad \text{and} \quad \sigma_{max,min} = \frac{\sigma_z}{2} \pm \tau_{max}$$

A *hollow box* is similar to an I beam, except that the single web is replaced by two webs, as shown in Fig. 8.8. To calculate the value of Q, it is necessary to start from a free edge. There is no such free edge in a box section, but because of symmetry, the box may be cut into two channel sections, each of which may be analyzed separately. (Figure 8.8 applies only for central loading.)

At the plane of symmetry the distributed shear force is zero, and it increases linearly until it reaches the sides of the box, as shown in Fig. 8.8b. The distribu-

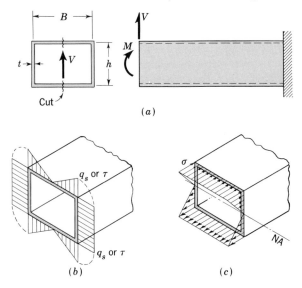

Figure 8.8. Distribution of shear and bending stresses in a box beam.

tion over the webs will be nearly constant. The maximum combined stresses will occur at the corners of the box.

The sketches of Fig. 8.8 do not indicate how the shear force is applied to the box beam. If this force is applied as a concentrated load at the free end, it will be necessary to use a rib or bulkhead to distribute it over the web members. If the resultant transverse force (or shear) does not coincide with the plane of symmetry of the cross section, an additional effect (torsion) will occur. This is treated in Chap. 10.

EXAMPLE 8.4 Calculation of maximum shear and normal stresses in I beam.
For the 10-WF-49 beam (Example 8.3):

$$I_x = 273 \text{ in.}^4 \qquad t_{web} = 0.34 \text{ in.}$$
$$h = 10.0 \text{ in.} \qquad t_{fl} = 0.56 \text{ in.}$$

Let $V = 20,000$ lb, $M = 800,000$ in.-lb
AT OUTER FIBER ($y = 5$ in.),

$$\sigma_z = \frac{My}{I} = \frac{800,000 \times 5.0}{273} = 14,000 \text{ psi}$$

AT EDGE OF WEB ($y = 4.44$ in.),

$$\sigma_z = \frac{800,000 \times 4.44}{273} = 13,000 \text{ psi}$$

$$\tau_{yz} = \frac{VQ}{tI}$$

Neglecting area of fillets,

$$Q_{fl} = A_{fl} \times y_{centroid}$$
$$= (10.0 \times 0.56)(5.0 - 0.28) = 26.4 \text{ in.}^3$$
$$\tau_{yz} = \frac{20,000 \times 26.4}{0.34 \times 273} + 5,700 \text{ psi}$$
$$\tau_{max} = \sqrt{\left(\frac{13,000}{2}\right)^2 + 5,700^2} = 8,650 \text{ psi}$$
$$\sigma_{max} = \frac{13,000}{2} + 8,650 = 15,150 \text{ psi}$$

This value is 16.7 percent greater than the normal stress at the outer fiber.

To compare shear stresses, calculate τ_{yz} at the neutral axis (where $\sigma_z = 0$):

$$Q_{NA} = Q_{fl} + Q_{half \ web}$$
$$= 26.4 + (5.0 - 0.56) \times 0.34 \times \frac{5.0 - 0.56}{2}$$
$$= 26.4 + 3.35 = 29.75 \text{ in.}^3$$
$$\tau_{max} = \tau_{yz} = \frac{20,000 \times 29.75}{0.34 \times 273} = 6,400 \text{ psi}$$

The value previously calculated at the juncture of flange and web is 35 percent higher, showing that yielding will tend to occur first near the junction.

8.4 Tapered beams

For efficiency, beams are often tapered in depth.* For moderate taper, the bending theory developed in Chap. 7 is sufficiently accurate, but the effect of taper on shear stress can be very large. To see this, consider a simplified conceptual model of an I beam in which *the bending moment is resisted entirely by the axial loads in the flanges; the web resists only shear (no bending)*.

* Galileo was the first to calculate the optimum shape of a variable-depth beam (Ref. 7).

Figure 8.9a shows a shear force and a bending moment acting on a section. The horizontal components of the flange forces must be, for moment equilibrium,

$$P_H = \pm \frac{M}{h} \tag{a}$$

where h is the distance between flange centroids.

Because of the taper, the actual flange force must be

$$P_{fl} = \frac{P_H}{\cos(\alpha/2)} \tag{b}$$

When α is small, the taper causes very little increase in the flange force, as compared with a nontapered beam.

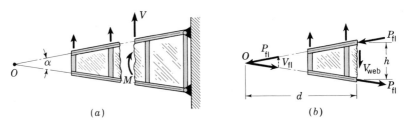

Figure 8.9. Shear resisted by nonparallel flanges.

The vertical component of each flange force is

$$P_V = P_{fl} \sin \frac{\alpha}{2} \tag{c}$$

Substituting for P_{fl} from Eq. (b),

$$P_V = P_H \tan \frac{\alpha}{2} \tag{d}$$

The total shear resisted by the axial flange forces is twice this value (since both components act downward). Therefore

$$V_{fl} = 2P_H \tan \frac{\alpha}{2}$$

Figure 8.9b shows the resisting forces from both flanges and webs. For vertical force equilibrium:

$$V - 2P_H \tan \frac{\alpha}{2} - V_{web} = 0$$

or

$$V_{web} = V - 2P_H \tan \frac{\alpha}{2} \tag{e}$$

For small angles this is approximately equal to

$$V_{web} = V - P_H \tan \alpha \tag{8.3}$$

where $P_H = M/h$.

Another interpretation is obtained by noting that the closed vector diagram (shown at point O) has a base equal to V_{fl} and a height equal to P_H. This triangle is similar to the triangle with base h and height d; that is,

$$\frac{V_{fl}}{P_H} = \frac{h}{d}$$

But $P_H h = M$. Therefore

$$V_{fl} = \frac{M}{d}$$

and

$$V_{web} = V - \frac{M}{d} \tag{8.4}$$

This equation may be used for any beam in which the flanges, if extended, would meet at a point (for example, a moderately tapered truncated cylinder).

8.5 Shear axis and shear center

Figure 8.10 shows a beam consisting of two large flanges, connected by a relatively thin, curved shear web. The cross section can be approximated

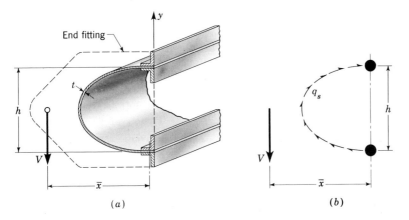

Figure 8.10. Two-flange beam with curved shear web.

by the two-flange model previously used. The web is represented by a line along which the internal shear force is distributed as a *constant line force* (shear flow) q_s. Figure 8.10b represents equilibrium at a section.

Surprisingly, the resultant of such a line force lies considerably outside of the area enclosed by the flanges and web, at a distance $\bar{x}$. To prove this, we find first the value of the resultant force. In Fig. 8.11 the shear force acting on an element ds is, by definition of q_s,

$$dF = q_s \, ds \tag{a}$$

(Note that this force is being transmitted along a path *normal* to the plane of the paper.) The component parallel with the line joining the two ends of the curve is

$$dF_y = q_s \, ds \sin \alpha = q_s \, dy \qquad (b)$$

The vertical component of the resultant is the line integral of dF_y between the two ends of the curve, from $y = 0$ to $y = h$:

$$F_y = \int_0^h q_s \, dy = q_s h \qquad (c)$$

Since $F_y = V$, we can write Eq. (c) in the following form:

$$\boxed{V = q_s h} \qquad (8.5)$$

where h is the length of a straight line between the ends of the curved

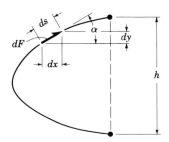

Figure 8.11. Computation of resultant of a constant shear flow.

member (this line need not be vertical). Note that Eq. (8.5) is identical with the equation for a two-flange member with straight web of height h.

Integrating the horizontal components between the two ends of the curve:

$$F_x = \int q_s \, dx = 0$$

Equation (8.5) leads to two important rules:

1. The resultant of a constant shear flow q_s acting over a curved line is equal to the product of q_s and the distance h between the two ends of the line.

2. The resultant acts parallel with the line h.

To locate the resultant, we must find a distance $\bar{x}$ such that the moment of the resultant, about any point in the plane, equals the moment of the shear flow in the curved member. In Fig. 8.12 the moment of dF about point 0 is*

$$dM = rq_s \, ds \sin \beta$$

* In vector algebra this is written $\mathbf{dM} = \mathbf{r} \times \mathbf{dF}$

This can be written as $dM = 2q_s\,d\text{Ⓐ}$, where $d\text{Ⓐ}$ is the area of the triangle formed by ds and r. Integrating with respect to A gives

$$M = 2q_s\text{Ⓐ} \qquad (8.6)$$

where Ⓐ is the area enclosed by the web and by lines drawn from ends of the web to point 0 (see Fig. 8.12*b*).

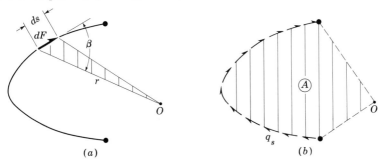

Figure 8.12. Moment of a constant shear flow.

Equation (8.6) leads to a third important rule:

3. The resultant moment of a constant curved shear flow q_s about a point in the plane of the cross section is equal to twice the product of q_s and the area enclosed by the web and two straight lines which connect its ends to the point.

To find the location of the resultant shear force, the moments are equated:

$$\bar{x}V = 2q_s\text{Ⓐ}$$

Replacing V by $q_s h$ and solving for $\bar{x}$ give

$$\bar{x} = \frac{2\text{Ⓐ}}{h} \qquad (8.7)$$

The axis thus determined is called the *shear axis* (see Fig. 8.13).

It is convenient to select a point on the line joining the two ends of the web. Then the distance $\bar{x}$, measured normal to this line, is equal to twice the width of a rectangle having the same area as that enclosed by the web and the line joining the two flanges (see Fig. 8.13).

The practical significance of the shear axis is illustrated by the model shown in Fig. 8.14. (Such a model can be made from cardboard. It should be relatively slender, to avoid end effects.) When a transverse force is applied along the shear axis, no twist will be observed.

A relatively thin-walled section* is shown in Fig. 8.15. Under transverse loading, the shear flow is not constant around the section. It is possible to find a point in the plane cutting the cross section at which shear loads may be applied, *in any direction in the plane,* without causing torsion. This point is called the *shear center.*

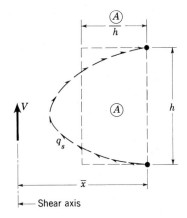

Figure 8.13. Location of resultant shear axis for constant shear flow.

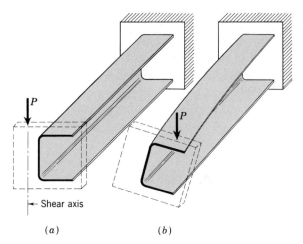

Figure 8.14. Model for demonstrating effects of eccentric transverse loading with respect to shear axis.

In Fig. 8.15 the section has a line of symmetry; this is the shear axis for shear loads applied in the x direction. The shear axis with respect to loading in the y direction is found by a method similar to that used for the two-flange beam, except that the shear flow q_s is not constant.

---

* In this model each element of cross-sectional area can resist normal stresses caused by bending moment.

The value of q_s at any point along the median line of the cross section is found from the equation

$$q_s = \frac{VQ}{I} \qquad (8.8)$$

[See Eqs. (8.1) and (8.2) for meaning of symbols.] This equation is derived in exactly the same way as the shear stress equation, (8.2), except that the shear force per unit length is *not* divided by t (or b).

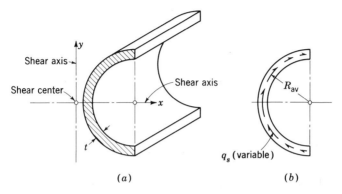

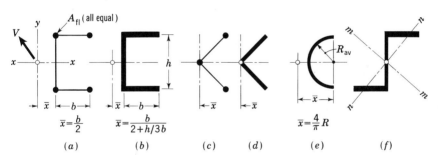

Figure 8.15. Shear center for an open section.

Figure 8.16. Shear centers for various cross sections.

The moment of q_s about an arbitrary point (say the centroid) is computed as for Eq. (8.6) (see Fig. 8.12).

$$M = \int_s \mathbf{r} \times d\mathbf{F} = \int_s |r| q_s \sin \theta \, ds \qquad (8.9)$$

Then

$$\bar{x} = \frac{M}{V}$$

Figure 8.16 shows the location of shear centers for various cross sections.

EXAMPLE 8.5. The shear axis of a channel can be located as follows. For a thin-walled channel of constant thickness (Fig. E8.5), the value of I can be closely expressed by

$$I = 2bt\left(\frac{h}{2}\right)^2 + \frac{th^3}{12} \qquad (a)$$

(This neglects I_0 of the flanges about their own centroidal axes.) The static moment of an entire flange is

$$Q_{\text{fl}} = bt\,\frac{h}{2} \qquad (b)$$

The value of q_s at the juncture is

$$q_1 = \frac{VQ_{\text{fl}}}{I} = \frac{Vbt(h/2)}{bth^2/2 + th^3/12} = \frac{Vb}{bh + h^2/6} \qquad (c)$$

The resultant horizontal shear force in each flange is

$$P_H = \frac{1}{2}\,q_1 b = \frac{Vb^2}{2bh + h^2/3}$$

Substituting these values in the equation for $\Sigma M = 0$ about a point at the corner gives

$$V\bar{x} - P_H h = 0$$
$$\bar{x} = \frac{P_H h}{V} = \frac{b^2 h}{2bh + h^2/3} = \frac{b}{2 + h/3b} \qquad (d)$$

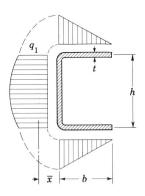

Figure E8.5

EXAMPLE 8.6. Figure E8.6 represents an "unbalanced" I beam under lateral loading. The vertical shear axis can be located by inspection. The horizontal axis is found by calculating the values of q in the cross section, under lateral loading only. The resultant of these values must equal V, and the location of this resultant gives the shear axis.

A close approximation can be made by idealizing the section into two separate beams, each resisting part of the total shear force. The web will obviously contribute very little to the lateral bending resistance. The shear forces resisted by the flanges are indicated by V_1 and V_2. Since the axial stress distribution will be linear for both "beams," both have the same type of distribution of q_s over their depth (parabolic). The values of V_1 and V_2 are proportional to the areas under the q_s curves, which in turn are given by $\frac{2}{3}q_s h$, where q_s represents the maximum value.

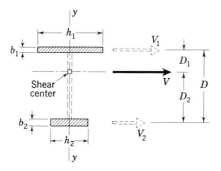

Figure E8.6

From Eq. (8.8),

$$q_{s_1} = \frac{VQ_1}{I} \qquad q_{s_2} = \frac{VQ_2}{I} \tag{a}$$

(Note that V is used because this represents the change in bending moment for the entire beam.) Then,

$$V_1 = \tfrac{2}{3}q_{s_1}h_1 \qquad V_2 = \tfrac{2}{3}q_{s_2}h_2$$
$$V_1 = \frac{2}{3}\frac{VQ_1 h_1}{I} \qquad V_2 = \frac{2}{3}\frac{VQ_2 h_2}{I}$$

from which,

$$\frac{V_1}{V_2} = \frac{Q_1 h_1}{Q_2 h_2} \tag{b}$$

For a flange of rectangular section,

$$Q = (\tfrac{1}{2}A) \times (\text{centroidal distance of half flange})$$

$$Q_1 = \left(\frac{1}{2}h_1 b_1\right)\left(\frac{1}{4}h_1\right) = \frac{b_1 h_1{}^2}{8}$$

$$Q_2 = \left(\frac{1}{2}h_2 b_2\right)\left(\frac{1}{4}h_2\right) = \frac{b_2 h_2{}^2}{8}$$

Substituting,

$$\frac{V_1}{V_2} = \frac{b_1 h_1{}^3}{b_2 h_2{}^3} \tag{c}$$

The location of the resultant shear V is found by equating moments about the upper flange [$\Sigma M = 0$]:

$$VD_1 = V_2D$$

$$\frac{D_1}{D} = \frac{V_2}{V} = \frac{V_2}{V_1 + V_2} = \frac{b_2h_2^3}{b_1h_1^3 + b_2h_2^3} \tag{d}$$

The same result can be obtained by finding the location of V at which there would be no rotation of the cross section (twist) if each flange were to bend as a separate beam. This requires that both of these beams must bend about the same neutral axis (yy) and to the *same radius of curvature*. This requirement means that the bending moments resisted by each flange must be in proportion to their moments of inertia. The bending moments are caused by the shear forces; hence V_1 and V_2 must be proportional to the respective moments of inertia I_1 and I_2. Therefore

$$\frac{V_1}{V_2} = \frac{b_1h_1^3}{b_2h_2^3}$$

8.6 Shear deflections and shear energy

The elastic shear strains in a beam are computed from the basic formula Eq. (4.3):

$$\gamma = \frac{\tau}{G}$$

When the shear stress varies over the depth (as for a solid rectangular cross section), the maximum value of shear stress can be used as an approximation.

For members in which the shear (or depth) varies over the length, it is necessary to integrate the local values of shear strain over the length of the beam. Treating γ (in radians) as $d\delta_s/dz$, one obtains, for the straight cantilever beam (see Fig. 8.5),

$$\delta_s = \int_0^L \gamma \, dz + C \tag{8.10}$$

The shear deflection of slender beams is usually insignificant as compared with the deflections caused by bending moment.

Since γ represents the rate of change of transverse deflection per unit length, the *elastic shear energy* for an incremental length ds (or dz, for straight beams) is

$$dU_s = \tfrac{1}{2}V\gamma \, ds$$

or, using the equivalent area from Sec. 8.2,

$$\boxed{\frac{dU_s}{ds} = \frac{1}{2}\frac{V^2}{A_sG}} \tag{8.11}$$

PROBLEMS

8.1. For an assigned beam from Fig. P6.2, determine the actual dimensions required for shapes dimensionally similar to each of the cross-sectional shapes shown in Fig. P7.1. (The beam is to have a constant cross section.) The design criterion shall be the attainment of a maximum normal stress $\sigma_{allow} = \pm 0.5\sigma_y$, for a designated material from Table A.1. Another criterion is that the maximum shear stress shall not exceed $\tau_{allow} = 0.5\sigma_{allow}$. (Use elastic theory.)

(*a*) As a first approximation, omit consideration of combined stresses; i.e., treat bending and shear stresses separately.

(*b*) For cross sections 2 and 3 only, include the effect of combined stresses.

Suggestion: The actual properties of the cross sections of Fig. P7.1 may be used as trial values in calculating stresses. The required dimensions are then found by determining a factor by which all cross-sectional dimensions are to be multiplied to satisfy the design criteria. (Note that stresses caused by a constant bending moment vary inversely as the cube of a dimension and that those caused by a constant shear vary inversely as the square of a dimension, for dimensionally similar shapes.)

8.2. A wood beam is constructed by glueing together three planks, as shown in Fig. P8.2. For an assigned set of dimensions from the table:

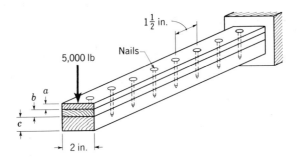

Figure P8.2

(*a*) Calculate the shear stress in each glued joint (neglect nails).

(*b*) Calculate the maximum shear load per nail, assuming that there is no glue bond.

a, in.	0.60	0.50	0.40	0.70	0.80
b, in.	0.90	0.75	0.95	0.85	0.80
c, in.	1.10	1.30	1.50	1.40	1.20

8.3. *Maximum combined stress.* For an assigned wide-flange beam from Table B.4, apply a shear loading (in the y direction) so that the average (allowable) shear stress in the web (V/A_{web}) equals 10,000 psi.

(a) Calculate the allowable pure bending moment, assuming that the allowable stress in the outer fiber is 20,000 psi.

(b) Find the length of the beam (as a cantilever) for which the shear load V will produce the moment M (this is the maximum allowable length).

(c) Find the bending stress at the juncture of web to flange, neglecting fillets.

(d) Calculate the maximum (combined) shear and normal stresses at the juncture. (Check by Mohr's circle.)

(e) Determine a new allowable length at which the maximum combined stresses will not exceed either of the above prescribed values. Note the reduction (percentage) involved.

8.4. The beam of Prob. 8.2 is replaced by a composite beam like that shown in Fig. P7.9. The wood and aluminum-alloy laminates are bonded together by a strong adhesive (such as epoxy resin). Find the shear stresses in the bonds (caused by transverse shear only). Assume elastic behavior, disregarding yield stresses in Table P7.9. (If Prob. 7.9 has previously been assigned, use the same selection of parameters.)

8.5. (a) Derive the equation for the location of the shear axis of the half tube shown in Fig. 8.16e. [*Note:* Use the thin-wall approximation, for which I (of the entire tube) equals $\pi R_{\text{av}}^3 t$. Bending stresses are resisted by the cross section; i.e., there are no flanges.]

(b) Repeat for the section shown in Fig. P8.5. (Use b/R as a variable.)

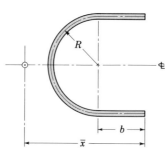

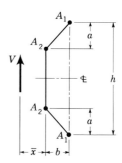

| Figure P8.5 | Figure P8.6 |

8.6. (a) Find the location of the shear center for the symmetrical cross section of Fig. P8.6, using the flange-web model (webs transmit no bending but transmit shear flow q). Numerical values are to be assigned from Table P8.6. (*Suggestion:* Select one of the internal juncture points about which to write the equation of moment equilibrium, thereby eliminating moment of shear flow in two webs.)

(b) Calculate q_s for each web.

TABLE P8.6

	1	2	3	4	5	6	7
V, lb	10,000	10,000	8,000	8,000	6,800	6,000	7,500
h, in.	15.0	15.0	15.8	13.0	13.6	12.0	12.4
a, in.	5.0	5.0	5.3	4.0	4.2	4.4	3.0
b, in.	6.0	6.0	5.0	5.1	4.0	4.2	3.3
A_1, in.²	1.20	1.20	0.80	0.80	0.90	0.90	1.10
A_2, in.²	0.45	0.65	0.45	0.65	0.35	0.45	0.75

8.7. Refer to Fig. 8.8 and place the transverse shear force vector so as to coincide with the left vertical side of the box. Find the net shear flow q in each vertical wall, in terms of V, h, and B. *Method:* Consider the unsymmetrically loaded box to be represented by two different loadings:

(a) Symmetrical loading, such as shown in Fig. 8.8.

(b) A torsional loading M_z equal to $Vb/2$. The shear flow for the latter case is, from Eq. (8.6), $q_1 = M_z/2\text{Ⓐ}$.

The shear flow at any point is then found by superposition. (*Note:* Use the approximation $q_{\text{web}} = \text{const.}$)

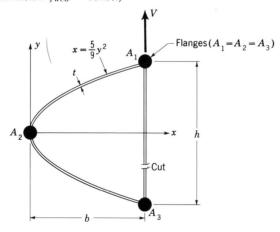

Figure P8.8

8.8. A parabolic "D tube" with three flanges is illustrated in Fig. P8.8. Such a closed structure can resist shear, bending, and torsion. Using the idealized web-flange model, calculate the shear flows $q_{1,2}$, $q_{2,3}$, $q_{3,1}$ in terms of V, b, and h, when V is applied as shown. [*Note:* One method is to start by "cutting" the vertical web and computing q' and the moment of this (constant) shear flow about A_1. Superpose a constant shear flow q'' caused by the unbalanced torsion acting on the closed section. (Flanges do not enter into this calculation.)]

8.9. A built-up I beam is constructed by welding three plates together, as shown in Fig. P8.9a.

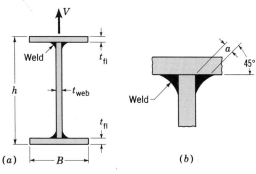

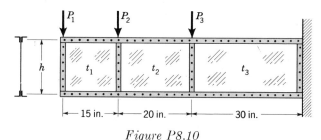

Figure P8.9

(*a*) Derive a formula for the total "longitudinal" shear flow q between flange and web, for the case when both flanges have the same thickness. Do this by two methods, one for q_{web} = constant, the other (more accurate) using Eq. (8.8).

(*b*) For a weld "throat" depth a, as shown in Fig. P8.9b, extend the above formulas to predict the maximum shear stress in the welds (see also Sec. 12.8).

Figure P8.10

8.10. For Fig. P8.10 and for an assigned set of values from Table P8.10:

(*a*) Compute the shear flows q_s across the webs. (Use the 2-flange approximation, with h representing the distance between flange centroids.)

(*b*) Find the required web thicknesses using a value of 15,000 psi for the allowable shear stress.

(*c*) Neglecting the possibility of web buckling (Sec. 11.7), calculate the vertical deflection at the free end caused by shear *only;* i.e., omit bending deflection. (Use steel, with $E = 29 \times 10^6$ psi, $\nu = \frac{1}{3}$.)

(*d*) Calculate the total elastic energy in the webs, corresponding to shear only.

Note: Flanges and vertical stiffeners not designed.

TABLE P8.10

	1	2	3	4	5	6	7
h, in.	16	13	20	19	14	24	12
P_1, kips	4.8	4.0	6.0	8.0	7.5	3.5	5.0
P_2, kips	7.5	9.0	12.0	11.0	8.0	13.0	10.0
P_3, kips	8.0	7.0	13.0	13.0	12.0	15.0	9.0

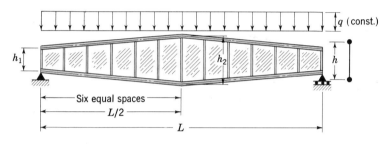

Figure P8.11

8.11. For an assigned set of values for Fig. P8.11:

(*a*) Draw the shear and bending-moment diagrams (calculate values for stations at which verticals are located, neglecting beam weight).

(*b*) Calculate and plot (for half the beam) the values of P_{flange} and q_{web}, using the approximate 2-flange–beam theory and Sec. 8.4.

TABLE P8.11

	1	2	3	4	5	6	7
L, in.	114	108	122	128	135	147	152
h_1, in.	13	9	7	11	12	15	17
h_2, in.	42	34	38	29	27	40	40
q, lb/in.	410	430	370	390	350	380	425

Chapter 9

Deflections of Beams

9.1 General equations

For the elastic range, the equation $d\phi/ds = M/EI$, previously derived, gives the curvature caused by a bending moment M and resisted by the cross-sectional stiffness EI. Curvature is defined by $1/R \equiv d\phi/ds$.

For the small curvatures usually caused by bending moments, the following approximations may be made for initially straight beams (see Fig. 9.1):

$$\text{Slope} \qquad \phi \doteq \frac{dy}{dz} \qquad \text{radians} \qquad (a)$$

$$\text{Curvature} \qquad \frac{d\phi}{ds} \doteq \frac{d\phi}{dz} \qquad (b)$$

where z is the distance along the structural axis, and y is the deflection* of the structural axis in the y direction.

For an initially straight beam, the relationships between loading (q), shear (V), and bending moment (M) are given by Eqs. (6.1) and (6.2). The complete sequence of equations can be written as follows:

Rate of change of shear	$\dfrac{dV}{dz} = q$	$(9.1a)$
Rate of change of moment	$\dfrac{dM}{dz} = V$	$(9.1b)$

---

* A more appropriate designation would be δ_y. However, it is customary to use y, which is *not the same* as that used in Eq. (7.9), in which y refers to a dimension of a cross section.

Rate of change of slope	$\dfrac{d\phi}{dz} = \dfrac{M}{EI}$	*(9.1c)*
Rate of change of deflection	$\dfrac{dy}{dz} = \phi$	*(9.1d)*

The *loading function* q includes not only distributed forces but also local forces and moments. This is made mathematically possible by the use of *singularity functions* (Sec. 6.3).

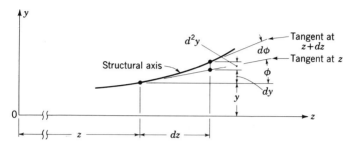

Figure 9.1. Approximations in bending-deflection theory.

Successive integration of Eqs. (9.1) gives the values of the various quantities at point z along the axis:

$$V = \int_0^z q\, dz + C_1 \qquad (9.2a)$$

$$M = \int_0^z V\, dz + C_2 \qquad (9.2b)$$

$$\phi = \int_0^z \frac{M}{EI}\, dz + C_3 \qquad (9.2c)$$

$$y = \int_0^z \phi\, dz + C_4 \qquad (9.2d)$$

The constants of integration are evaluated from a knowledge of the required end conditions, which are referred to generally as *constraints*. Various types of constraints are shown in Fig. 9.2. These sketches represent conceptual models, that is, abstractions of actual situations.

In using Eqs. (9.2), any consistent set of conventions may be employed. We shall use those already established in Chap. 6. The positive conventions for deflection y and slope ϕ must be consistent with the effects of a positive bending moment. As indicated in Fig. 9.1, positive values of y are measured upward and positive ϕ is counterclockwise. This agrees with the action of a positive state of bending, which causes a counterclockwise change of slope over a length dz, as shown in Fig. 9.3.

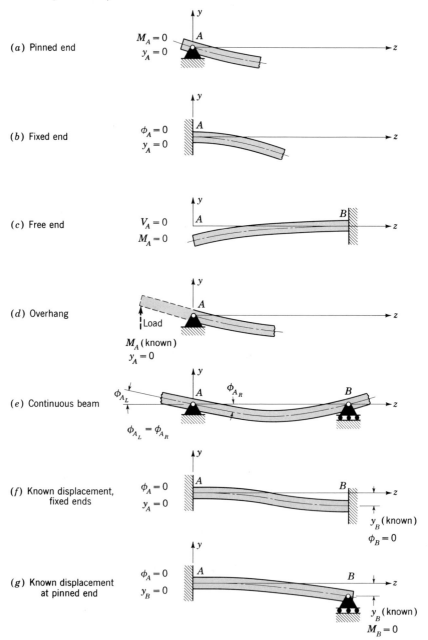

(a) Pinned end

$M_A = 0$
$y_A = 0$

(b) Fixed end

$\phi_A = 0$
$y_A = 0$

(c) Free end

$V_A = 0$
$M_A = 0$

(d) Overhang

Load

M_A (known)
$y_A = 0$

(e) Continuous beam

ϕ_{A_L} ϕ_{A_R}

$\phi_{A_L} = \phi_{A_R}$

(f) Known displacement,
fixed ends

$\phi_A = 0$
$y_A = 0$

y_B (known)
$\phi_B = 0$

(g) Known displacement
at pinned end

$\phi_A = 0$
$y_B = 0$

y_B (known)
$M_B = 0$

Figure 9.2. Various end conditions (constraints).

9.2 Methods of integration

Various methods of performing the integrations of Eqs. (9.2) are used. When q can be expressed as an integrable mathematical function, the usual integration formulas may be employed. For elementary loading functions (such as those represented by rectangles, triangles, etc.) the *area-moment method* of Sec. 6.4 is convenient.

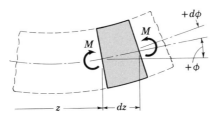

Figure 9.3. Change of slope caused by positive state of bending.

If the loading function is quite irregular, it may be represented by a table of values at relatively small intervals (Δz) along the structural axis. A numerical method of integration is then employed.

In Eqs. (9.2), if the constants of integration C_1 and C_2 can be determined from Eqs. (a) and (b) only, the beam is classified as *statically determinate*. If not, it is necessary to proceed further in the integration sequence before C_1 and C_2 can be determined. Such beams are classified as *statically indeterminate*.

A point of inflection is defined as any point on the deflected structural axis at which the curvature is zero. This point is located where the value of M/EI is zero.

The *area-moment theorems*, as applied to slope and deflection, can be stated as follows (see Fig. 9.4, in which "area" is denoted by A*):

1. The change of slope (in radians) between two points A and B on the deflection curve is equal to the corresponding area under the $1/R$ curve. (In the elastic range, $1/R = M/EI$.)*
2. The deflection of point B relative to the tangent to the curve at point A is equal to the moment of the corresponding area under the $1/R$ curve, with respect to point B.
3. The tangents to the deflection curve at points A and B intersect at a point which is determined by the location of the centroid of the corresponding area of the $1/R$ diagram.

Proof of the above theorems follows directly from Eqs. (9.2c) and (9.2d) when the M/EI curve is known. The use of the tangent as a base in theorem 2 implies the omission of C_3 and C_4.

* For inelastic bending use $1/R$ as determined by methods outlined in Sec. 7.7.

In the original derivation of theorems 1 and 2, Saint-Venant (Ref. 1, p. 137) used the following reasoning: An element of area under the $1/R$ curve, of width dz, represents the change of slope $d\phi$ over this elemental length (Fig. 9.5). The effect of this change of slope on the deflection at some particular point B is determined by multiplying the elemental area $d\phi$ by the distance to the point $(L - z)$. The

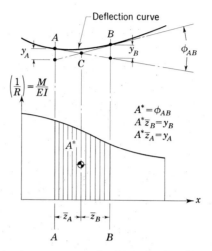

Figure 9.4. Area-moment theorems for bending deflections.

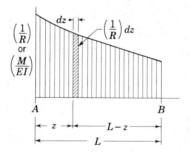

Figure 9.5. Derivation of area-moment theorems.

total change of deflection at B, with respect to the tangent to the deflection curve at A, is therefore found by integrating the quantity $[(1/R)\,dz](L - z)$ between the limits $z = A$ and $z = B$. But the resulting quantity can also be interpreted as the moment of the area under the $1/R$ curve with respect to point B, thus leading to theorem 2.

EXAMPLE 9.1 Cantilever beam with concentrated load. The equation for bending moment* is, by inspection of Fig. E9.1a,

$$M = P_1 z \qquad (a)$$

* Weight of beam omitted unless otherwise noted.

For constant EI, Eq. (9.2c) becomes

$$\phi = \frac{1}{EI} \int P_1 z \, dz + C_3 = \frac{P_1}{EI} \frac{z^2}{2} + C_3 \qquad (b)$$

From Fig. E9.1a we see that at B, where $z = L$, the slope ϕ must be zero:

$$0 = \frac{P_1}{EI} \frac{L^2}{2} + C_3 \qquad C_3 = -\frac{P_1}{EI} \frac{L^2}{2} \qquad (c)$$

Substituting this in Eq. (b), we obtain the equation for slope:

$$\phi = \frac{P_1}{EI} \left(\frac{z^2 - L^2}{2} \right) \qquad (d)$$

Substitute this in Eq. (9.2d) and integrate, obtaining

$$y = \frac{P_1}{EI} \left(\frac{z^3}{6} - \frac{L^2 z}{2} \right) + C_4 \qquad (e)$$

At B, where $z = L$, $y = 0$:

$$0 = \frac{P_1}{EI} \left(\frac{L^3}{6} - \frac{L^3}{2} \right) + C_4 \qquad C_4 = \frac{1}{3} \frac{P_1 L^3}{EI} \qquad$$

Substituting this in (e) gives

$$y = \frac{P_1}{EI} \left(\frac{z^3}{6} - \frac{L^2 z}{2} + \frac{1}{3} L^3 \right) \qquad (f)$$

The maximum deflection occurs where $z = 0$:

$$y_{\max} = + \frac{1}{3} \frac{P_1 L^3}{EI} \qquad (g)$$

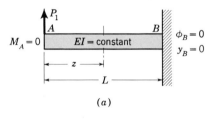

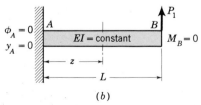

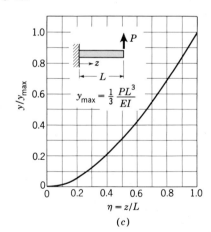

Figure E9.1. (a) *Cantilever beam with concentrated force at free end.* (b) *Beam reversed.* (c) *Dimensionless plot of deflection.*

Note that this value is positive, which tells us that the direction of the deflection is the same as the direction of the load.

As an exercise, let us now turn the beam around, placing the fixed end at A, as shown in Fig. E9.1b. The following equations are obtained:

$$M = P_1(L - z) \qquad \phi = \frac{P_1}{EI}\left(Lz - \frac{z^2}{2}\right) \qquad y = \frac{P_1}{EI}\left(\frac{Lz^2}{2} - \frac{z^3}{6}\right)$$

Since $y_{\max}$ occurs where $z = L$,

$$y_{\max} = \frac{1}{3}\frac{P_1 L^3}{EI}$$

To obtain a *dimensionless deflection curve* for all beams of this class and type of loading we normalize the distance along the beam and also the deflection. Let

$$\eta = \frac{z}{L}$$

Also divide y by $y_{\max}$. This gives

$$\frac{y}{y_{\max}} = \frac{3}{2}\eta^2 - \frac{1}{2}\eta^3$$

The results are shown in Fig. E9.1c.

EXAMPLE 9.2 Simply supported beam with uniform loading.   In Fig. E9.2a all forces are shown positive upward. Substituting in Eqs. (9.2) we have

$$V = \int q \, dz + C_1 = q_1 z + C_1$$

$$M = \int V \, dz + C_2 = q_1 \frac{z^2}{2} + C_1 z + C_2$$

at $z = 0$, $M = 0$; therefore $C_2 = 0$. Also, at $z = L$, $M = 0$, giving

$$0 = q_1 \frac{L^2}{2} + C_1 L$$

$$C_1 = -\frac{q_1 L}{2}$$

Substituting these values of C_1 and C_2, we obtain

$$V = q_1 z - \frac{q_1 L}{2} \tag{a}$$

$$M = q_1 \frac{z^2}{2} - \frac{q_1 L z}{2} \tag{b}$$

To find the reaction at A note that

$$R_A = V_{z=0} = C_1$$

Therefore $$R_A = -\frac{q_1 L}{2} \quad \text{(down)}$$

Also, $R_B = R_A$.

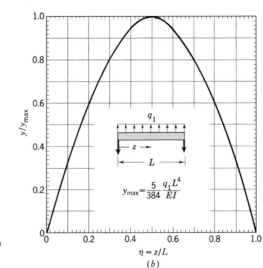

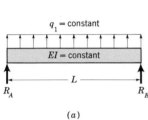

(a)

(b)

Figure E9.2. (a) *Uniformly loaded simply supported beam (all forces shown positive upward).* (b) *Dimensionless plot of deflection.*

The maximum moment occurs at $z = L/2$, therefore

$$M_{\text{max}} = -\frac{q_1 L^2}{8}$$

The slope is

$$\phi = \int \frac{M}{EI}\, dz + C_3$$

$$= \frac{1}{EI}\left(q_1 \frac{z^3}{6} - \frac{q_1 L z^2}{4} \right) + C_3$$

The deflection is

$$y = \int \phi\, dz + C_4$$

$$= \frac{1}{EI}\left(\frac{q_1 z^4}{24} - \frac{q_1 L z^3}{12} \right) + C_3 z + C_4$$

At $z = 0$, $y = 0$; therefore $C_4 = 0$, and at $z = L$, $y = 0$:

$$0 = \frac{1}{EI}\left(\frac{q_1 L^4}{24} - \frac{q_1 L^4}{12} \right) + C_3 L$$

$$C_3 = +\frac{q_1 L^3}{24 EI}$$

Substituting for C_3,

$$\phi = \frac{1}{EI}\left(q_1\frac{z^3}{6} - \frac{q_1Lz^2}{4} + \frac{q_1L^3}{24}\right) \tag{c}$$

$$y = \frac{1}{EI}\left(\frac{q_1z^4}{24} - \frac{q_1Lz^3}{12} + \frac{q_1L^3z}{24}\right) \tag{d}$$

From inspection, y_{max} occurs at $z = L/2$:

$$y_{max} = \frac{1}{EI}\left(\frac{q_1L^4}{384} - \frac{q_1L^4}{96} + \frac{q_1L^4}{48}\right)$$

$$y_{max} = \frac{5}{384}\frac{q_1L^4}{EI} \tag{e}$$

The normalized deflection equation is

$$\frac{y}{y_{max}} = \frac{16}{5}\left(\eta^4 - 2\eta^3 + \eta\right) \tag{f}$$

This is plotted in Fig. E9.2.

Equation (e) can be used to find the sag of a horizontal beam under its own weight, when it is simply supported at the ends. In that case, $q_1 = -wA$, where w is the density and A is the cross-sectional area (constant).

When new situations are being analyzed, the resulting equations should be checked for dimensional consistency. To illustrate, substitute the dimensional units involved in Eq. (e).

$$y_{max} \sim \frac{(\text{lb/in.})(\text{in.}^4)}{(\text{lb/in.}^2)(\text{in.}^4)} = \text{in.}$$

EXAMPLE 9.3 Simply supported beam with concentrated load at $z = a$.   Using the *singularity function* method of Sec. 6.3 for the beam in Fig. E9.3a, the loading can be expressed as

$$q = P\langle z - a\rangle_{-1}$$

Integrating q to find the shear, we have

$$V = \int q\,dz + C_1 = P\int\langle z - a\rangle_{-1}\,dz + C_1$$
$$= P\langle z - a\rangle^0 + C_1$$

Integrating V to find the moment:

$$M = P\langle z - a\rangle^1 + C_1z + C_2$$

At $z = 0$, $M = 0$, therefore $C_2 = 0$; at $z = L$, $M = 0$. Substituting in the above equation, we have

$$0 = P(L - a) + C_1L \qquad C_1 = -P\left(1 - \frac{a}{L}\right)$$

Therefore

$$V = P\langle z - a\rangle^0 - P\left(1 - \frac{a}{L}\right) \tag{a}$$

$$M = P\langle z - a\rangle^1 - P\left(1 - \frac{a}{L}\right)z \tag{b}$$

Divide M by EI (= constant) and integrate to find ϕ:

$$\phi = \frac{P}{EI}\left[\frac{\langle z - a\rangle^2}{2} - \left(1 - \frac{a}{L}\right)\frac{z^2}{2}\right] + C_3$$

Integrate ϕ to find y:

$$y = \frac{P}{EI}\left[\frac{\langle z - a\rangle^3}{6} - \left(1 - \frac{a}{L}\right)\frac{z^3}{6}\right] + C_3 z + C_4$$

When $z = 0$, $y = 0$; therefore $C_4 = 0$. When $z = L$, $y = 0$. Substituting, we have

$$0 = \frac{P}{EI}\left[\frac{(L - a)^3}{6} - \left(1 - \frac{a}{L}\right)\frac{L^3}{6}\right] + C_3 L$$

$$C_3 = -\frac{PL^2}{6EI}\left[\left(1 - \frac{a}{L}\right)^3 - \left(1 - \frac{a}{L}\right)\right]$$

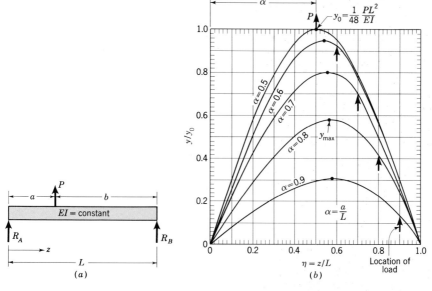

Figure E9.3. (a) *Simply supported beam with concentrated load at* $z = a$ *(all forces shown positive).* (b) *Dimensionless deflection curves.*

Substituting for C_3 in equations for ϕ and y:

$$\phi = \frac{P}{EI}\left\{\left[\frac{\langle z - a\rangle^2}{2} - \left(1 - \frac{a}{L}\right)\frac{z^2}{2}\right] - \frac{L^2}{6}\left[\left(1 - \frac{a}{L}\right)^3 - \left(1 - \frac{a}{L}\right)\right]\right\} \quad (c)$$

$$y = \frac{P}{6EI}\left\{\langle z - a\rangle^3 - \left(1 - \frac{a}{L}\right)z^3 - L^2 z\left[\left(1 - \frac{a}{L}\right)^3 - \left(1 - \frac{a}{L}\right)\right]\right\} \quad (d)$$

Let us find the value of y when $a = L/2$ and $z = L/2$.

$$y = \frac{P}{6EI}\left\{0 - \left(1 - \frac{1}{2}\right)\frac{L^3}{8} - \frac{L^3}{2}\left[\left(1 - \frac{1}{2}\right)^3 - \left(1 - \frac{1}{2}\right)\right]\right\}$$

$$y_{max} = \frac{1}{48}\frac{PL^3}{EI} \quad (e)$$

To normalize, let $\eta = z/L$, $\alpha = a/L$, and $\beta = 1 - \alpha = b/L$. Let y_0 be the value from Eq. (e). Then

$$\frac{y}{y_0} = 8[\langle \eta - \alpha\rangle^3 - \beta\eta^3 - \eta\beta^3 + \eta\beta] \quad (f)$$

Let $\beta = \frac{1}{2}$ and $\eta \leq \frac{1}{2}$:

$$\frac{y}{y_0} = 3\eta - 4\eta^3 \quad (g)$$

By setting the derivative of Eq. (f) equal to zero and solving for η, we obtain the value of η for maximum deflection (η assumed greater than α):

$$\eta = \sqrt{\tfrac{1}{3}(1 - \beta^2)}$$

Substituting in (f) to find y_{max}/y_0,

$$\frac{y_{max}}{y_0} = \frac{8\beta}{\sqrt{3}}\sqrt{1 - \beta^2}\left[-\frac{1}{3}(1 - \beta^2) - \beta^2 + 1\right] \quad (h)$$

Values from Eq. (f) are plotted in Fig. E9.3b for values of α.

EXAMPLE 9.4 Discontinuous uniform loading. In Example 6.3, the equation for moment was found to be

$$M = 275z - 5[\langle z - 20\rangle^2 - \langle z - 70\rangle^2] \quad (a)$$

The maximum bending moment was 9,280 in.-lb.

To make the problem realistic, select a tube which will transmit this bending moment without exceeding a prescribed allowable stress of 20,000 psi. The section modulus required is

$$Z_{req'd} = \frac{M}{\sigma_{allow}} = \frac{9,280}{20,000} = 0.464 \text{ in.}^3$$

From Appendix Table B.3, we select a steel tube 3 in. OD with 0.083-in. wall thickness, for which

$$Z = 0.5398 \text{ in.}^3 \qquad I = 0.8097 \text{ in.}^4 \qquad A = 0.7606 \text{ in.}^2$$

We have $E = 29 \times 10^6$ psi; therefore $EI = 23.48 \times 10^6$ lb-in.^{2}

Now calculate the bending deflection:

$$\phi = \int \frac{M}{EI} \, dz + C_3 = \frac{1}{23.48 \times 10^6} \int \{275z - 5[\langle z - 20 \rangle^2 - \langle z - 70 \rangle^2]\} \, dz + C_3$$

$$= 4.258 \times 10^{-8} \left\{ 275 \frac{z^2}{2} - 5 \left[\frac{\langle z - 20 \rangle^3}{3} - \frac{\langle z - 70 \rangle^3}{3} \right] \right\} + C_3$$

$$y = \int \phi \, dz + C_4$$

$$= 4.258 \times 10^{-8} \left\{ 275 \frac{z^3}{6} - 5 \left[\frac{\langle z - 20 \rangle^4}{12} - \frac{\langle z - 70 \rangle^4}{12} \right] \right\} + C_3 z + C_4$$

When $z = 0$, $y = 0$; therefore $C_4 = 0$.

When $z = L = 100$ in., $y = 0$; substituting,

$$0 = 4.258 \times 10^{-8} \left\{ 275 \frac{10^6}{6} - \frac{5}{12} [(100 - 20)^4 - (100 - 70)^4] \right\} + C_3 100$$

$$C_3 = -1.24 \times 10^{-2} \qquad \text{radians.}$$

Substituting this in the above equation for y,

$$y = 4.258 \times 10^{-8} \{45.8z^3 - \tfrac{5}{12}[\langle z - 20 \rangle^4 - \langle z - 70 \rangle^4]\} - 1.24 \times 10^{-2} z$$

The deflection curve can be plotted from this equation, or the slope equation may be set equal to zero to find the location of the maximum deflection. However, it is evident from Fig. E9.3b that y_{max} will occur very close to $z = L/2$. Therefore we shall calculate the value at midpoint by letting $z = 50$ in.:

$$y = 4.258 \times 10^{-8} \{45.8(50)^3 - \tfrac{5}{12}[(50 - 20)^4 - 0]\} - 1.24 \times 10^{-2} \times 50$$

$$= -0.39 \text{ in.} \qquad \text{(down)}$$

The deflection of the tube under its own weight is, from Example 9.2, Eq. (e),

$$y = \frac{5}{384} \frac{qL^4}{EI}$$

where $q = -wA = 0.29 \times 0.761 = -0.221$ lb/in.; thus

$$y = \frac{5}{384} \times \frac{-0.221 \times 100^4}{23.48 \times 10^6} = -0.0123 \text{ in.} \qquad \text{(down)}$$

EXAMPLE 9.5 Beam with overhang moments (method of superposition). Figure E9.5 shows a beam with overhang moments at the supports. If the central span is assumed to be unloaded, the slope and deflection in this span are easily determined. The results can be added to the solution for the central span treated as a simple beam without end moments. The overhang shears have no effect on the central span (they affect the reactions, however).

Figure E9.5*b* shows the free-body diagram for the central span with $q = 0$. The values of V and M are shown for positive *states* of loading, not for the loading shown in *a*.

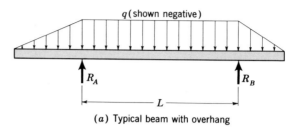

q (shown negative)

R_A R_B

L

(*a*) Typical beam with overhang

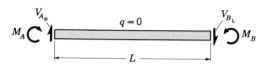

$q = 0$

V_{A_R} V_{B_L}

M_A M_B

L

(*b*) Free-body diagram for overhang loading only (positive states of V and M)

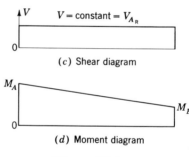

V $V = \text{constant} = V_{A_R}$

0

(*c*) Shear diagram

M_A

M_B

0

(*d*) Moment diagram

Figure E9.5

The shear and moment diagrams can be drawn immediately. Sketch *d* shows that the moment must vary linearly from M_A to M_B. The shear in the central span is constant and equal to

$$V = \frac{M_B - M_A}{L}$$

To find the deflection (caused by overhang moments only) we shall follow the formal procedure of Eqs. (9.2), without referring to the above results. Let $q = 0$; from Eq. (9.2*a*),

$$V = C_1$$

At $z = 0$, $V = V_{A_R}$; therefore

$$C_1 = V_{A_R} \quad \text{and} \quad V = V_{A_R} = \text{constant}$$

From Eq. (9.2b),

$$M = \int V_{A_R}\, dz + C_2 = V_{A_R}z + C_2$$

At $z = 0$, $M = M_A$,

$$M_A = 0 + C_2$$

Therefore $\qquad C_2 = M_A \qquad$ and $\qquad M = V_{A_R}z + M_A$

At $x = L$, $M = M_B$,

$$M_B = V_{A_R}L + M_A$$

Solving for V_{A_R},

$$V_{A_R} = \frac{M_B - M_A}{L}$$

From Eq. (9.2c),

$$\phi = \int \frac{M}{EI}\, dz + C_3$$

$$= \frac{1}{EI}\left(\frac{V_{A_R}z^2}{2} + M_A z\right) + C_3$$

(C_3 cannot be determined at this stage, because the slope at $z = 0$ is not known.)
From Eq. (9.2d),

$$y = \int \phi\, dz + C_4$$

$$= \frac{1}{EI}\left(\frac{V_{A_R}z^3}{6} + M_A \frac{z^2}{2}\right) + C_3 z + C_4$$

At $z = 0$, $y = 0$. Substituting, $0 = C_4$
At $z = L$, $y = 0$. Substituting,

$$0 = \frac{1}{EI}\left(\frac{V_{A_R}L^3}{6} + M_A \frac{L^2}{2}\right) + C_3 L$$

$$C_3 = -\frac{1}{EI}\left(\frac{V_{A_R}L^2}{6} + M_A \frac{L}{2}\right)$$

Substituting for C_3,

$$y = \frac{1}{EI}\left[\frac{V_{A_R}}{6}(z^3 - L^2 z) + \frac{M_A}{2}(z^2 - Lz)\right]$$

where $\qquad V_{A_R} = \dfrac{M_B - M_A}{L}$

If the central span is actually loaded, the above values of y must be added (algebraically) to those representing the deflection of a simply supported beam having the same loading (method of superposition).

9.3 Statically indeterminate beams

In integrating the general equations (9.2), the number of end constraints may be such that the constants of integration C_1 and C_2 cannot be determined before going on to evaluate slope and deflection. The *fixed-end*

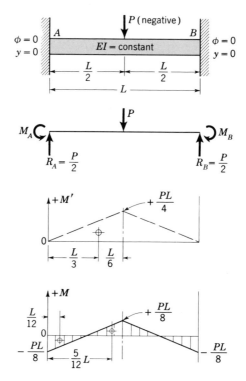

Figure 9.6. Fixed-end beam with concentrated force at midspan.

beam is an example. Such a beam is statically indeterminate. As shown in Fig. 9.6, the conditions of constraint are

$$\phi_A = 0, \qquad y_A = 0, \qquad \phi_B = 0, \qquad y_B = 0$$

Neither the shear nor the moment is zero at either end.

For the simple loading condition shown (concentrated downward load at midspan), conditions of symmetry provide an easy solution. *The slope at midspan must be zero.* For zero end slope, this means that there can be no net change in area of the M/EI diagram over either half of the span (or for the entire span). Consequently, *if EI is constant*, the M' diagram for the simple beam (shown by dashed line) must be "shifted downward" by an amount $-PL/8$. The moment at midspan then becomes $+PL/8$,

$$M_A = M_B = -\frac{PL}{8}$$

The shear diagram will be unchanged from that of the simple beam.

To calculate the maximum deflection (at midspan), we can apply the *second area-moment theorem* (page 209) by calculating the moment of half the M/EI diagram with respect to the end point of the beam (where the slope and deflection are zero).

The area of one small triangle in Fig. 9.6 is

$$\text{Area} = \frac{1}{2}\frac{PL}{8}\frac{L}{4} = \frac{PL^2}{64}$$

The moment arms to the centroids are shown on the sketch. The net moment is

$$\text{Moment of area} = +\frac{PL^2}{64}\left(\frac{5}{12}L - \frac{1}{12}L\right) = \frac{PL^3}{192}$$

The deflection is found by dividing this result by EI:

$$y = \frac{1}{192}\frac{PL^3}{EI} \tag{a}$$

For the corresponding *simply supported beam*, the deflection relative to the center (where the slope is zero) is found by computing the moment of area for one-half the dashed diagram, about the end. [See also Example 9.3, Eq. (e)].

$$\text{Moment of area} = \left(\frac{1}{2}\frac{PL}{4}\times\frac{L}{2}\right)\times\frac{L}{3} = \frac{1}{48}PL^3$$

$$y_{\max} = \frac{1}{48}\frac{PL^3}{EI} \tag{b}$$

Thus the maximum deflection for this type of loading is reduced to one quarter of that for a simply supported beam, by fixing both ends.

Figure 9.7 shows a *fixed-end beam with uniform loading*. The moment diagram for the simply supported beam (shown by the dashed curve of M') is parabolic. It has an area equal to two-thirds that of the superscribed rectangle.

Since $M_A = M_B$ (from symmetry), the area represented by the fixed-end moments (alone) is M_AL. We therefore set this area equal and opposite to that for the simple beam, to give zero change of slope:

$$-M_AL = \frac{2}{3}\times\frac{qL^2}{8}L$$

$$M_A = M_B = -\frac{qL^2}{12}$$

When the moment diagram is shifted downward by this amount, the moment at *mid-span* becomes

$$M_{L/2} = \frac{qL^2}{8} - \frac{qL^2}{12} = \frac{qL^2}{24}$$

The fixed-end moments are now the maximum moments. Fixing the ends has reduced the value of M_{max} in the ratio of $\frac{1}{12}$ to $\frac{1}{8}$, or to two-thirds its value for a simple beam.

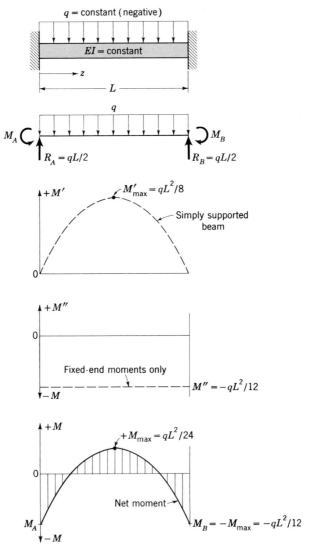

Figure 9.7. Fixed-end beam under uniform loading.

EXAMPLE 9.6 Deflection of fixed-end beam with uniform loading. Although several shortcuts are possible because of symmetry, the routine mathematical procedure will be followed. The loading q is assumed positive upward (opposite to that of Fig. 9.7):

$$V = \int q \, dz + C_1 = qz + C_1 \qquad (a)$$

$$M = \int V \, dz + C_2 = q\frac{z^2}{2} + C_1 z + C_2 \qquad (b)$$

Neither V nor M is zero at either end. Therefore neither C_1 nor C_2 can be evaluated at this stage:

$$\phi = \int \frac{M}{EI} \, dz + C_3 = \frac{1}{EI}\left(\frac{qz^3}{6} + C_1\frac{z^2}{2} + C_2 z\right) + C_3 \qquad (c)$$

At $z = 0$, $\phi = 0$. In Eq. (c), $0 = 0 + C_3$; therefore $C_3 = 0$. At $z = L$, $\phi = 0$. Substituting,

$$0 = \frac{1}{EI}\left(\frac{qL^3}{6} + C_1\frac{L^2}{2} + C_2 L\right) \qquad C_2 = -\left(\frac{qL^2}{6} + C_1\frac{L}{2}\right) \qquad (d)$$

$$y = \int\phi \, dz + C_4$$

$$= \frac{1}{EI}\left(\frac{qz^4}{24} + C_1\frac{z^3}{6} + C_2\frac{z^2}{2}\right) + C_4$$

At $z = 0$, $y = 0$; therefore $C_4 = 0$. At $z = L$, $y = 0$ (also substitute for C_2):

$$0 = \frac{1}{EI}\left[\frac{qL^4}{24} + C_1\frac{L^3}{6} - \frac{L^2}{2}\left(\frac{qL^2}{6} + C_1\frac{L}{2}\right)\right] \qquad C_1 = -\frac{qL}{2}$$

From Eq. (d),

$$C_2 = -\left(\frac{qL^2}{6} - \frac{qL^2}{4}\right) = +\frac{qL^2}{12}$$

The final equations are found by substituting the values of C_1 and C_2:

$$V = qz + C_1 = qz - \frac{qL}{2} = q\left(z - \frac{L}{2}\right) \qquad (e)$$

$$M = q\frac{z^2}{2} + C_1 z + C_2 = q\left(\frac{z^2}{2} - \frac{Lz}{2} + \frac{L^2}{12}\right) \qquad (f)$$

$$\phi = \frac{q}{EI}\left(\frac{z^3}{6} - \frac{Lz^2}{4} + \frac{L^2 z}{12}\right) \qquad (g)$$

$$y = \frac{q}{EI}\left(\frac{z^4}{24} - \frac{Lz^3}{12} + \frac{L^2 z^2}{24}\right) \qquad (h)$$

These equations will now be used to find the following quantities:

At $z = 0$,
$$M = \frac{qL^2}{12}$$

At $z = \frac{L}{2}$,
$$M = q\left(\frac{L^2}{8} - \frac{L^2}{4} + \frac{L^2}{12}\right) = -\frac{qL^2}{24}$$

At $z = \frac{L}{2}$,
$$y_{max} = \frac{q}{EI}\left(\frac{L^4}{384} - \frac{L^4}{96} + \frac{L^4}{96}\right) = \frac{1}{384}\frac{qL^4}{EI} \tag{i}$$

Note that the maximum deflection is reduced to *one-fifth* of that for a similarly loaded beam with simply supported ends (see Example 9.2).

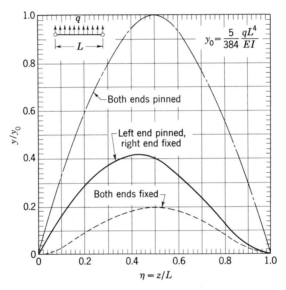

Figure E9.6. Dimensionless deflection curves for uniformly loaded beams.

Equation (h) can be normalized by letting y_0 equal the maximum deflection for a *simply supported beam*, giving

$$\frac{y}{y_0} = \frac{16}{5}(\eta^4 - 2\eta^3 + \eta^2) \tag{j}$$

where
$$y_0 = \frac{5}{384}\frac{qL^4}{EI}$$

The normalized deflection curve is shown in Fig. E9.6, which shows also the curves for the simply supported beam and for the beam with one end simply supported, one end fixed.

9.4 Deflection of initially curved beams

A curved cantilever beam transmitting the forces $\mathbf{P}_1$, $\mathbf{P}_2$, $\mathbf{P}_3$ is shown in Fig. 9.8. Arbitrary z and y axes have been selected as shown, with the origin at the fixed end. Distances along the curved centroidal axis are designated by s. The bending moment M at any point along the centroidal axis can be determined by the methods of Sec. 6.5.

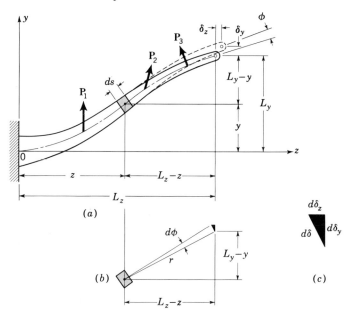

Figure 9.8. Deflection of a curved beam.

In the elastic range the change of slope (due to bending moment only) over the length ds is given by

$$d\phi = \frac{M}{EI} ds \qquad (a)$$

The total change of slope at the free end is found from the line integral

$$\phi = \int_0^{L_s} \frac{M}{EI} ds \qquad (b)$$

where L_s is the total developed length.

To find the deflection δ at the free end it is convenient to work with the components δ_z and δ_y (shown positive in Fig. 9.8a). First we imagine the beam to be "cut" at the point (z, y), each portion of the beam remaining rigid. The outer portion of the beam is then allowed to rotate as a rigid body through the angle $d\phi$ as shown in Fig. 9.8b. The outer beam is represented by a straight line of length r as shown. Sketch c shows an enlarged view of the situation at the tip. The arc line representing $d\delta$ may be treated as a straight line normal to r for the very small angle $(d\phi)$ involved. Then the small triangle whose sides are $d\delta_z$, $d\delta_y$, and $d\delta$ (sketch c) is similar to the large triangle whose sides are $(L_z - z)$, $(L_y - y)$, and r in sketch b, giving the following relationships (note negative sign in first equation):

$$\frac{d\delta_z}{d\delta} = -\frac{(L_y - y)}{r} \qquad \frac{d\delta_y}{d\delta} = \frac{(L_z - z)}{r}$$

But $d\delta = r\,d\phi$. Substituting this in the above equations, we obtain

$$d\delta_z = -(L_y - y)\,d\phi \qquad (c)$$
$$d\delta_y = (L_z - z)\,d\phi \qquad (d)$$

The values of δ_x and δ_y are now obtained by substituting from Eq. (a) and integrating, giving the line integrals

$$\delta_z = -\int_0^{L_s} (L_y - y)\,\frac{M}{EI}\,ds$$
$$\delta_y = \int_0^{L_s} (L_z - z)\,\frac{M}{EI}\,ds \qquad (9.3)$$

The constants of integration are zero because the beam is fixed at the origin. In Fig. 6.9 the free end was selected as the origin, in determining bending moments. If that system is also used to determine deflections, constants of integration must be added to Eqs. (b) and (9.3). See Ref. 19 for statically indeterminate curved beams.

PROBLEMS

9.1. For one or more assigned beams from Fig. P6.1, sketch the M/EI, slope, and deflection diagrams, assuming all beams have constant EI. Sketches need not be to scale but should have correct shape.

9.2. For one or more assigned beams from Fig. P6.1, derive equations for slope and deflection at station z, in terms of loading function and EI (constant). Also derive equations for the maximum value of deflection and the value of z at which it occurs.

9.3. *Continuation of Prob.* 8.1. For one or more assigned beams from Fig. P6.2 and for a particular assigned cross section (constant over length of beam) determined in Prob. 8.1, derive the equations for the deflections of the beams, using the numerical values given for the loading functions. Also determine the maximum deflection of the beams between supports, if simply supported, or at a free end (if this applies).

9.4. Derive the equation for the deflected shape of the beam of Fig. P9.4 and plot the deflection curve (to an exaggerated scale). Compare this deflection curve to that of a similarly loaded beam having constant depth $h_{av} = (h_1 + h_2)/2$.

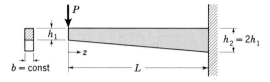

Figure P9.4

9.5. For a specified I beam from Table B.5, apply a concentrated force **P** at the free end, at an angle of 30°, as indicated in Fig. P9.5. Determine the value of this force so that the maximum stress due to bending (only) at the fixed end will be 20,000 psi. Calculate the vertical and horizontal components of the elastic deflection at the free end, and draw a sketch showing the direction and resultant of the deflection (end view). Use steel, with $E = 29 \times 10^6$ psi.

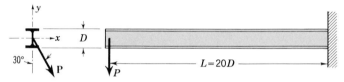

Figure P9.5

9.6. A horizontal steel beam is to be designed (cross section chosen) to transmit a downward line force q of 54 lb/in. over a span of 18 ft. The specified allowable bending stress at this loading is 20,000 psi. The beam weight is to be added to q. Omit consideration of shear stresses. $E = 29 \times 10^6$ psi. The beam is simply supported at each end.

(a) Select a wide-flange section from Table B.4, which will satisfy strength requirements. (Try to find the one which has minimum cross-sectional area.)

(b) Redesign, using a thin-walled square tube having an average depth D and a value of $D/t = 50$. Compare the cross-sectional area with that found in case a. (*Note:* Use the approximate formula $I = \frac{2}{3}D^3t$.)

(c) Repeat case b for a thin-walled round tube of the same D/t, using $I = \pi R^3 t$.

(d) Compare the cross-sectional areas of designs a, b, and c.

(e) Calculate the deflection at mid-span for case a, omitting beam weight. Calculate also for cases b and c by proportion.

9.7. Identical with Prob. 9.6 except that the ends of beam are to be fixed.

9.8. A beam of constant EI and length L is simply supported (pinned) at each end and is unloaded except for a bending moment M_A applied at the left end ($M_B = 0$). Draw shear and moment diagrams and derive an equation for the deflected shape. Find the location of the maximum deflection and its value (in terms of M_A, EI, L).

9.9. *Statically indeterminate beam.* A beam of constant EI and length L is simply supported (pinned) at the left end (A) and fixed at the right end (B). The beam is unloaded except for a moment M_A applied at the left end. Sketch the beam and calculate the "fixed-end moment" M_B in terms of M_A. Draw shear and bending-moment curves. Derive an equation for slope ϕ_A at the left end. (*Note:* The quantity M_A/ϕ_A represents the resistance to rotation, or "stiffness.")

9.10. *Statically indeterminate beam.* Determine M_B and ϕ_A for the beam of Prob. 9.9 if the applied moment M_A is replaced by a line force q_0 (constant) acting over the entire span.

9.11. *Statically indeterminate beam.* Draw shear, bending-moment, slope, and deflection curves for the uniformly loaded two-span beam shown in Fig. P9.11. Assume EI constant.

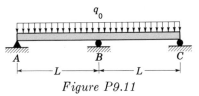

Figure P9.11

Method 1. Treat the central reaction as an unknown force, applying required boundary conditions (slope and deflection at center support must be zero).

Method 2. Use the principle of superposition by calculating the central deflection with the support at B removed, and again with q_0 removed but with the reaction at B acting. Use both methods as a check.

9.12. A cantilever beam is made from a wide-flange steel section (to be assigned) from Table B.4. Let the length L equal $15D$, where D is the depth of the section. $E = 29 \times 10^6$ psi, $w = 0.29$ lb/in.^{3}

(*a*) Calculate the vertical deflection of the free end, caused by beam weight only. Also calculate bending stress at the fixed end.

(*b*) Apply a vertical load P at the free end such that the maximum bending stress at the fixed end equals 20,000 psi for loading P only. Calculate the total elastic energy in the beam. Shear stresses may be ignored.

(*c*) Assume that, to reduce weight, each flange is to be tapered so that its width varies linearly from the nominal width at the root to a value of 2 in. at the tip. Calculate the tip deflection caused by load P (omit beam weight).

9.13. *Curved beam.* Find the vertical deflection at the free end of the beam of Prob. 6.5. Assume EI constant. Answer to be in terms of EI. (*Note:* Solution may be found by numerical integration, if desired, using about ten stations along the span.)

Chapter 10

Torsion

10.1 Introduction

We now take up the last of the four basic modes of force transmission (axial force, transverse force, bending moment, torsional moment). *Torsion* may be defined as the transmission of a moment along an axis having the same direction as that of the moment vector.

The general solution for torsion of members of any cross section was developed by Saint-Venant, in 1853 (see Ref. 1, p. 83). Before that time, formulas similar to those for bending had been used, but tests had shown that these were in error (except for circular cross sections).

Classes of cross sections are shown in Fig. 10.1. Simple engineering methods are available for analyzing members of circular and thin-walled cross sections (*a* and *b*). However, there is no simple theory that applies to case *c*, the "thick" bar of noncircular cross section. For this situation, it is necessary to employ the differential equations of the theory of elasticity, which is beyond the scope of this text. Tables are available giving results that have been worked out for various shapes of cross sections (see Table 10.2). It is also possible to use various analogies, one of which is described in Sec. 10.4.

10.2 Torsion in members of circular cross section

Figure 10.2 shows a uniform circular bar that has been twisted through the angle ϕ, over the length L. The postulate is made that *cross sections which are originally plane and parallel rotate with* respect to each other and remain plane, parallel, and undistorted in the plane. This means that there is no warping of cross sections out of their own planes.

In Fig. 10.3, a very thin element is "sliced" out of the bar, representing two cross sections separated by the distance Δz. When the bar is twisted,

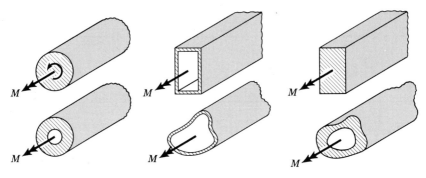

(*a*) Circular; any thickness   (*b*) Thin-walled; any shape   (*c*) Thick; noncircular

Figure 10.1. Classification of members transmitting torsion.

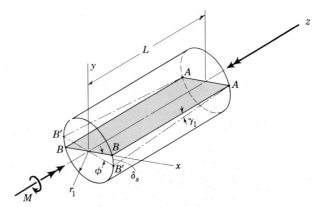

Figure 10.2. Torsion of solid round bars.

a radial line OB rotates to the position OB' through the angle $\Delta\phi$. In accordance with the above postulates, *this line remains straight*.

Let $\Delta\delta$ represent the displacement of point B relative to the corresponding point on the adjacent cross section. From the definition of shear strain we have, *for small angles*,

$$\gamma = \frac{\Delta\delta}{\Delta z} \quad \text{(radians)} \qquad (a)$$

This shear strain is measured on the outer surface of the member, in Fig. 10.3.

The angle $\Delta\phi$, measured in the plane of the cross section, is equal to

$$\Delta\phi = \frac{\Delta\delta}{r} \quad \text{(radians)} \tag{b}$$

By equating the values of $\Delta\delta$ from (a) and (b) we obtain

$$\gamma = r\left(\frac{\Delta\phi}{\Delta z}\right)$$

Letting Δz approach zero as a limit, we have

$$\boxed{\gamma = r\frac{d\phi}{dz}} \tag{10.1}$$

Equation (10.1) applies at any value of r. Thus, for circular cross sections in torsion, *the shear strain varies linearly with radius*, reaching a maximum

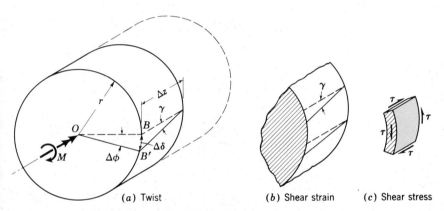

(a) Twist   (b) Shear strain   (c) Shear stress

Figure 10.3. Model for analysis of torsion.

value at the outer surface, where $r = R$. Equation (10.1) should be compared with Eq. (7.2), for bending strains. The term $d\phi/dz$ represents the rate of change of angle (twist) along the structural axis.* It is comparable to curvature in bending, where $d\phi/dz$ represents rate of change of slope.

An element located at a distance r from the centerline of the bar is in a state of pure shear strain. For the model analyzed (twist assumed small) there are no axial strains in the longitudinal, circumferential, or radial directions.

In the elastic range, the *shear stress* at any point on the cross section is found by multiplying γ by G. From Eq. (10.1),

$$\tau = Gr\frac{d\phi}{dz}$$

---

* The rate of twist is sometimes denoted by θ, but this notation is not used here.

The direction of the shear stress τ is circumferential, as indicated by the small element in Fig. 10.3c. An equal shear stress in the longitudinal direction is required for equilibrium.

To find the torsional moment required to produce the rate of twist $d\phi/dz$, we apply the shear stress to each element of the cross section and multiply the resulting incremental force by the radius r, as indicated in Fig. 10.4:

$$dM = r\,dF = r\tau\,dA = Gr^2\frac{d\phi}{dz}\,dA$$

Integrating over the area, we obtain

$$M = \int_A dM = G\frac{d\phi}{dz}\int_A r^2\,dA$$

The integral quantity is called the *polar moment of inertia* (or polar second

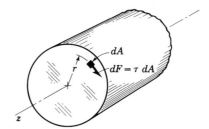

Figure 10.4. Elemental torsional moment.

moment of area):

$$\boxed{I_p \equiv \int_A r^2\,dA} \tag{10.2}$$

Substituting this and solving for $d\phi/dz$ gives

$$\boxed{\frac{d\phi}{dz} = \frac{M}{GI_p}} \tag{10.3}$$

Where $d\phi/dz$ = rate of twist (elastic)
M = twisting moment
G = shear modulus of elasticity (modulus of rigidity)
I_p = polar moment of inertia
Note: $I_p = I_x + I_y$. For a solid circular cross section,

$$I_p = 2I_x = \frac{\pi R^4}{2} = \frac{\pi D^4}{32}$$

To find the shear stress at a point on the cross section, the shear strain from Eq. (10.1) is multiplied by G. When $d\phi/dz$ is replaced by its value from Eq. (10.3) we have

$$\tau = \frac{Mr}{I_p}$$ (10.4)

Equations (10.1), (10.3), and (10.4) can be used for hollow circular bars or tubes. (The polar moment of inertia is found by subtracting that of the hole from that of the solid bar.) The equations also apply to circular bars or tubes that vary gradually in cross section along the length. (Abrupt changes cause stress concentrations, but do not appreciably affect the total value of twist.)

For the *solid round bar* of outside radius R, Eq. (10.4) becomes

$$\tau = \frac{2M}{\pi R^3}$$

The *elastic energy* in torsion can be expressed in terms of energy per unit length. In the elastic range,

$$U = \tfrac{1}{2}M\phi \qquad (\phi \text{ in radians})$$

Therefore, substituting from Eq. (10.3),

$$\frac{dU}{dz} = \frac{1}{2}\frac{M^2}{GI_p}$$ (10.5a)

This equation can also be expressed in terms of shear stress or strain by making the appropriate substitutions. From Eq. (10.5a) the elastic energy over a length L is obtained by integration, giving

$$U = \frac{1}{2}\int_0^L \frac{M^2}{GI_p}\,dz$$ (10.5b)

Warning: The equations in this section cannot be used for cross sections of noncircular shape.

EXAMPLE 10.1. A solid round steel bar $1\frac{1}{2}$ in. in diameter must transmit a torque of 8,000 in.-lb over a length of 9 ft, $G = 11 \times 10^6$ psi. Find the maximum shear stress and the twist in degrees and also the elastic energy.

$$I_x = \frac{\pi R^4}{4}$$

$$I_p = 2I_x = \frac{\pi R^4}{2} = \frac{\pi \times 0.75^4}{2} = 0.497 \text{ in.}^4$$

The stress is

$$\tau = \frac{MR}{I_p} = \frac{8,000 \times 0.75}{0.497} = 12,070 \text{ psi}$$

The twist is

$$\phi = \frac{ML}{GI_p} = \frac{8{,}000 \times 108}{11 \times 10^6 \times 0.497} = 0.158 \text{ radian}$$

$$\phi = 0.158 \times 57.3 = 9.05°$$

The energy is

$$U = \tfrac{1}{2}M\phi = \tfrac{1}{2} \times 8{,}000 \times 0.158 = 632 \text{ in.-lb}$$

10.3 Torsion of thin-walled members

We now take up case *b* of Fig. 10.1, the thin-walled member of any cross-sectional shape. The member must be *closed*, that is, tubular, as indicated in Fig. 10.5. However, the thickness may vary around the periphery of the tube. Such members are also classified as shells.

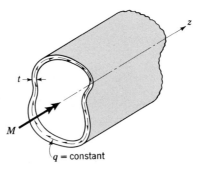

Figure 10.5. Line force (shear flow) caused by torsional moment in thin-walled member.

In Fig. 10.5 the thickness is small, compared with an outside dimension (width) of the tube. The following postulates are used as a basis for analysis.

1. *The shear stress is uniformly distributed across the thickness.*
2. *The resultant line force ("shear flow") is constant around the periphery of the cross section and acts at mid-thickness.*
3. *The ends of the tube are free to warp out of their (unloaded) plane.*

In Sec. 8.4, it was found that the moment of a (constant) shear line force acting over a curved path is given by Eq. (8.6):

$$M = 2q \text{Ⓐ}$$

For the closed section in torsion, this equation can be used directly; the term Ⓐ is the entire area enclosed by the median line of the wall thickness.*

* The force resultant of a closed "shear flow" is zero; that is, *h* is zero in Eq. (8.5).

The shear flow is

$$q = \frac{M}{2\,\textcircled{A}}$$ (10.6)

The shear stress is

$$\tau = \frac{q}{t}$$ (10.7)

EXAMPLE 10.2. A torsion box is constructed of $\frac{1}{8}$-in. steel sheet, with a rectangular cross section 10 by 20 in. (mean dimensions). A torque of 100,000 in.-lb is applied. Find the shear stress in the sheet.

$$q = \frac{M}{2\,\textcircled{A}} = \frac{100,000}{2 \times 10 \times 20} = 250 \text{ lb/in.}$$

$$\tau = \frac{q}{t} = \frac{250}{\frac{1}{8}} = 2,000 \text{ psi}$$

To find the torsional deflection we shall use the method of *virtual work.** Imagine that, *before* the moment M is applied, a very small "virtual" moment M_Q has been applied as shown in Fig. 10.6. This will produce a

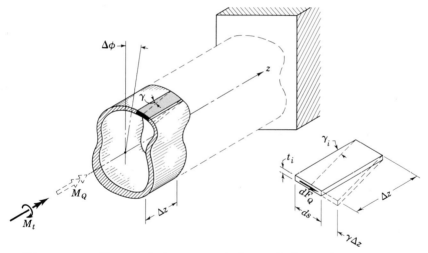

Figure 10.6. Torsional deflection of thin-walled member, by energy method.

constant, virtual distributed shear force q_Q. For an elemental length ds along the periphery the virtual force $dF_Q = q_Q ds$. Therefore

$$dF_Q = \frac{M_Q}{2\,\textcircled{A}}\, ds$$ (a)

* See also Sec. 15.3.

After this force is applied, the real moment M is applied. This moment produces a real shear stress $\tau = q/t$ which causes a shear strain $\gamma = \tau/G$. For an element having a length Δz, the relative motion over this length is $\gamma \Delta z$, as shown. The internal virtual work done by the force dF_Q when it moves through this distance is

$$\Delta dU_{\text{int}} = dF_Q \gamma \, \Delta z \tag{b}$$

Now substitute for dF_Q its value from (a). Also substitute for γ the value obtained from the foregoing theory. Then

$$\gamma = \frac{\tau}{G} = \frac{M}{2\textcircled{A}tG} \tag{c}$$

The result is

$$\Delta dU_{\text{int}} = \frac{M_Q M}{4\textcircled{A}^2 tG} \, ds \, \Delta z \tag{d}$$

The total virtual work done internally is given by the line integral of dU_{int} around the periphery:

$$\Delta U_{\text{int}} = \Delta z \int_s \frac{M_Q M}{4\textcircled{A}^2 tG} \, ds \tag{e}$$

The virtual work done by the external virtual moment M_Q during the actual twist $\Delta\phi$ (over the length Δz) is

$$\Delta U_{\text{ext}} = M_Q \Delta\phi \tag{f}$$

From the law of conservation of energy,

$$\Delta U_{\text{int}} = \Delta U_{\text{ext}}$$

Therefore we equate the expressions from (e) and (f). Letting $\Delta z \to 0$, replace Δz by dz, giving

$$\frac{d\phi}{dz} = \frac{M}{4\textcircled{A}^2 G} \int_s \frac{1}{t} \, ds \tag{10.8}$$

Equation (10.8) can be put into a form similar to that for a round bar by writing

$$\boxed{\frac{d\phi}{dz} = \frac{M}{GJ}} \tag{10.9}$$

where

$$J = \frac{4\textcircled{A}^2}{\int_s \frac{1}{t} \, ds} \tag{10.10}$$

When t is constant,

$$J = \frac{4\text{\textcircled{A}}^2 t}{s}$$

where s is the periphery of the median line of the cross section.

In the model description it was stated that the ends of the shell must be free to warp out of their original (unloaded) plane. If one of the ends is compelled to remain plane (as by bolting it to a "rigid wall"), some of the torsion will be resisted by shear forces resulting from this constraint. Axial stresses will also be introduced. This effect will tend to disappear at some distance from the "rigid" end, in accordance with Saint-Venant's principle. The magnitude of the effect will depend on the geometry of the cross section; it becomes smaller as the cross section approaches a circular shell of constant thickness, for which there is no effect of constraint. All of these facts indicate that the thin-walled model is inaccurate for short noncircular members with end constraint.

The distributed-force concept may be used for *closed frameworks* made up of individual axial members (trusses). The value of q is found from Eq. (10.6). This value is multiplied by the depth of one of the plane trusses to find the shear carried by the truss members.

EXAMPLE 10.3. Find the shear stress and the torsional deflection (twist) of an aluminum-alloy tube 12 ft long, having a mean diameter of 4 in. and a wall thickness of $\frac{1}{8}$ in., when transmitting a torsional moment of 15,000 in.-lb. Let $G = 3.75 \times 10^6$ psi.

$$\tau = \frac{q}{t} = \frac{M}{2\text{\textcircled{A}}t} = \frac{15,000}{2 \times \pi \times 2^2 \times \frac{1}{8}} = 4{,}775 \text{ psi}$$

From Eq. (10.10),

$$\frac{d\phi}{dz} = \frac{M}{GJ}$$

$$J = \frac{4\text{\textcircled{A}}^2 t}{s} = \frac{4(\pi 2^2)^2 \times \frac{1}{8}}{4\pi} \doteq 2\pi \text{ in.}^4$$

$$\frac{d\phi}{dz} = \frac{15,000}{3.75 \times 10^6 \times 2\pi} = 6.37 \times 10^{-4} \text{ rad/in.}$$

$$\phi = 6.37 \times 10^{-4} \times 144 \times 57.3 = 5.26°$$

10.4 Torsion of thick noncircular members

When the cross section of a member is neither circular nor thin, the use of either of the preceding theories can lead to large errors. For example, if Eq. (10.4) for round members is used to determine the shear stress in a rectangular cross section, it appears that the maximum stress would occur at the corners, where r is a maximum. Actually the maximum shear stress occurs where the radius to the surface is a minimum, that is, at the midpoint of the longer side of the rectangle. The shear stress at the corners is zero.

Saint-Venant showed that the longitudinal displacements of the cross section, in torsion, must satisfy a certain partial differential equation. (This same equation applies also for the displacements of a thin membrane under normal pressure.) The solution has been worked out for many shapes (boundary conditions), and some of the results are tabulated in Table 10.2 (see Sec. 10.5).

Prandtl (see Ref. 1, p. 393) showed that the shear stress in a cross section of arbitrary shape could be found by the *membrane analogy*. A hole of the same shape is cut in a plate. A soap film covering this hole is subjected to a small pressure differential. Because of the identity in the basic differential equations it turns out that at a given point the maximum slope of the deflected film is proportional to the shear stress. It can also be shown (Ref. 19, pp. 500–503) that the contour lines formed on the film by passing planes at constant spacing h describe "tubes," each of which has the same shear flow q, given by the formula

$$q = \frac{Mh}{2\circled{V}} \qquad (10.11)$$

where M = torsional moment

h = spacing of planes (measured normal to cross-sectional plane)

$\circled{V}$ = volume enclosed between original plane and deflected membrane

The shear stress in a "tube" is found by Eq. (10.7):

$$\tau = \frac{q}{t}$$

where t is the thickness of the imaginary tube, that is, the distance between contour lines.

Therefore $$\tau = \frac{Mh}{2\circled{V}t} \qquad (10.12)$$

EXAMPLE 10.4.   As a check on the membrane analogy, we shall derive the equation for the shear stress in a solid round bar. Figure E10.4 shows a linear distribution of shear stress. If the slope of the membrane is to be proportional to the stress, the deflection must be parabolic, that is, $w \approx r^2$. But the actual deflection under constant pressure will be spherical, as shown in Fig. E10.4.

Therefore the value for t determined for the outer "tube" will not be exact, even when h approaches zero. However, we shall calculate the slope at the edge of the membrane by assuming the section to be parabolic. One property of a parabola is that the slope at any point is equal to twice the slope of a line drawn from the origin to that point, as indicated in the figure by α_1 and α_2. The ratio h/t at the edge of the member, as $h \to 0$, is given by the slope dw/dr, which is equal to $2C/R$:

$$\frac{h}{t} = \frac{2C}{R} \qquad (a)$$

The volume of a paraboloid of revolution is

$$\textcircled{V} = \tfrac{1}{2}\pi R^2 C \qquad (b)$$

Substituting this in Eq. (10.12), we obtain

$$\tau = \frac{Mh}{\pi R^2 C t}$$

Substituting for h/t from Eq. (a),

$$\tau = \frac{2M}{\pi R^3}$$

This checks Eq. (10.4).

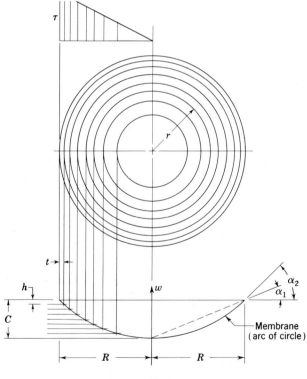

Figure E10.4

EXAMPLE 10.5.   The membrane analogy can be used to determine the maximum shear stress in an elliptical member. Figure E10.5 shows such a cross section, with a membrane sketched below it. Let B and D represent the longer and shorter axes. Let C be the maximum depth of the membrane. Then the volume enclosed by the paraboloid is

$$\textcircled{V} = \frac{1}{2}\pi \frac{B}{2}\frac{D}{2} C = \frac{\pi}{8} BDC \qquad (a)$$

The slope at point (x, y) on a parabola is found by differentiating an equation of the type $y = cx^2$. The result shows that the maximum slope of the membrane

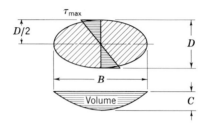

Figure E10.5

at the edge of the longer side is (as $h \to 0$)

$$\frac{h}{t} = \frac{2C}{D/2} = 4\frac{C}{D} \qquad (b)$$

Substituting from (a) and (b) in Eq. (10.12), we obtain

$$\tau = \frac{16}{\pi}\frac{M}{BD^2}$$

EXAMPLE 10.6.   The *thin plate in torsion* is of particular interest in structures (Fig. E10.6). If the plate cross section is considered to be an infinitely long

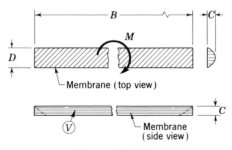

Figure E10.6

rectangle, the volume under the parabolic membrane is

$$\textcircled{V} = \tfrac{2}{3}BDC$$

Substituting this in Eq. (10.12), with $h/t = 4C/D$, gives

$$\tau_{\max} = \frac{3M}{BD^2}$$

This equation can be used to find the shear stress in an *open section* (for example, a split tube) formed from a thin plate of constant thickness t. The width B is taken as the developed length of the cross section; D is the thickness. This model neglects any effects of end constraint; that is, the approximation is best for "long" members. The torsional stiffness of a long tube is greatly reduced by splitting it.

The torsional stiffness of a noncircular thick section can be approximated by using J for an elliptical section having the same area and the same polar moment of inertia (Ref. 1, p. 237).

10.5 Summary of elastic-torsion equations and constants

Tables 10.1 and 10.2 give a summary of useful information for torsion in the elastic range.

10.6 Special topics (torsion)

Inelastic torsion can be analyzed by the use of the shear stress-strain diagram (τ plotted against γ), which can be obtained by conversion of the tension stress-strain diagram (see Chap. 5). The procedures of Sec. 7.7 for inelastic bending can be adapted to torsion, to determine residual stresses, modulus of rupture, and springback. (For detailed methods see Ref. 19.)

Failure of a solid round bar in torsion may be caused by cracking at an angle of 45° if the material is brittle in nature. Such failure is caused by the maximum tensile stress, which is equal in magnitude to the shear stress. (Demonstrate by twisting a piece of chalk.) For ductile materials, large, permanent, torsional deflections (twist) usually occur before actual failure of material occurs. For relatively thin-walled tubes and shells failure is usually caused by *buckling* under the influence of the diagonal compressive stresses (see Chap. 11).

Highly curved torsion members experience an increase in shear strain on the inside surface, above that predicted by the theory for straight members. The phenomenon is similar to the effect described in Prob. 7.12, for bending.

TABLE 10.1

*Summary of torsion formulas (elastic)**

Round sections, any thickness (t = constant)	Thin-walled sections, any shape (t = variable)	Noncircular thick sections (membrane analogy)
Distributed force: (Not used in this case)	Distributed force: $$q = \frac{M}{2\text{Ⓐ}}$$ Ⓐ = area enclosed by median line	Distributed force: $$q = \frac{Mh}{2\text{Ⓥ}}$$ Ⓥ = volume enclosed by membrane h = distance between planes
Shear stress: $$\tau = \frac{Mr}{I_p}$$ $$I_p = \tfrac{1}{2}\pi R^4 = \tfrac{1}{32}\pi D^4$$ $$\tau_{max} = \frac{16}{\pi}\frac{M}{D^3} \text{ (solid section)}$$	Shear stress: $$\tau = \frac{q}{t} = \frac{M}{2\text{Ⓐ}t}$$ t = thickness at given point	Shear stress: $$\tau_{max} = \frac{q}{t_{min}}$$

Deflection formulas

$$\text{Rate:} \frac{d\phi}{dz} = \frac{M}{GJ} \qquad \phi_L = \frac{ML}{GJ}\left(\frac{\text{const } M}{\text{const } J}\right), \text{ radians} \qquad G = \frac{E}{2(1+\nu)}$$

$$J = I_p$$	$$J = \frac{4\text{Ⓐ}^2}{\int_0^s \frac{1}{t}\,ds}$$ For constant t: $$\frac{d\phi}{dz} = \frac{\tau s}{2\text{Ⓐ}G}$$	$$J \doteq \frac{A^4}{4\pi^2 I_p}$$ For equivalent ellipse of same A and same I_p

Energy formulas

$$\frac{dU}{dz} = \frac{1}{2}M\frac{d\phi}{dz} \qquad U = \frac{1}{2}M\phi \qquad U = \frac{1}{2}\frac{M^2 L}{GJ}\left(\frac{\text{const } M}{\text{const } J}\right)$$

* Basic assumption: cross section free to warp.

TABLE 10.2

Torsional stresses and deflections (elastic)

Shape	Area A	Maximum shear stress τ_{max}	Rate of twist $d\phi/dz$ ϕ = radians (57.3°)
	$\dfrac{\pi D^2}{4}$	$\dfrac{16M}{\pi D^3}$ $(16/\pi = 5.1)$	$\dfrac{32M}{\pi D^4 G}$
	$\dfrac{\pi(D^2 - d^2)}{4}$	$\dfrac{16MD}{\pi(D^4 - d^4)}$	$\dfrac{32M}{\pi(D^4 - d^4)G}$
Thin tube	$\pi \bar{D} t$	$\dfrac{2M}{\pi \bar{D}^2 t}$	$\dfrac{4M}{\pi \bar{D}^3 t G}$
	$\dfrac{\pi BD}{4}$	$\dfrac{16M}{\pi BD^2}$	$\dfrac{16(B^2 + D^2)M}{\pi B^3 D^3 G}$
	B^2	$4.8\dfrac{M}{B^3}$	$7.2\dfrac{M}{B^4 G}$
	BD	$K_1\dfrac{M}{BD^2}$ See figure	$K_2\dfrac{M}{BD^3 G}$ See figure
	$0.433B^2$	$20\dfrac{M}{B^3}$	$46\dfrac{M}{B^4 G}$
(hex.)	$0.866B^2$	$5.7\dfrac{M}{B^3}$	$8.8\dfrac{M}{B^4 G}$

PROBLEMS

10.1. For a set of assigned values from Table P10.1:

(a) Calculate the maximum shear stress in a straight tube of constant circular cross section, transmitting the torsional moment M_z. (Assume elastic behavior.)

(b) Calculate the torsional deflection (twist) in degrees, for two different materials, steel and aluminum alloy, using $G = 11 \times 10^6$ and 4×10^6 psi, respectively.

(c) Find the elastic energy stored in each tube at the designated value of M_z.

Note: D_o = outside diameter, D_i = inside diameter.

TABLE P10.1

	1	2	3	4	5	6	7
M_z, in.-lb	20,000	650,000	7,000	15,000	50,000	80,000	25,000
L, in.	60	38	54	72	80	86	48
D_o, in.	2.0	3.25	1.50	1.75	3.5	4.0	2.5
D_i, in.	1.5	2.75	1.25	1.25	3.2	3.6	2.2

10.2. For an assigned set of values from Table P10.2:

(a) Calculate the diameter of a solid round shaft at which the maximum shear stress would equal 20,000 psi.

(b) Select a tube size from Table B.3 such that the shear stress developed will be equal to, or less than, 20,000 psi (tube to have the lowest cross-sectional area of those tubes available).

(c) Calculate relative material volumes for the tube and the solid shaft.

(d) Calculate twist (in degrees) of the two different designs (solid and tube) using actual properties from Table B.3. Let $E = 29 \times 10^6$ psi, $\nu = \frac{1}{3}$. [See Eq. (4.4).]

TABLE P10.2

	1	2	3	4	5	6	7
M_z, in.-lb	2,000	5,000	3,500	10,000	40,000	20,000	30,000
L, in.	20	30	35	40	45	50	60

10.3. For an assigned tube size from Table B.3 let the length L be equal to 24 times the outside diameter. The tube is to be twisted (elastically) through an angle of 5°. Calculate:

(a) The maximum shear strain

(b) The maximum shear stress for an aluminum-alloy tube, using $G = 4 \times 10^6$ psi

(c) The torsional moment M_z required

(d) The elastic energy stored in the tube

10.4. Using an assigned material in Table A.1, for which the tensile yield stress (0.002 offset) is given:

(a) Calculate the corresponding yield stress τ_y in pure shear, using the octahedral shear-stress theory of Sec. 5.2. (*Note:* "Corresponding" means that the plastic normal strain along a principal axis equals 0.002; see Example 3.2.)

(b) Find the torsional moment that would develop the above value of τ_y in a tube having an average diameter of 5.0 in. and a wall thickness of 0.20 in. (Use the thin-wall theory of Sec. 10.3.) (*Note:* Ignore the possibility of buckling, which is taken up in Sec. 11.8.)

10.5. A schematic drawing of a simple torsion-bar spring is shown in Fig. P10.5. Using a steel alloy ($G = 11 \times 10^6$ psi) and for an assigned set of

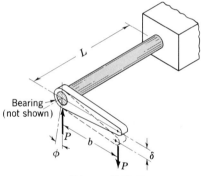

Figure P10.5

values from Table P10.5, calculate:

(a) The diameter required for a solid round shaft to provide the required deflection δ, assuming that the maximum allowable shear stress is 20,000 psi. (Neglect deflection of lever arm.)

TABLE P10.5

	1	2	3	4	5	6	7
L, in.	20	15	12	13	17	14	18
b, in.	10	8	8	8	9	9	7
δ, in.	1.0	1.0	0.5	0.3	0.5	0.7	0.8

(b) The force P.

(c) The elastic energy at maximum deflection. (Calculate both internal and external energy and show that they are equal.)

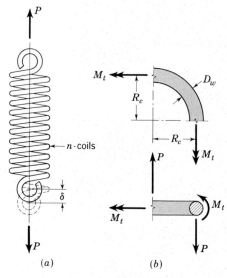

Figure P10.6

10.6. Derive the following approximate formulas for the maximum shear stress and deflection for a "close-coiled" spring, such as that shown in Fig. P10.6.

$$\tau_{\max} = \frac{16PR_c}{\pi D_w{}^3} \qquad \delta = \frac{4PR_c{}^3 n}{GR_w{}^4}$$

The following assumptions may be made:

(a) Neglect the slope of each coil; i.e., use sketch b as a basis.

(b) Neglect the transverse shear stress (given by $\tau = P/A_s$).

(c) Neglect the fact that shear strain on the inner surface of a coil will be increased somewhat by the curvature effect.

(d) Assume that stresses remain in elastic range.

(*Suggestion:* For calculating deflection, use actual energy: $U_{\text{ext}} = \frac{1}{2}P\delta$, $U_{\text{int}} = $ torsional energy of straight wire of equivalent length.)

10.7. A thin-walled square box of average dimensions 12 in. by 12 in. has a wall thickness of 0.100 in. and a length of 12 feet. Using $G = 11 \times 10^6$ psi (for steel), derive a formula for use directly in computing the twist ϕ (degrees) in terms of a numerical constant times the torsional moment M_z (in.-lb). (Possible variations for assignment: use triangular, rectangular, or hexagonal box section.)

10.8. A linearly tapered thin-walled rectangular tube has the following average dimensions at one end: $B_1 = 48$ in. and $D_1 = 12$ in. At the opposite end, the dimensions are $B_2 = 16$ in. and $D_2 = 4$ in. The box is 16 ft long and is made from an aluminum-alloy sheet of constant thickness $t = 0.080$ in. Neglecting the possibility of buckling, find the torque M_z, in in.-lb, required to cause a twist of one degree between the two ends. ($E = 10 \times 10^6$ psi, $\nu = \frac{1}{3}$.) (*Suggestion:* As a check, plot a few points along the span and draw a curve through them giving values of $d\phi/dz$. The area under the curve will give the answer. The curve will also show how torsional stiffness varies for a tapered structure of this type.)

10.9. A design office wishes to add to Table 10.2 a column indicating the relative efficiency of various cross-sectional shapes in resisting a given torsional moment M_0, on a *strength* basis. Using the solid round bar as a base for normalization, calculate the ratios of cross-sectional area required (A/A_0), assuming that failure occurs when $\tau_{\max}$ reaches a certain "allowable" stress τ_0, which has the same value in all cases. [*Notes:* (a) Assume elastic action. (b) For thick tube let $d = 0.75D$; for thin tube let $\bar{D} = 40t$; for ellipse let $B = 2D$; for rectangle let $B = 2D$.]

10.10. Extend Prob. 10.9 by adding another column indicating the relative efficiency (A/A_0) for the same sections on a *stiffness* basis. That is, let each member have the same length and be required to develop the, same torsional stiffness M/ϕ.

10.11. A solid bar of constant cross section has a diameter of 0.50 in. and is to be subjected to a tensile load of 6,000 lb, which is held constant while a torsional moment M_z is gradually applied. In a previous test of a similar bar an abrupt yielding took place when a pure tensile load of 9,860 lb was applied. Predict the value of M_z at which abrupt yielding can be expected to occur under the combined loading condition, using the two different theories of plasticity covered in Sec. 5.2.

Notes: (a) In this case it is only necessary to equate values of the effective stress $\bar{\sigma}$.

(b) The shear stress in pure torsion is not uniformly distributed over the cross section, as it is in tension; consequently the yielding would not be abrupt but would be expected to start at the value of M_z predicted above.

10.12. A shaft which transmits a torsional moment M_z is also subjected to a bending moment M_x. (A practical example is a power shaft which has a pulley or gear located at some distance from the bearings.)

(a) Derive two formulas for the maximum values of shear stress and normal stress, respectively, for *solid* bars of round cross section, in terms of M_x, M_z, and D.

(b) Assume that failure under the above combined loading occurs when the maximum shear stress reaches a certain value τ_0. Derive the following formula (frequently found in handbooks) for the required outside diameter of a *hollow* circular shaft, where n is the ratio of inside to outside diameter.

$$D = 1.72 \frac{(M_x{}^2 + M_z{}^2)^{\frac{1}{3}}}{\tau_0{}^{\frac{1}{3}}(1 - n^4)^{\frac{1}{3}}}$$

Note: For maximum efficiency the tube must be "thinned" and "expanded" (n increased). Such expansion will lower the local buckling stress (Sec. 11.8). Therefore, analytical optimization cannot be accomplished until the subject of buckling is covered.

Chapter 11

Buckling

11.1 The Euler column

Columns are defined as members that transmit axial compressive loads. Columns usually fail by buckling, a form of instability. The conceptual model is that of a perfectly straight, centrally loaded member with no lateral loads or bending moments. We shall follow the original analysis of Euler (1757).*

Figure 11.1 shows the structural axis of a member that has been displaced from its original straight position by a small bending deflection (shown exaggerated). The mathematical problem is to find the "critical" axial load at which the column will remain in static equilibrium in the deflected position. The solution of the problem will also determine the shape of the deflection curve.

In the deflected configuration the presence of the axial load P causes bending moments of magnitude Py. These moments cause bending deflections. We postulate that at some *critical* load P_{cr} the moments will be such that the column will remain in the deflected position (neutrally stable). In this condition the column cannot support an additional load statically; it will bend indefinitely.†

The only physical law needed is that of Eq. (7.2), which, for small deflections from a straight configuration, can be closely approximated by

$$\frac{d\phi}{dx} = -\frac{M}{EI} \tag{a}$$

---

* See Timoshenko's discussion, Ref. 1, pp. 30–36, also Van den Broek's translation of the original paper in *Am. J. Physics*, vol. 15, no. 4, July–August, 1947, pp. 309–318.

† If the load P is applied very rapidly over a short period, inertial forces permit an increase in the maximum load that can be supported. This phenomenon is called *dynamic buckling*.

The negative sign is important. It expresses the fact that the moments shown in Fig. 11.1c cause a *decrease* of slope over a length dx. Since ϕ can be expressed by dy/dx,

$$\frac{d^2y}{dx^2} = -\frac{M}{EI} \qquad (b)$$

But $M = Py$. Substituting, we have

$$\frac{d^2y}{dx^2} = -\frac{Py}{EI} \qquad (c)$$

This differential equation tells us that y must be a function of x such that its second derivative is equal to $-y$, multiplied by the constant term

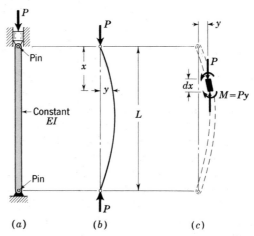

Figure 11.1. *Buckling of a pinned-end column.*

P/EI. One way of solving this type of differential equation is to put it in the form

$$\frac{d^2y}{dx^2} + p^2y = 0 \qquad (d)$$

where $p^2 = P/EI$. The general solution of (d) is

$$y = C_1 \sin px + C_2 \cos px \qquad (e)$$

where C_1 and C_2 are constants of integration.* To evaluate these constants, we utilize the boundary conditions. Substituting in Eq. (e), we have

At $x = 0$, $y = 0$,

$$0 = C_1(0) + C_2 \cos (0)$$

* This solution can be verified by differentiating twice.

Therefore $C_2 = 0$ and Eq. (e) becomes

$$y = C_1 \sin px \tag{f}$$

At $x = L$, $y = 0$; in Eq. (f) either C_1 or p must have a value such that

$$0 = C_1 \sin pL \tag{g}$$

where C_1 is the half-wave amplitude, that is, the bending deflection at midlength. A trivial solution is $C_1 = 0$, that is, the column remains straight. When C_1 is not zero the value of $\sin pL$ will be zero only when $pL = 0$, π, 2π, . . . , $n\pi$ (where n is an integer). Therefore $y = 0$ at $x = L$ when

$$pL = n\pi \tag{h}$$

To find P_{cr}, the value of P at which this is possible, square Eq. (h), giving

$$p^2 = \frac{n^2\pi^2}{L^2}$$

Substituting for p^2 its value P/EI, we obtain

$$P_{cr} = \frac{n^2\pi^2 EI}{L^2} \tag{i}$$

When $n = 0$, $P_{cr} = 0$ (trivial solution). The smallest value of P at which buckling* is possible occurs when $n = 1$.

In Eq. (i), n represents the number of half waves. When $n = 2$, the column buckles into an S shape and the critical load is four times greater than for $n = 1$. However, without external support at midspan the column will *not* be able to develop this configuration.

Letting P_E represent the *Euler load* for an elastic pinned-pinned column, we obtain

$$\boxed{P_E = \frac{\pi^2 EI}{L^2}} \tag{11.1}$$

This is the fundamental equation in buckling theory. The following points should be specially noted.

1. The fundamental Euler load is that for a column pinned† at each end, with the ends constrained laterally so that their relative motion (column-shortening) occurs along the axis of loading (see Fig. 11.1).

---

* The term *bifurcation of equilibrium configurations* is often used to define this phenomenon. It means that two alternate stable configurations become possible, one straight, the other curved.

† "Pinned" means that there is zero moment at each end. Such a condition is approached in tests in which cylindrical or spherical end fittings bear on a flat plate.

2. The bending occurs about that *principal axis* for which the moment of inertia is a minimum; the "pin" is located accordingly at the neutral axis.
3. The normal stress P/A remains in the elastic range.
4. The cross section does not vary in shape or size over the column length.
5. Axial deflections do not enter into the solution. However, the column as a whole shortens as a result of bending, when buckling occurs.
6. Lateral deflections caused by shear forces are omitted. This simplification causes only insignificant errors unless the column is relatively "weak" (that is, not stiff) in shear. Such deflections can be included in the theory by suitable modifications.
7. Buckling is a *force-deflection* phenomenon. (This is often overlooked because buckling formulas are generally expressed in terms of *stress*.)
8. The "small-deflection" approximation (using dx instead of ds) gives the result that P_{cr} is independent of lateral deflection. For large deflection, a more accurate theory shows that this is not true. The load increases slowly beyond P_{cr}, with increasing lateral deflection. (Euler solved this problem also.)

The foregoing method of deriving the buckling load equation may be classified as an *eigenvalue* solution. Other methods are possible; for example, Prob. 11.1 illustrates the direct use of the equilibrium equation for a simple case. For more complicated situations a solution on the energy level, using the law of conservation of energy, is usually employed (see Prob. 11.2 and Sec. 15.3).

The buckling load can be converted to buckling stress by dividing by the cross-sectional area:

$$\sigma_E = \frac{P_E}{A} = \frac{\pi^2 EI}{AL^2} \tag{a}$$

We can substitute for I/A the identity

$$\rho^2 \equiv \frac{I}{A}$$

where ρ is the radius of gyration measured from the neutral axis. It is customary to divide L by ρ, giving the *slenderness ratio*, L/ρ. (The letter r is often used instead of ρ.) Equation (a) then becomes

$$\boxed{\sigma_E = \frac{\pi^2 E}{(L/\rho)^2}} \tag{11.2}$$

This is the *Euler stress for an elastic column with pinned ends*. Since the Euler buckling stress is governed by a dimensionless ratio (the slenderness ratio), any two columns which have the same E and are dimensionally similar* will have the same buckling stress.

When Eq. (11.2) is plotted as σ_E versus L/ρ, a single curve is obtained for each different material, as shown in Fig. 11.2. The differences in these curves are caused by the differences in E.

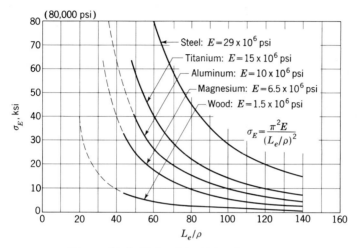

Figure 11.2. Euler (elastic) column curves.

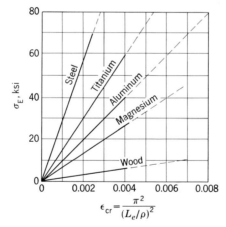

Figure 11.3. Linear plot of Euler column curves.

Another way to plot the Euler stress is shown in Fig. 11.3. When an elastic buckling equation is divided through by E, the critical stress is converted to *critical strain*. Equation (11.2) then becomes, for the basic

---

* That is, all dimensions of one structure may be multiplied by a constant to obtain the dimensions of the other.

case,

$$\epsilon_{cr} = \frac{\sigma_E}{E} = \frac{\pi^2}{(L/\rho)^2} \qquad (11.3)$$

Then
$$\sigma_E = \epsilon_{cr}E \qquad (11.4)$$

The Euler stress, when plotted against critical strain, gives a family of straight lines, as shown in Fig. 11.3. In both sets of curves the lines are extended by dashed lines. This is to indicate that the theory will not be correct when the stress (P/A) exceeds the elastic range.

EXAMPLE 11.1. A column is made from a solid round bar of steel, 5 ft long, $\frac{1}{2}$ in. in diameter, pinned at each end. Calculate the elastic (Euler) buckling load, using $E = 29 \times 10^6$ psi. Also calculate average axial stress at which buckling will begin, using P/A. Check by Euler stress formula.

$$I = \frac{\pi D^4}{64} = \frac{\pi(0.5)^4}{64} = 3.068 \times 10^{-3} \text{ in.}^4$$

$$L = 60 \text{ in.}$$

$$P_E = \frac{\pi^2 EI}{L^2} = \frac{\pi^2 \times 29 \times 10^6 \times 3.068 \times 10^{-3}}{60^2}$$

$$= 244 \text{ lb}$$

$$\sigma_E = \frac{P}{A} = \frac{244}{\pi(0.25)^2} = \frac{244}{0.1963} = 1,240 \text{ psi}$$

To calculate the Euler stress directly:

$$\rho = \sqrt{\frac{I}{A}} = 0.1250 \text{ in.}$$

$$\frac{L}{\rho} = \frac{60}{0.125} = 480$$

$$\sigma_E = \frac{\pi^2 E}{(L/\rho)^2} = \frac{\pi^2 \times 29 \times 10^6}{(480)^2} = 1,240 \text{ psi}$$

11.2 Effects of end constraint

The results for the basic pinned-end column can be extended to other end conditions by a simple concept, that of *effective length*. Figure 11.4 shows members with different end conditions, starting with the basic case (pinned-pinned). Sketch *b* shows the *fixed-free* ("flagpole") column. The reflection concept (illustrated) shows that the Euler buckling load (or stress) would be the same as that for a pinned-pinned column twice as long. The effective length is therefore $2L$.

The *effective-length coefficient** is defined as

$$\alpha \equiv \frac{L_e}{L} \qquad (11.5)$$

---

* In structural engineering, the symbol K is often used for this coefficient.

where L_e is the effective and L the actual length. By using either L_e or αL in place of L, the basic Euler equations (11.1) and (11.2) are extended to include all conditions of constraint at the ends. For example, the effective-length coefficient for case b in Fig. 11.4 is given by $\alpha = 2$. The Euler load is thereby reduced to *one-fourth* of the basic load.

Sketch c shows the fixed-fixed column, where both ends are constrained against rotation ($\phi = 0$). From Eq. (*e*) we know that the deflected structural axis must be composed of either sine or cosine functions of x. For zero slope at each end, the shape must be that of a cosine function. Two

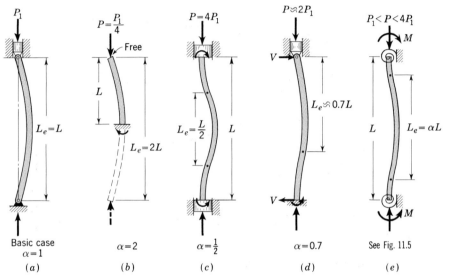

Figure 11.4. Various types of column end constraints.

points of inflection occur (where $M = 0$) at one quarter of the length from the ends. The center portion therefore has an effective length of $L/2$, and the Euler load (or stress) becomes four times as great as that for the basic case.

Sketch d shows a *pinned-fixed* column. Note that the conditions of static equilibrium require a transverse force V to be applied at the pinned end. This force must be included in the differential equation. It is found (Ref. 20) that the effective length is very close to $0.7L$. This fact is indicated in Fig. 11.4d.

Another case of practical interest occurs when end constraints are elastic, as indicated in Fig. 11.4e. The effective length will then depend on the relative stiffness of the constraints and the column. For the case of equal end constraints, the relationship is shown in Fig. 11.5 from Ref. 19. (For other situations see Ref. 20.)

In Fig. 11.5 note that a relatively small end constraint will reduce the effective length considerably. On the other hand, the required support stiffness (relative to the column stiffness) increases very rapidly as we attempt to approach the fixed-end value of $\alpha = 0.5$. It is obviously impossible to develop "absolute" fixity in a structure or testing machine.

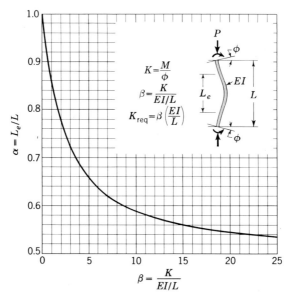

Figure 11.5. Effective-length coefficient for columns with elastic end constraint.

The effective length is strongly affected by a change of direction of the applied load during buckling. Figure 11.6 shows a case in which the force is applied through a cable which passes through a fixed point. The effective-length factor can be determined from Table 2-1, p. 55, Ref. 20. When $C = L$, the value of α is unity.

As previously noted, Eq. (11.2) can be written to provide for end effects merely by adding the subscript e to the term L, or by replacing L by αL. An alternative method (*not recommended*) is to use a *coefficient of fixity* c as a multiplying factor in Eqs. (11.1) and (11.2). The relationship is, in the elastic range,

$$c = \frac{1}{\alpha^2}$$

For example, $c = 4$ for the fixed-fixed column. However, *this method is invalid in the inelastic range.*

EXAMPLE 11.2.   A wide-flange steel beam 10 in. by 10 in. by 89 lb/ft is used as a column 30 ft long. Both ends are pinned through the x axis (see Appendix Table B.4). The constraint about the y axis is estimated to be such that the effective length is reduced to 0.70*L*. Calculate the Euler load for buckling independently about each axis and predict the maximum axial load that can be

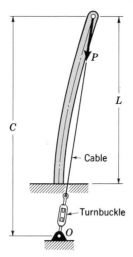

Figure 11.6. Fixed-free column with load axis through fixed point. (For buckling in plane shown; provision must be made against buckling out of plane.)

transmitted. Assume elastic action, $E = 29 \times 10^6$ psi. From Appendix Table B.4,

$$A = 26.19 \text{ in.}^2 \qquad \rho_x = 4.55 \text{ in.}$$
$$I_x = 542.4 \text{ in.}^4 \qquad \rho_y = 2.63 \text{ in.}$$
$$I_y = 180.6 \text{ in.}^4$$

(*Note:* x axis used here is *not* column axis.) For buckling about the x axis,

$$L_e = L = 360 \text{ in.}$$
$$\frac{L_e}{\rho} = \frac{360}{4.55} = 79.1$$
$$\sigma_E = \frac{\pi^2 \times 29 \times 10^6}{79.1^2} = 45,700 \text{ psi}$$

For buckling about the y axis,

$$L_e = 0.70L = 0.70 \times 360 = 252 \text{ in.}$$
$$\frac{L_e}{\rho} = \frac{252}{2.63} = 95.8$$
$$\sigma_E = \frac{\pi^2 \times 29 \times 10^6}{95.8^2} = 31,170 \text{ psi}$$

The column will therefore buckle about the y axis at the load

$$P_E = \sigma_E A = 31,170 \times 26.19 = 816,500 \text{ lb}$$

EXAMPLE 11.3. The structure shown in Fig. E11.3 is composed of steel tubes 1 in. OD with a 0.120 in. wall. The horizontal tubes are welded to the column at each end and thereby supply an elastic constraint. Find the buckling load for the tube, (a) as a pinned-pinned column, and (b) with the elastic constraint. Also compute the buckling stress for each case. Assume $E = 29 \times 10^6$ psi.

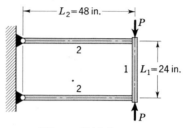

Figure E11.3

From Appendix Table B.3, $A = 0.332$ in.², $I = 0.0327$ in.⁴

(a) For a pinned-pinned column,

$$P_E = \frac{\pi^2 EI}{L^2} = \frac{\pi^2 \times 29 \times 10^6 \times 0.0327}{24^2} = 16,250 \text{ lb}$$

$$\sigma_E = \frac{P_E}{A} = \frac{16,250}{0.332} = 49,000 \text{ psi}$$

(b) The spring constant for each horizontal tube is found from the equation for the slope produced by a moment acting at one end of a simply supported beam. From Sec. 9.7,

$$\phi = \frac{1}{3} \frac{ML_2}{E_2 I_2}$$

$$K = \frac{M}{\phi} = \frac{3E_2 I_2}{L_2}$$

In Fig. 11.5,

$$\beta = \frac{K}{E_1 I_1 / L_1} = \frac{3E_2 I_2 L_1}{L_2 E_1 I_1} = \frac{3L_1}{L_2} = \frac{3 \times 24}{48} = 1.5$$

From the curve, $\alpha = 0.81$. The effective length is $0.81 \times 24 = 19.4$ in.

It is not necessary to recalculate the buckling load, because the Euler equation shows that it will vary as $(1/\alpha)^2 = 1.23^2 = 1.52$.

$$P_{cr} = 1.52 \times 16,250 = 24,800 \text{ lb}$$
$$\sigma_{cr} = 1.52 \times 49,000 = 74,500 \text{ psi}$$

Since the above method is based on the assumption of elastic action, it would be necessary that the proportional limit of the material be at least 74,500 psi.

11.3 Inelastic-column theory

Euler's column theory has been adequately confirmed by tests, except for situations in which the average applied stress exceeds the proportional limit, that is, is in the inelastic range. Then Young's modulus E cannot be used. In 1889 Engesser* proposed the use of the *tangent modulus, E_t,* defined as

$$E_t \equiv \frac{d\sigma}{d\epsilon}$$

where $d\sigma/d\epsilon$ represents the slope of the compressive stress-strain diagram at the value of $\sigma(= P/A)$. Equation (11.2), modified in this manner becomes, with the substitution of the effective length,

$$\boxed{\sigma_{cr} = \frac{\pi^2 E_t}{(L_e/\rho)^2}} \qquad (11.6)$$

This equation is usually called the *tangent-modulus* formula. It accounts for both inelastic effects and end constraint, and has been shown by experiments to predict accurately the maximum load that can be reached in columns which buckle by bending. (It does not apply to local buckling of thin-walled tubes or shells.)

After the appearance of Engesser's original paper in 1889, the tangent-modulus theory was criticized by Considère because it did not account for the fact that, during bending, a portion of the cross section would be subjected to a decreasing stress, for which the elastic modulus would apply. Using this concept as a basis, Von Kármán developed the *double-modulus theory*, in which a *reduced modulus E_r* was determined (see Ref. 21, pp. 9–14). This modulus contains both E and E_t and depends on the shape of the cross section. Since the reduced modulus is always greater than the tangent modulus, the predicted inelastic-buckling loads from the double-modulus theory are greater than those for the tangent-modulus theory.

The double-modulus theory was considered to be the correct theory of inelastic column action until 1946, when the author (Refs. 23, 24) showed that it represents a paradox. In order to exceed the Engesser load, it is necessary that the effective modulus be greater than E_t. Such a situation can occur only if a portion of the cross section is subjected to a decreasing stress. But this means that the column would begin to bend *before* reaching the double-modulus load. These conclusions have since been confirmed by many investigators. It is now clear that for an idealized (straight) column in the inelastic range the Engesser load represents the maximum load below which the column has only one equilibrium configuration (*straight*); beyond this load it may (theoretically) either bend or

---

* See Bleich's historical account (Ref. 21). Von Kármán also independently proposed the use of the tangent modulus (Ref. 22).

remain straight. For a given material, the maximum load that can be developed will generally be only slightly greater than the Engesser load, because of the rapid decrease in E_t with increasing stress. Therefore the Engesser load is a practical upper limit for column strength (for a more detailed discussion see Ref. 19).

In plotting the inelastic-column curve, values of E_t are obtained graphically from the stress-strain diagram or mathematically from an empirical equation. The E_t curve is shown in Fig. 11.7, with E_t plotted horizontally.

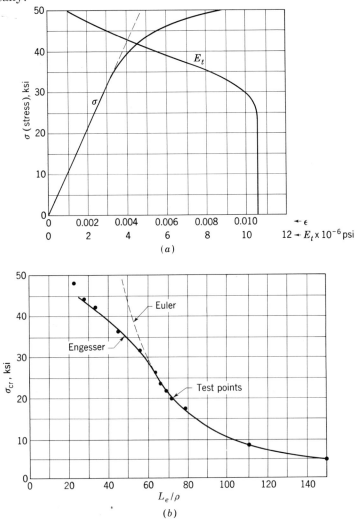

Figure 11.7. Inelastic-column curve determined from stress-strain diagram. (Data from Ref. 28; material is aluminum alloy.)

If Eq. (11.6) were used directly, it would be necessary to select a value of L_e/ρ, assume a value of E_t, and solve for σ_{cr}. The value of E_t at this stress would then be determined from the graph. If it did not coincide with the assumed value, the process would have to be repeated.

This difficulty can be avoided by starting with a value of σ and solving for the slenderness ratio L_e/ρ at which this stress would become critical. Equation (11.6) is therefore rewritten so that the functionally related quantities appear on the same side of the equation:

$$\left(\frac{L_e}{\rho}\right)_{cr} = \pi \sqrt{\frac{E_t}{\sigma}} \qquad (11.7)$$

The calculations used to obtain Fig. 11.7b are shown in Table 11.1.

TABLE 11.1

Calculation of column curve

σ, ksi	E_t, ksi Fig. 11.7a	$\dfrac{E_t}{\sigma} = (2)/(1)$	$\sqrt{\dfrac{E_t}{\sigma}} = \sqrt{(3)}$	$\dfrac{L}{\rho} = \pi \times (4)$
(1)	(2)	(3)	(4)	(5)
0	10,600	∞	. . . .	∞
5	10,600	2,120	46.0	145
10	10,600	1,060	32.6	102
15	10,600	706	26.6	84
20	10,600	530	23.0	72
25	10,600	424	20.6	65
30	9,800	327	18.1	57
35	8,200	234	15.3	48
40	5,500	138	11.7	37
45	2,800	62	7.9	25

The shape of the inelastic portion of the column curve will depend on the shape of the stress-strain diagram around the knee. This is shown by the sketches of Fig. 11.8. Note that, if the stress-strain diagram becomes straight again after rounding the knee (Fig. 11.8), the column curve "picks up" along a new Euler curve. The latter is obtained by substituting the constant value of E_{t_2} in the Euler equation. (It should be remembered that the stress-strain diagram for compression tends to continue to rise, in contrast to that for tension, which may reach a maximum value before actual failure occurs.)

Figure 11.8d illustrates the effect of a "double yield point" caused by a sudden yielding of the material at the "upper yield point," followed by a drop in stress

to the "lower yield point." (Low-carbon steel shows such behavior.) Because of
the small eccentricities that are inevitably present, it is customary to use the
lower yield point as the upper limit for the buckling stress.

The effects of improving the yield strength of a base metal by alloying and
heat treatment are shown in Fig. 11.9. The stress-strain diagrams are typical
of various alloys of heat-treated steel. A similar set of curves is obtained for

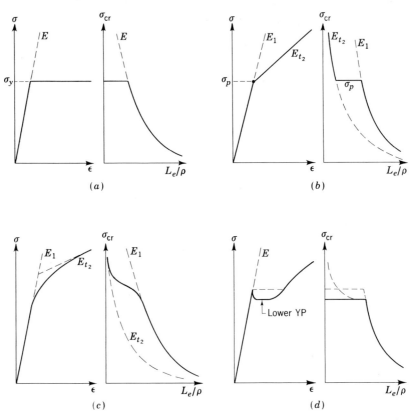

Figure 11.8. Effect of shape of stress-strain diagram on column curve.

aluminum alloys. *Residual stresses* (such as found in rolled shapes) tend to lower
the effective value of the tangent modulus, thereby lowering the inelastic portion
of the column curve.

Two different ways of plotting the column curves are shown. In Fig. 11.9b
note that, in order to take advantage of the higher buckling stresses, the value
of L_e/ρ may have to be reduced.

In Sec. 11.2 a warning was given against using the coefficient of fixity as a
multiplying factor in the inelastic range. This can be demonstrated by referring
to Fig. 11.10a, in which the *actual* slenderness ratio L/ρ is used. For example,
assume that a column is analyzed (or tested) at a slenderness ratio $(L/\rho)_1$, with

pinned ends. If the ends are now completely fixed, the column curve will appear as shown for $c = 4$. (This curve was obtained by the effective-length method.) Although the original column may have been in the elastic range, it would be wrong to predict the effects of complete end constraint by multiplying the original stress (or load) by 4. The predicted stress would be much too high.

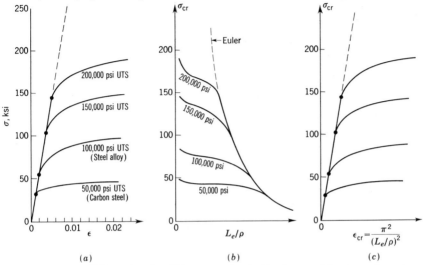

Figure 11.9. Effects (on buckling stress) of alloying and heat treatment of steel.

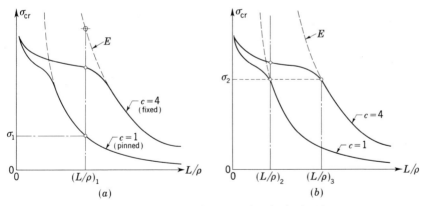

Figure 11.10. Effects of end constraint in inelastic range.

If the original column were in the inelastic range, as in Fig. 11.10*b*, the use of the fixity coefficient as a multiplying factor would lead to even greater errors. The main advantage of applying end constraint to a column already in the inelastic range is to permit a greater unsupported length or a smaller radius of gyration, as shown in Fig. 11.10*b*.

Column formulas and curves may be normalized (put in dimensionless form) by dividing the buckling stress by a base stress and by dividing the effective slenderness ratio by a base value of slenderness ratio. Empirical formulas for the stress-strain diagram may be employed [e.g., Eq. (1.16a)].

11.4 Empirical column formulas

In structural design, the effects of inelastic action have long been provided for by empirical short-column formulas. Such formulas are still used in structural specifications; they will therefore be reviewed briefly.

The *straight-line formula* is obtained simply by fitting a straight line to the test points in the inelastic range. For example, the test data shown in Fig. 11.7

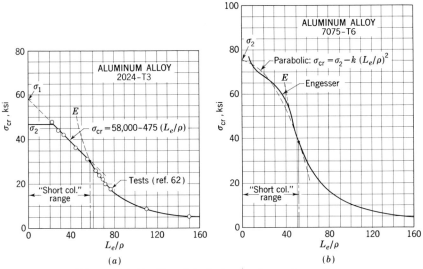

Figure 11.11. Empirical short-column formulas.

can be fitted reasonably well with a straight line, as indicated in Fig. 11.11a. Formulas of this type appear as

$$\sigma_{cr} = \sigma_1 - k_1 \frac{L_e}{\rho} \tag{11.8}$$

where k_1 is a constant. There may also be an overriding requirement that the stress should not exceed a certain value. This amounts to adding another horizontal straight line in Fig. 11.11a (shown at maximum stress σ_2).

The straight line does not give a good fit for a material having a stress-strain diagram with a relatively sharp knee. The *parabolic formula* provides a curved line that gives a better fit. Figure 11.11b shows such an equation in comparison with the Engesser curve for a different aluminum alloy. These equations have the form

$$\sigma_{cr} = \sigma_2 - k_2 \left(\frac{L_e}{\rho}\right)^2 \qquad (11.9)$$

The constants in the above equations are often adjusted so that the empirical curve is tangent to the Euler curve, as shown in Fig. 11.11b.

Both of the above formulas give irrational results when used beyond the range of slenderness ratios for which they apply. This range is arbitrarily defined as the *short-column range*, as indicated in Fig. 11.11.

The *eccentric-column formula* is sometimes used as a basis for design in the inelastic range. This is called the *secant formula* and is usually written as

$$\sigma_y = \sigma_{cr} \left(1 + \frac{ec}{\rho^2} \sec \frac{L}{2\rho} \sqrt{\frac{\sigma_{cr}}{E}}\right) \qquad (11.10)$$

This equation is discussed in Sec. 11.5.

Various other empirical and semiempirical column formulas are employed. For civil structures, the formulas usually incorporate a *factor of safety* by arbitrarily reducing the buckling stress to give an "allowable" or "working" stress. The engineer who must design a structure to meet a particular code will probably find that the allowable stresses for columns are specified by certain arbitrary formulas which are based to some extent on experience. (See also Sec. 15.5.)

11.5 *Eccentric columns and beam-columns*

A "straight" column may be loaded eccentrically, that is, the axial load P does not pass through the centroids of cross sections. No real column is "perfectly straight"; it is therefore also necessary to be able to predict the effect of an initial curvature of the structural axis. The *beam-column* is a member that transmits both bending moment and axial load simultaneously. All three of these cases fall in the same general category; the common feature is that the axial compressive load causes *secondary* bending moments.

The simplest case is the eccentric column which has an initial sinusoidal shape and is centrally loaded at the ends. The analysis is identical to that for a beam-column for which the *primary* bending moment is distributed sinusoidally over the length. (*Primary* refers to the bending moment that would exist if the axial load were absent.)

Figure 11.12 shows a beam loaded by a downward force distributed sinusoidally. The loading function is (using x for distance along beam)

$$q = -q_0 \sin\left(\frac{\pi x}{L}\right) \qquad (a)$$

Using the general beam equations (9.2), we find that*

$$M = M_0 \sin\left(\frac{\pi x}{L}\right) \tag{b}$$

where $\qquad M_0 = q_0 \dfrac{L^2}{\pi^2} \qquad$ and $\qquad y = -\dfrac{M_0}{EI}\dfrac{L^2}{\pi^2}\sin\left(\dfrac{\pi x}{L}\right)$ $\qquad$ (c)

or, dropping the negative sign,

$$y = \delta_0 \sin\left(\frac{\pi x}{L}\right)$$

where $\qquad\qquad\qquad \delta_0 = \dfrac{M_0}{EI}\dfrac{L^2}{\pi^2}$ $\qquad\qquad\qquad$ (d)

But the term $\pi^2 EI/L^2$ represents the fundamental Euler load P_E. Therefore the maximum deflection of the beam is

$$\delta_0 = \frac{M_0}{P_E} \tag{11.11}$$

---

* This derivation should be assigned as an exercise because it demonstrates an important point. It will be found that *both* constants of integration C_1 and C_2 are zero; that is, the shear at $x = 0$ is *not* given by C_1 as in the case of uniform loading.

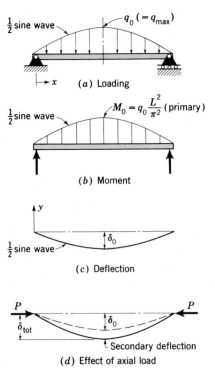

(a) Loading

(b) Moment

(c) Deflection

(d) Effect of axial load

Figure 11.12. Beam-column with initial sinusoidal loading.

This is the *primary* deflection without axial loading. Now assume that a compressive force P is acting. This will cause an additional increment of *secondary* moment having a maximum value equal to

$$\Delta M = P\delta_0 \tag{e}$$

But this causes additional deflection, which causes additional moment, and so on. This action may be either convergent or divergent. If it is convergent, there will be a final (total) value for the maximum bending moment, which we shall call M_{tot} (the sum of primary and final secondary moments). At this value, the deflection at midspan will be

$$\delta_{\text{tot}} = \frac{M_{\text{tot}}}{P_{\text{E}}} \tag{f}$$

But we know that

$$M_{\text{tot}} = M_0 + P\delta_{\text{tot}} \tag{g}$$

Substituting from (f),

$$M_{\text{tot}} = M_0 + \frac{PM_{\text{tot}}}{P_{\text{E}}} \tag{h}$$

The *amplification factor* is defined as $k_a \equiv M_{\text{tot}}/M_0$. Dividing Eq. (h) by M_0, we obtain

$$k_a = 1 + \frac{P}{P_{\text{E}}}\frac{M_{\text{tot}}}{M_0} = 1 + \left(\frac{P}{P_{\text{E}}}\right)k_a$$

From this,

$$\boxed{k_a = \frac{1}{1 - P/P_{\text{E}}}} \tag{11.12}$$

This important equation shows that as the value of P approaches P_{E} the amplification factor approaches infinity; that is, at P_{E} the action becomes divergent and the beam continues to bend indefinitely. For an eccentric column with an initial sinusoidal shape Eq. (11.12) may be used to determine the lateral deflection δ. The maximum deflection at midspan can be expressed in dimensionless form as

$$\frac{\delta}{e} = \frac{1}{1 - P/P_{\text{E}}} \tag{11.13}$$

where e is the amplitude of initial sinusoidal eccentricity.

A plot of this equation is shown in Fig. 11.13. Note that the curve is asymptotic to the line $P = P_{\text{E}}$ and that P_{E} could be attained only at infinite deflection!

A different expression for k will be obtained for initial moment distributions (or deflections) other than sinusoidal (see Ref. 20). However, the various formulas give approximately the same numerical results. Therefore, for general purposes the simple formula of Eq. (11.12) may be used.

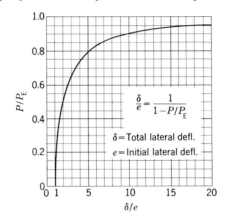

Figure 11.13. Dimensionless load-deflection diagram for sinusoidally eccentric column.

The reciprocal of the amplification factor can be thought of as a *reduction factor for the effective bending stiffness*. This can be expressed by

$$\frac{(EI)_R}{EI} = \frac{1}{k_a} = 1 - \frac{P}{P_E} \qquad (11.14)$$

where $(EI)_R$ is the reduced bending stiffness.

For the sinusoidal case, the reduction is linear with axial load P, as shown in Fig. 11.14.

When the primary bending moment (or initial eccentricity) is constant, the amplification factor can be derived by adding to the differential equation for the straight column a term representing the constant eccentricity e, giving

$$\frac{d^2y}{dx^2} + p^2y = -p^2e$$

This equation was solved by Thomas Young in 1807. Let k_e represent the amplification factor for constant eccentricity. Its value is

$$k_e = \frac{1}{\cos\left(\dfrac{\pi}{2}\sqrt{P/P_E}\right)} \qquad (11.15)$$

Then the stiffness reduction factor becomes

$$\frac{(EI)_R}{EI} = \cos\left(\frac{\pi}{2}\sqrt{\frac{P}{P_E}}\right) \qquad (11.16)$$

This factor is plotted on Fig. 11.14 to show the difference between the two formulas. Many other cases of combined bending and axial loading are worked out in Ref. 20, which also includes the case of combined eccentric loading (at distance e) and initial sinusoidal curvature (with amplitude a). By using the princi-

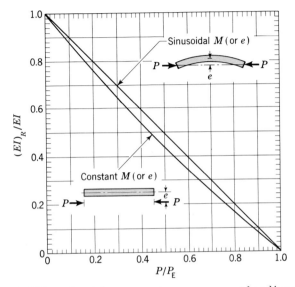

Figure 11.14. Effect of axial compression on apparent bending stiffness.

ple of superposition, it is shown that the two different amplification factors may be added, giving

$$\delta_{\text{tot}} = k_a a + k_e e \qquad (11.17)$$

The maximum compressive stress in a column subjected to combined bending and compression can now be expressed as

$$\sigma_{\max} = -\frac{P}{A} - k\frac{Mc}{I} \qquad (11.18)$$

where k is the amplification factor from Eq. (11.12) or Eq. (11.15).

For the eccentric column, Eq. (7.23) is modified to account for secondary bending, as follows:

$$\sigma_{\max} = -\frac{P}{A}\left(1 + k\frac{e}{r_c}\right) \qquad (11.19)$$

where k = amplification factor
$\quad e$ = initial eccentricity
$\quad r_c$ = core radius = p^2/c or Z/A (see Sec. 7.6)
$\quad e/r_c$ = eccentricity ratio

Equation (11.19) is the basis for one of the oldest column-design formulas, called the *secant formula*. The theory postulates that the eccentric column will fail when the maximum compressive stress (σ_{max}) reaches the value of the compressive yield stress (σ_y). Making these substitutions and using Eq. (11.15), we obtain (with $P/A = \sigma_{av}$)

$$\sigma_y = \sigma_{av}\left[1 + \frac{e/r_c}{\cos\left(\frac{\pi}{2}\sqrt{\sigma_{av}/\sigma_E}\right)}\right]$$

The most common form of the formula is obtained by making the following substitutions:

$$\sigma_{av} = \sigma_{cr}, \qquad \sigma_E = \frac{\pi^2 E}{(L/\rho)^2}, \qquad r_c = \frac{\rho^2}{c}$$

Then
$$\sigma_y = \sigma_{cr}\left(1 + \frac{ec}{\rho^2}\sec\frac{L}{2\rho}\sqrt{\frac{\sigma_{cr}}{E}}\right) \qquad (11.20)$$

For a given yield stress, slenderness ratio, and eccentricity ratio, the value of σ_{cr} can be determined. A plot of σ_{cr} against L/ρ, for different values of e/r_c constitutes a family of column curves.

A typical plot is shown in Fig. 11.15, where $E = 30 \times 10^6$ psi, $\sigma_y = 36,000$ psi. Note that the intercepts at $L/\rho = 0$ represent Eq. (7.23).

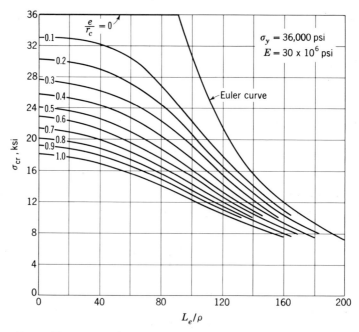

Figure 11.15. Eccentric column curves from secant formula (from Ref. 20).

The secant formula implies that the compressive stress-strain diagram has a "sharp" yield point; that is, the *elastoplastic* approximation is used. This procedure is satisfactory for relatively low-strength steel, but not for heat-treated steel alloys or for other materials such as aluminum alloys.

See Ref. 20 for secant formulas and secant column curves for members having unequal eccentricities at each end.

EXAMPLE 11.5. A 1-in.-square steel bar, 20 ft long, in a horizontal position, is simply supported at each end. There is no transverse force, except the weight of the bar itself. (*a*) Find the maximum stress and deflection. (*b*) Assume that an axial compressive load of 200 lb is applied at each end, through the centroid of cross-sectional area. Find the maximum stress and deflection under this loading condition.

For steel, the density is approximately 0.29 lb/in.^{3}, $E = 29 \times 10^6$ psi. The distributed loading due to dead weight is equal to the density times the cross-sectional area (1 in.^{2}); therefore $q = 0.29$ lb/in.

$$M_{max} = \frac{qL^2}{8} = \frac{0.29 \times 240^2}{8} = 2{,}090 \text{ in.-lb}$$

For a 1-in.-square section, $I = \frac{1}{12}$ in.^{4}, $Z = \frac{1}{6}$ in.^{3},

$$\sigma_{max} = \frac{M}{Z} = 2{,}090 \times 6 = 12{,}540 \text{ psi}$$

From Eq. (9.5),

$$\delta = \frac{5}{384} \frac{qL^4}{EI}$$

$$= \frac{5 \times 0.29 \times 240^4}{384 \times 29 \times 10^6 \times \frac{1}{12}} = 0.0518 \text{ in.}$$

The Euler column load in the elastic range is

$$P_E = \frac{\pi^2 EI}{L^2} = \frac{\pi^2 \times 29 \times 10^6 \times \frac{1}{12}}{240^2} = 414 \text{ lb}$$

From Eq. (11.12),

$$k = \frac{1}{1 - \frac{200}{414}} = \frac{1}{0.517} = 1.934$$

Both the maximum bending stress and the bending deflection must be multiplied by this factor.

$$\sigma_{bending} = 12{,}540 \times 1.934 = 24{,}250 \text{ psi}$$

$$\sigma_{axial} = \frac{P}{A} = 200 \text{ psi}$$

$$\sigma_{tot} = 24{,}250 + 200 = 24{,}450 \text{ psi (compression)}$$
$$\delta = 0.0518 \times 1.934 = 0.100 \text{ in.}$$

Note that, if the axial load were doubled, the factor k would become 29.4.

11.6 *Interaction method for eccentric columns and beam-columns*

When two different loading conditions are applied to a member, the presence of one condition will, in general, affect the degree of loading that can be applied in the other condition without causing failure. ("Failure" can be defined in various ways, such as buckling, development of permanent strains, fracture, and so on.) Figure 11.16 shows schematically the

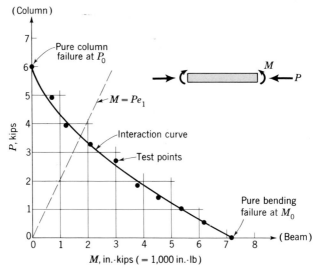

Figure 11.16. Interaction curve for combined bending and compression.

results of tests of a member under combined bending and compression. (The cross section, length, and material are the same in all the tests.) The curve fitting the test points is called an *interaction curve*.

Figure 11.17 (heavy line) shows a normalized interaction curve for which each value of P has been divided by P_0 and each value of M by M_0, where P_0 and M_0 are the failure values for pure axial compression and pure bending, respectively. These ratios are designated as R_a and R_b, respectively. For a relatively short member in which *secondary bending effects are negligible*, the maximum stress, from elastic theory, is

$$\sigma_{\max} = \frac{P}{A} + \frac{Mc}{I} \qquad (a)$$

This can be expressed as

$$\sigma_{\max} = \sigma_a + \sigma_b \qquad (b)$$

Assume first that σ_0 represents the failure stress for both axial loading and bending. Dividing Eq. (*b*) by σ_0 and rearranging give

$$\frac{\sigma_a}{\sigma_0} + \frac{\sigma_b}{\sigma_0} = 1 \qquad \text{or} \qquad R_a + R_b = 1 \qquad\qquad (11.21)$$

This represents a *straight-line interaction curve*, shown in Fig. 11.18.

Equation (11.21) may be generalized by substituting for σ_0 the actual failure stresses for pure axial loading (σ_{a_0}) and pure bending (σ_{b_0}), respectively.

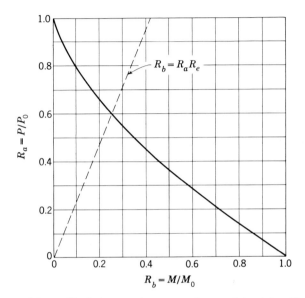

Figure 11.17. Normalized interaction curve for combined bending and compression.

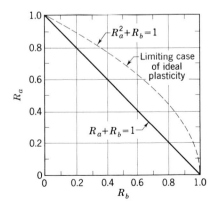

Figure 11.18. Straight-line interaction curve for combined axial loading and bending (secondary bending effect negligible).

For ductile materials the modulus of rupture (Sec. 7.7) is used for σ_{b_0} in bending. This may cause test data to fall somewhat above the straight line. The particular case of a solid rectangular cross section with ideal plasticity (Sec. 1.8) is represented by the parabolic formula:

$$R_a{}^2 + R_b = 1 \tag{11.22}$$

This formula is shown as a dashed curve on Fig. 11.18. For cross sections (such as I beams) that are efficient in bending, the inelastic effect is usually negligible; it will be omitted in what follows.

For slender members, we introduce the elastic amplification factor, which gives the interaction curve

$$R_a + kR_b = 1 \tag{a}$$

For *sinusoidal* distribution of primary bending moment this becomes, from (11.12),

$$R_a + \frac{1}{1 - (P/P_\mathrm{E})} R_b = 1 \tag{b}$$

We now introduce the following *buckling ratio:*

$$\eta \equiv \frac{P_0}{P_\mathrm{E}} \equiv \frac{\sigma_0}{\sigma_\mathrm{E}} \tag{11.23}$$

which is defined as the ratio between the actual failing load of a column and the theoretical Euler load. It provides for inelastic effects and also for local buckling (to be discussed later).

Substituting $P_\mathrm{E} = P_0/\eta$ in Eq. (b), we obtain

$$R_a + \frac{1}{1 - \eta(P/P_0)} R_b = 1$$

Solving for R_b and replacing P/P_0 by R_a give the interaction equation

$$R_b = (1 - R_a)(1 - \eta R_a) \tag{11.24}$$

This equation represents the family of interaction curves plotted on Fig. 11.19.

If the primary bending moment is constant, the amplification factor of Eq. (11.15) is used. This gives the following interaction equation:

$$R_b = (1 - R_a) \cos\left(\frac{\pi}{2} \sqrt{\eta R_a}\right) \tag{11.25}$$

This family of interaction curves is plotted on Fig. 11.20.

Note that the curves of Fig. 11.20 are somewhat lower than those of Fig. 11.19 (except when $\eta = 0$). This reflects the difference in the shape of the primary bending-moment curve.

The eccentric column is also provided for by these charts. On the *dimensional* interaction curve (Fig. 11.16), a straight line through the origin represents a certain eccentricity e (because $M = Pe$). On the normalized chart (Fig. 11.17), the eccentricity is replaced by the *eccentricity ratio*, determined as follows:

$$R_e \equiv \frac{R_b}{R_a} \equiv \frac{M/M_0}{P/P_0} \qquad (a)$$

but

$$\frac{M}{P} = e \qquad (b)$$

Therefore

$$R_e = \frac{e}{M_0/P_0} \qquad (c)$$

or

$$R_e = \frac{e}{e_0} \qquad (11.26)$$

The term e_0 represents the *base eccentricity* and is given by

$$e_0 = \frac{M_0}{P_0} \qquad (11.27)$$

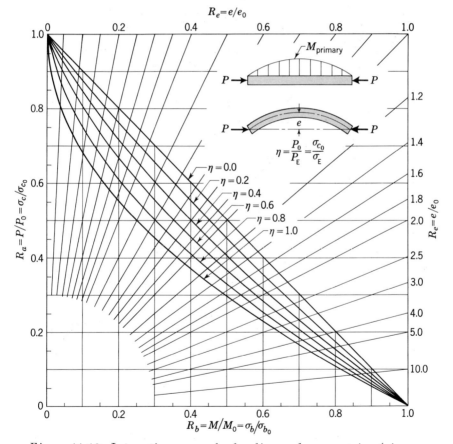

Figure 11.19. Interaction curves for bending and compression (sinusoidal primary-bending moment or column eccentricity).

To express e_0 in terms of stress, replace M_0 by $\sigma_{b_0}Z$ and P_0 by $\sigma_{a_0}A$. Then, since the term Z/A represents the *core radius* r_c, we have

$$e_0 = \frac{\sigma_{b_0}}{\sigma_{a_0}} r_c \qquad (11.28)$$

and

$$R_e = \frac{e}{r_c} \frac{\sigma_{a_0}}{\sigma_{b_0}} \qquad (11.29)$$

where σ_{a_0} is the failure stress for pure compression. When $\sigma_{a_0} = \sigma_{b_0}$, the base eccentricity becomes the core radius and R_e becomes e/r_c.

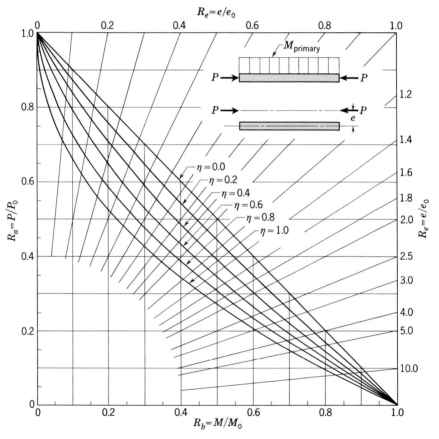

Figure 11.20. Interaction curves for bending and compression (constant primary-bending moment or column eccentricity).

A major advantage of the interaction charts is that the *primary*-bending moment is used in determining R_b. This permits a direct solution of beam-column or eccentric-column problems and is particularly useful in design.

The method also permits extension of the inelastic-buckling theory to eccentric columns,* as shown in the following example.

EXAMPLE 11.6 Reduction of column test data for eccentricity. Assume that a number of concentric-column tests have established the column curve of Fig. E11.6. One test has also been made in pure bending, to determine M_0. It is desired to find a column curve (buckling load versus length) for an eccentricity of 0.15 in. (constant). The necessary data are given on the figure.

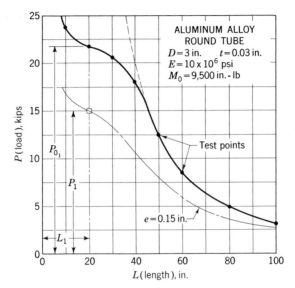

ALUMINUM ALLOY
ROUND TUBE
$D = 3$ in. $t = 0.03$ in.
$E = 10 \times 10^6$ psi
$M_0 = 9,500$ in.-lb

Figure E11.6. Reduction of basic column curve to account for eccentricity.

The computations are listed in Table 11.2. Values of L are selected, and the corresponding values of P_0 are read from the original column curve, while P_E is calculated for each length. The values of η, e_0, and R_e are determined. The value of R_a is found at the intersection of the proper η and R_e lines in Fig. 11.20. This gives the reduction factor R_a by which the value of P_0 is multiplied. The resulting eccentric-column curve is shown in Fig. E11.6 (dot-dash line).

EXAMPLE 11.7 Eccentric column curves. Plot a family of column curves for various eccentricity ratios e/r_c, given the column stress curve for the centrally loaded column. Assume that e is constant over length. A set of calculations for

---

* The use of the elastic amplification factor in the inelastic range might appear to be questionable. To settle this, nearly 200 tests were made by the author and R. D. Chipman. The results, reported in Ref. 26, showed conclusively that this method is quite accurate. See also Ref. 76.

one eccentricity ratio (e/r_c) is shown in Table 11.3. The resulting column curves
are shown in Fig. E11.7 for various values of eccentricity ratio.

Note that P_0 or σ_{a_0} should include the effects of local buckling, if the column
fails in that mode; similarly σ_{b_0} must represent the actual mode of failure in pure
bending. (For an I beam this could be either local or lateral buckling.) A special
method is required for I beams which fail by lateral buckling, when the eccentricity is in the plane of the web (see Ref. 19, Sec. 26.9).

TABLE 11.2

Computations for eccentric-column-load curve

$$M_0 = 9{,}500 \; in.\text{-}lb \qquad e = 0.15 \; in.$$

L, in.	P_0, lb	$P_E = \dfrac{\pi^2 EI}{L^2}$, lb	$\eta = \dfrac{P_0}{P_E}$	$e_0 = \dfrac{M_0}{P_0}$, in.	$R_e = \dfrac{e}{e_0}$	R_a from Fig. 11.20	$P = R_a P_0$ lb
10	23,700	318,000	0.075	0.401	0.374	0.71	16,800
20	21,700	78,500	0.277	0.438	0.342	0.69	15,000
30	20,600	34,900	0.590	0.461	0.324	0.65	13,400
40	18,100	19,600	0.922	0.525	0.286	0.58	10,500
50	12,500	12,500	1.000	0.760	0.197	0.63	7,900
60	8,700	8,700	1.000	1.094	0.137	0.68	5,900
80	4,900	4,900	1.000	1.940	0.077	0.74	3,600
100	3,200	3,200	1.000	2.970	0.050	0.82	2,600

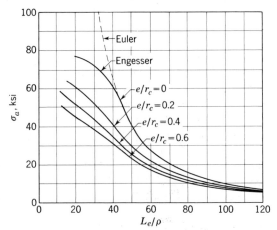

*Figure E11.7. Eccentric-column curves derived by interaction curve
method (aluminum alloy 7075-T6 tubing, $D/t = 50$).*

TABLE 11.3

Computations for eccentric-column-stress curve

$$\sigma_{b_0} = 82,500 \ psi \qquad \frac{e}{r_c} = 0.20$$

L_e/ρ	σ_{a_0}, psi	$\sigma_E = \dfrac{\pi^2 E}{(L_e/\rho)^2}$, psi	$\eta = \dfrac{\sigma_{a_0}}{\sigma_E}$	$R_e = 0.2\dfrac{\sigma_{a_0}}{\sigma_{b_0}}$	R_a from Fig. 11.20	$\sigma_a = R_a\sigma_{a_0}$, psi
20	76,000	247,000	0.325	0.184	0.80	60,800
30	72,500	110,000	0.659	0.176	0.72	52,200
40	61,000	61,700	0.989	0.148	0.67	40,900
50	39,500	39,500	1.000	0.096	0.72	28,400
60	27,400	27,400	1.000	0.066	0.76	20,800
70	20,100	20,100	1.000	0.049	0.79	15,900
80	15,400	15,400	1.000	0.037	0.81	12,500
90	12,200	12,200	1.000	0.029	0.83	10,100
100	9,900	9,900	1.000	0.024	0.85	8,400

11.7 Buckling of flat plates

Figure 11.21 shows two square plates loaded by a line compressive force q along two opposite edges. Case a shows the unloaded edges as "free," in the sense that they are not compelled to remain straight. The plate therefore behaves as a column.

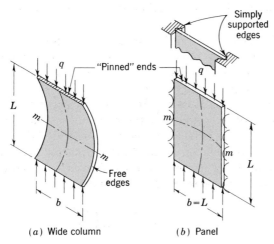

Figure 11.21. Wide column and panel.

If the width b is considerably greater than the thickness, the member is classified as a wide column. Except for a slight curling at the free edges such a plate will buckle by bending into a developable surface, that is, a section such as m–m will remain straight. The apparent modulus of elasticity for a wide plate in bending is (see Prob. 7.17)

$$E_{\text{app}} = \frac{E}{(1 - \nu^2)}$$

The Euler buckling stress becomes

$$\sigma_{\text{E}} = \frac{\pi^2 E}{(1 - \nu^2)(L_e/\rho)^2}$$

For a plate of thickness t,

$$\rho = \sqrt{\frac{I}{A}} = \frac{t}{\sqrt{12}}$$

Substituting this in the above equation we obtain

$$\sigma_{\text{E}} = \frac{\pi^2 E t^2}{12(1 - \nu^2)L_e^2} \tag{11.30}$$

For inelastic buckling, replace E by E_t. (Although Poisson's ratio ν changes in the inelastic range, this effect is negligible in the above formula.)

Figure 11.21b shows the square plate with *simply supported edges*. This means that all edges are compelled to remain straight but have no other constraints. Such a condition can be obtained in a test by using V blocks, as shown.

The effect of edge constraint is to compel the plate to bend about two different axes in order to buckle. This is indicated by the curvature of the two center lines. To distinguish this type of element from the wide column, the term *panel* will be used.

Edge constraint has a large effect on the elastic-buckling load of a panel. It might be expected that the buckling load of the wide column would be doubled, but in fact it is *four times as great*.[*] (The reason for this is that a strip "cut" off center must not only bend but must also twist.)

The elastic-buckling stress for the *square panel* is found by multiplying Eq. (11.30) by 4 and replacing L by b, giving

$$\sigma_{\text{cr}} = \frac{\pi^2 E}{3(1 - \nu^2)} \left(\frac{t}{b}\right)^2 \tag{11.31a}$$

[*] Mathematical proof is beyond the scope of this text (see Ref. 20).

This equation can be written in a more general form that applies to all types of plate buckling:

$$\sigma_{\mathrm{cr}} = K_c E \left(\frac{t}{b}\right)^2$$

(11.31b)

where K_c = constant depending on edge constraint

t = plate thickness

b = plate width

For the *square plate*, with Poisson's ratio = 0.30,

$$K_c = 3.62$$

The theory of elastic stability shows that when $L > b$ and L/b is an integer, the panel with simply supported edges will buckle as if it were a series of square panels, buckling alternately in opposite directions. Therefore Eq. (11.31b) can be used for such panels. (For nonintegral values of L/b, there is a small increase in the value of K_c, but this is usually neglected.) For "short" panels ($L/b < 1$), the value of K_c increases with decreasing L/b (see Ref. 19 or 20).

Equation (11.31b) is useful in the design of structures composed of thin-walled flat plates (a square tube is an example). The effects of other types of edge support and loading conditions are summarized in Table 11.4, based on $\nu = 0.30$. (The word "pinned" means simply supported. "Fixed" is sometimes called "clamped.")

TABLE 11.4

Buckling coefficients for flat plates

Loading (across b)	Constraint	K_c
Compression	All edges pinned	3.62
Compression	Unloaded edges fixed, others pinned	6.3
Compression	One unloaded edge fixed, other free	1.10
Compression	One edge free, others pinned ($L \gg b$)	0.375
Pure shear	All edges pinned ($L \gg b$)	4.8
Pure shear	All edges fixed ($L \gg b$)	8.1
Pure bending	All edges pinned	21.5

Inelastic buckling of flat plates is a complicated subject which will not be treated analytically in this text. As a rough guide, it is suggested that the elastic modulus be replaced by $\sqrt{EE_t}$, where E_t is found from the compressive stress-strain diagram at a value of $\sigma = \sigma_{\mathrm{cr}}$. (For pure shear use $\sigma = 2\tau_{\mathrm{cr}}$.)

In contrast to columns, flat panels usually do not fail completely when the critical stress is reached. The panel begins to buckle at the critical load, but in many cases the applied load may be increased considerably beyond that load. However, the buckles grow deeper during such "post-buckling" loading and may become permanent. For an elementary treatment of post-buckling effects see Ref. 19 (Sec. 25.6).

A square tube or flat-sided corrugation, when used as a column, may buckle in either of two modes: the *Euler* (column) mode or the *local buckling* mode, in which the sides buckle as flat plates. The strength in compression is governed by the lower of the two critical stresses.*

An "open" section, used as a column, may buckle locally in such a way that the column twists over its entire length. This type of buckling is sometimes referred to as torsional instability. An example is a thin-walled angle section (see Ref. 20, pp. 425–426).

EXAMPLE 11.8.   The structure of an airplane wing often consists of a thin aluminum-alloy sheet, to which internal spanwise stiffeners (stringers) are riveted. (The latter are supported by transverse ribs.) The "sheet-stringer" combination serves as the top flange of a box beam and receives its most severe loading in compression. Assume that the sheet is 0.050 in. thick and that the stringers are spaced at 5 in. Determine the axial stress at which the sheet between the stringers will begin to buckle. Assume aluminum-alloy material, $E = 10 \times 10^6$ psi. Assume that the panels have simply supported edges.

$$\sigma_{cr} = 3.62E \left(\frac{t}{b}\right)^2 = 3.62 \times 10 \times 10^6 \left(\frac{0.050}{5}\right)^2 = 3,620 \text{ psi}$$

This is obviously in the elastic range; hence the use of the elastic modulus is correct. This example shows that a structure so designed would buckle at relatively low loading. Although this would not mean complete failure, it would be undesirable. Therefore it would be necessary to use closer stringer spacing or thicker sheet, or both.

EXAMPLE 11.9.   A square tube is made from steel sheet $\frac{1}{16}$ in. thick. The outside width is 4 in. $E = 29 \times 10^6$ psi. Find the axial load at which a short specimen will begin to buckle locally.

The local buckles will tend to form inward and outward on adjacent sides. The sides may therefore be treated as flat plates with simply supported edges. The average width is $b = 4.000 - 0.0625 = 3.94$ in.:

$$\sigma_{cr} = 3.62E \left(\frac{t}{b}\right)^2 = 3.62 \times 29 \times 10^6 \times \left(\frac{0.0625}{3.94}\right)^2 = 26,400 \text{ psi}$$
$$P = \sigma A = 26,400 \times 4 \times 3.94 \times \tfrac{1}{16} = 26,000 \text{ lb}$$

* In Refs. 13 and 19 it is shown that the most efficient (lightest) design is usually obtained by equating the buckling stresses for the two modes. See also Sec. 15.10.

EXAMPLE 11.10. In Fig. E11.10 find the line loading over projected width B at which the square corrugation would begin to buckle locally, if the corrugations are 2 in. on a side and the sheet is 0.0625 in. thick. The material is aluminum alloy with $E = 10 \times 10^6$ psi. Assume elastic action.

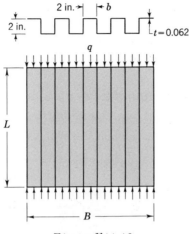

Figure E11.10

From Eq. (11.31b) with $K_c = 3.62$, the local buckling stress is

$$\sigma_{cr} = 3.62 \times 10 \times 10^6 \left(\frac{0.0625}{2.00}\right)^2 = 35,400 \text{ psi}$$

The area per inch of width (average thickness $\bar{t}$) is equal to $2t$ for the square corrugation; therefore the buckling load per inch of width is

$$q = \sigma_{cr}\bar{t} = 35,400 \times 2 \times 0.0625 = 4,400 \text{ lb/in.}$$

EXAMPLE 11.11. A flat-sided (square) corrugation (such as analyzed in Example 11.10) is used as a shear web in a beam for which the distance between flange centroids is 12 in. Corrugations are at right angles to the flanges, are 2 in. on a side, and the sheet thickness is 0.030 in. Material is steel with $E = 29 \times 10^6$ psi. Tensile yield stress is 60,000 psi. Find the transverse shear load V at which local buckling of the flat sides would begin.

From Eq. (11.31b), with $K_c = 4.8$ (Table 11.4),

$$\tau_{cr} = 4.8 \times 29 \times 10^6 \left(\frac{0.030}{2.00}\right)^2 = 31,400 \text{ psi}$$

The yield stress τ_y for pure shear is $0.577\sigma_y$, according to the octahedral shear theory (Example 5.2). Therefore

$$\tau_y = 0.577 \times 60,000 = 34,600 \text{ psi}$$

The buckling stress is thus in the elastic range.

For this type of beam the shear stress is constant over the depth (web ineffective in resisting bending). Therefore

$$V = qh = \tau_{cr}th = 31,400 \times 0.030 \times 12 = 11,300 \text{ lb}$$

Tests have shown that such high local buckling stresses are actually developed, provided that the corrugations are attached to the flanges on both faces. For very slender webs $(L \gg b)$ general instability may occur before the critical local buckling stress is reached (see Ref. 20, p. 428).

11.8 Local buckling of round tubes and shells*

If a short, thin-walled tube is loaded in compression, the failure will not cause bending of the tube as a whole but will involve local bending of the tube walls, as shown in Fig. 11.22.

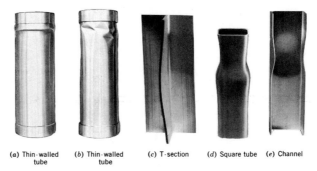

(a) Thin-walled tube   (b) Thin-walled tube   (c) T-section   (d) Square tube   (e) Channel

Figure 11.22. Types of local buckling in compression.

The most important shape-parameter in local buckling of cylindrical surfaces is the diameter–thickness ratio D/t. Length can affect the results to some extent (in the form of a ratio L/D), but in most structural applications the members are long enough so that length effects can be neglected.

If a series of short tubes having different D/t ratios is tested, the results will appear as indicated in Fig. 11.23. Although there is likely to be a considerable amount of scatter, the data in the elastic range can be fitted reasonably well by an equation of the type

$$\sigma_{cr} = \frac{K_c E}{D/t} \qquad (11.32)$$

where σ_{cr} is the local-buckling (crushing) stress, E the modulus of elasticity, and D/t the diameter–thickness ratio. The constant K_c has a

---

* As previously noted, the term *shell* is usually used for members of large diameter.

theoretical value of 1.2 (Ref. 20), and observed values of approximately 0.4 to 0.8.*

In the *inelastic range*, an effective modulus equal to the geometric mean of the elastic and tangent moduli gives conservative results. Equation (11.32) becomes

$$\sigma_{\text{cr}} = \frac{K_c \sqrt{EE_t}}{D/t} \qquad (11.33)$$

where E_t is the tangent modulus at the stress σ_{cr}. (See also Gerard, Ref. 31.)

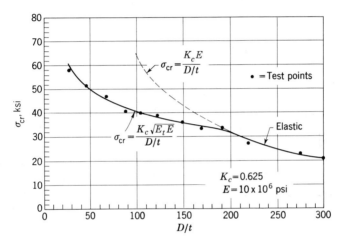

Figure 11.23. Typical test results for local buckling of tubes in compression (aluminum alloy).

EXAMPLE 11.12. A thin-walled tube has a mean diameter of 3 in., a wall thickness of 0.020 in., and a length of 80 in. (pinned ends). It is made from aluminum alloy, the column curve for which is given in Fig. 11.7 ($E = 10.6 \times 10^6$ psi). Determine the critical load, noting which type of failure will occur first, column failure or local buckling. Use Eq. (11.32) for local buckling, with $K_c = 0.40$ (conservative). For a thin-walled tube, $I = \pi R^3 t$, $A = 2\pi Rt$.

Substituting these values in the equation for radius of gyration,

$$\rho = \sqrt{\frac{I}{A}} = \sqrt{\frac{\pi R^3 t}{2\pi Rt}} = \frac{1}{\sqrt{2}} R = 0.707 R$$

In this example, $\rho = 0.707 \times 1.50 = 1.06$ in.:

$$\frac{L}{\rho} = \frac{80}{1.06} = 75.5$$

---

* Tests of "near-perfect" specimens have shown that the theoretical buckling coefficient can be approached rather closely. The scatter is evidently caused by small irregularities in the cross section.

From Fig. 11.7, it is evident that the stress remains in the elastic range. From this figure, the column stress is about 18,000 psi. Calculating this stress from the column equation,

$$\sigma_E = \frac{\pi^2 E}{(L/\rho)^2} = \frac{\pi^2 \times 10.6 \times 10^6}{75.5^2} = 18,400 \text{ psi}$$

For local buckling, the elastic equation will be used, with $K_c = 0.40$:

$$\sigma_{cr} = \frac{K_c E}{D/t} = \frac{0.40 \times 10.6 \times 10^6}{150} = 28,300 \text{ psi}$$

Since this is greater than the column-buckling stress, the failure will occur by Euler instability of the column as a whole, not by local buckling of the wall. There is therefore no need to consider inelastic effects for local buckling.

In *pure bending* of a round tube, there will be a compression field that is fairly uniform over a considerable fraction of the circumference. The buckling failure will therefore be practically the same as for pure compression. For general purposes, Eq. (11.33) can be used, with the same value of the effective modulus.

In *pure torsion* a diagonal compressive field acts spirally around the tube. This force will cause one or more diagonal wrinkles to form in a thin-walled tube when the critical shear stress is reached, as indicated in Fig. 11.24. Because of the fact that the buckle tends to form over a fairly long length (in contrast to compression or bending), the critical shear stress is strongly affected by the free length of the tube. For long tubes,

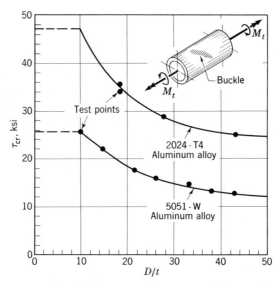

Figure 11.24. Buckling of tubes in torsion. (Data from Ref. 63.)

such as those used for shafts or control systems, the end effect is negligible. For such elements, the theoretical equation (Ref. 20) has the form

$$\tau_{cr} = \frac{K_s E}{(D/t)^{\frac{3}{2}}} \tag{11.34}$$

where $K_s = 0.73$ (theoretical for $\nu = 0.30$).

To allow for scatter, a lower value of K_s should be used, such as 0.60. To account for inelastic effects, a safe procedure is to use the ratio $\sqrt{E_t/E}$, from the compression stress-strain diagram, at values of $\sigma = 2\tau$.

For relatively short tubes, Batdorf's equation may be used (Ref. 32):

$$\tau_{cr} = \frac{K_s E}{(D/t)^{\frac{3}{2}}(L/D)^{\frac{1}{2}}} \tag{11.35}$$

where L is the distance between ends or bulkheads, and $K_s = 1.26$ (theoretical). This equation applies in the range where

$$\frac{25}{D/t} < \left(\frac{L}{D}\right)^2 < \frac{D}{t}$$

For very short cylinders, where $(L/D)^2(D/t) < \frac{1}{2}$, the cylinder wall may be treated as a flat shear web.

11.9 Lateral buckling of beams in bending

Figure 11.25 shows two narrow I beams which have buckled laterally by a twisting action, in a bending test. A narrow solid beam of rectangular cross section behaves in a similar manner, as shown in Fig. 11.26.

The critical bending moment has been derived by methods similar to those used to obtain the Euler load for columns (see Ref. 20). The basic equation for the *rectangular bar* is

$$M_{cr} = \frac{\pi \sqrt{(EI_y)(GJ)}}{L} \tag{11.36a}$$

If $G = \frac{3}{8}E$ (Sec. 4.3),

$$M_{cr} = \pi \sqrt{\frac{3}{8}} \frac{E \sqrt{I_y J}}{L} \tag{11.36b}$$

where M_{cr} = bending moment (constant) about x axis of cross section
EI_y = bending stiffness about y axis
GJ = torsional stiffness of entire section
J = cross-section property (see Chap. 10)
L = distance between ends (in Fig. 11.26 ends are constrained to remain vertical but are free to rotate about a vertical axis)

For *fixed ends* the effective length is reduced to one-half the total value, thereby doubling the critical moment (see Ref. 20).

The critical loadings have also been derived for beams in which the bending moment is not constant. A general equation can be written to cover all these cases:

$$P_{cr} = K_b \frac{\sqrt{(EI_y)(GJ)}}{L^2} \qquad (11.37)$$

where P is the transverse loading.

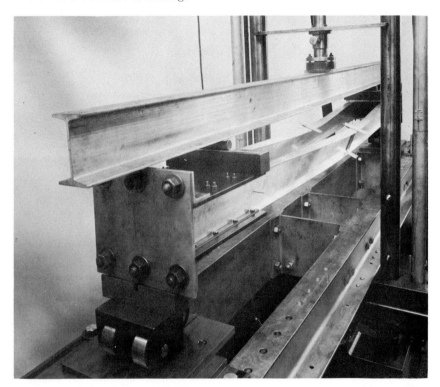

Figure 11.25. Lateral buckling of compression flanges of beams in bending. (Aluminum Company of America.)

Some values of K_b from Ref. 20, are listed below:

Cantilever beam, load P applied at the free end, $K_b = 4.013$
Cantilever beam, distributed loading q over entire length ($P_{cr} = qL$), $K_b = 12.85$
Simple beam, load P applied at the center, $K_b = 16.94$
Simple beam, distributed loading q over entire length ($P_{cr} = qL$), $K_b = 28.3$

If the maximum stress due to bending should exceed the proportional limit, a safe procedure is to assume that the values of EI_y and GJ are both reduced by the ratio $\eta = E_t/E$. The right side of Eq. 11.37 is then multiplied by η, which is a function of the compressive stress caused by bending.

EXAMPLE 11.13.   For a relatively thin beam of solid rectangular cross section, the value of J is only slightly greater than $BD^3/3$, where B is the larger dimension (Table 10.2). The value of I_y is $BD^3/12$. For a Poisson's ratio of $\frac{1}{3}$, $G = 0.375E$. Substituting these values in Eq. (11.37), a simple formula is obtained for the lateral buckling load:

$$P_{cr} = \frac{0.10K_bEBD^3}{L^2}$$

where B is the larger dimension of cross section, and D the smaller dimension of cross section.

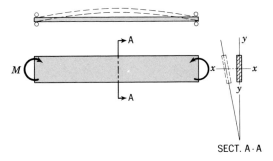

SECT. A-A

Figure 11.26. Lateral buckling of a rectangular beam in pure bending.

For I beams, Timoshenko (Ref. 20), Bleich (Ref. 21), and others have derived equations that can be simplified to the following form:

$$P_{cr_{fl}} = k_{fl}P_{y_{fl}} \tag{11.38}$$

where $P_{y_{fl}}$ is the lateral-buckling load (about y axis) for compression flange, acting alone, and k_{fl} is the torsional stiffness factor, by which the above load is increased. The value of k_{fl}, as derived from Bleich's equation, is

$$k_{fl} = \sqrt{1 + \frac{2m}{\pi^2}\left(\frac{L}{h}\right)^2} \tag{11.39}$$

where $m = GJ/EI_{y_{fl}}$

GJ = torsional stiffness of entire cross section

$I_{y_{fl}}$ = moment of inertia of compression flange about y axis

h = distance between centroids of compression and tension flanges

To provide for inelastic effects, E_t can be used in computing $P_{y_{fl}}$. The value of m can be assumed to be unchanged.

The above equation will give conservative results for cases in which the load P varies over the length of the flange. When P is caused by uniform loading of a constant-depth beam, the effective length is about $0.7L$. For more accurate methods, see Ref. 20.

For an I beam (with thin web) the web offers negligible resistance to bending about the y axis. Therefore, in using Eq. (11.38), the applied flange load P_y may be estimated by neglecting the web; that is, $P_y = M/h$. The critical bending moment for lateral buckling is then given by $M_{cr} = P_{crn}h$.

Because of the complications involved in a complete analysis, it has become customary to use semiempirical formulas for lateral buckling. A widely used formula for I beams and wide-flange beams has the form*

$$\sigma_{cr} = \frac{KE}{(L/b)(d/t)} \qquad (11.40)$$

where b = total width of flange

d = depth of beam

t = thickness of compression flange

K = 0.7 (based on average test values)

For structural steel, the value of KE is usually specified as 12,000,000 psi. This includes reduction by dividing by a factor of safety. An upper limit (yield stress) is also specified for the stress, giving a horizontal cutoff on the buckling curve.

In structural design it is usually possible to prevent lateral buckling by using lateral bracing members. For typical requirements see the *Manual of Steel Construction* (Ref. 68).

11.10 Local buckling under combined loading

The interaction method of predicting failure under combined loading was introduced in Sec. 11.6. This can be applied also to local buckling. The loading ratio R is defined as the ratio between the buckling load (or stress) under combined loading and the buckling load (or stress) under pure loading.

Figure 11.27, based on Ref. 33, shows a number of points representing tests of tubing under *combined bending and torsion*. Using R_b for bending and R_s for torsion,† it was found that the test points were well fitted by a circular interaction curve, the equation of which is

$$R_b{}^2 + R_s{}^2 = 1 \qquad (11.41)$$

Tests of thin-walled cylinders under *combined axial loading and torsion* are represented by Fig. 11.28 (Ref. 34). (Specimens were short, to exclude column effects.) A cubic interaction curve fits the test points rather well.

---

* This formula, originally developed by De Vries (Ref. 29), has been shown by Winter (Ref. 30) to be a simplified form of a more accurate theory. See also Ref. 68.

† The subscript s stands for shear, since torsion is a shearing phenomenon. The subscript t could have been used, but might be confused with tension.

The interaction equation is

$$R_a + R_s{}^3 = 1 \qquad (11.42)$$

Note that the presence of a tension load increases the buckling load beyond that for pure torsion.

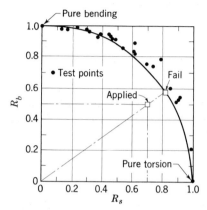

Figure 11.27. Strength of tubing under combined bending and torsion. (Data from Ref. 33.)

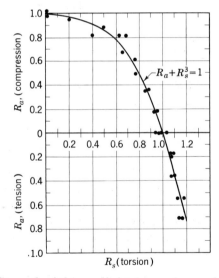

Figure 11.28. Strength of thin-walled tubes under combined axial loading and torsion. (After Bridget, Jerome, and Vosseler, Ref. 34.)

EXAMPLE 11.14. A tube has been designed to buckle at simultaneous bending and torsional moments of 6,000 and 7,000 in.-lb, respectively (factor of safety included). Assume that several similar tubes had previously been tested in pure bending and pure torsion and that the average failing moments were found to be 12,000 and 10,000 in.-lb, respectively.

(a) Find the *margin of safety* * under the applied loading, using a circular interaction curve. Assume that the applied bending and torsional moments remain in proportion at all times.

The values of the loading ratios are

$$R_b = \frac{6,000}{12,000} = 0.50$$

$$R_s = \frac{7,000}{10,000} = 0.70$$

The margin of safety (MS) can be computed by comparing the length of the diagonal representing the applied loading with the radius of a unit circle, as shown in Fig. 11.27.

$$\text{Diagonal length} = \sqrt{0.50^2 + 0.70^2} = 0.86$$
$$\text{MS} = 1 - 0.86 = 0.14$$

This means that the tube is 14 percent overstrength with respect to the required loads.

(b) Assume that the specifications for the structure require that actual failing stresses be divided by a *factor of safety* of 2.0, to give the allowable stresses (see Sec. 15.5).

$$R_b = \frac{6,000}{6,000} = 1.0$$

$$R_s = \frac{7,000}{5,000} = 1.40$$

$$\text{MS} = 1 - \sqrt{1.0^2 + 1.40^2} = 1 - 1.72 = -0.72$$

Although the tube was just satisfactory for pure bending, it fails by 72 percent to provide the required factor of safety for *combined* loading.

EXAMPLE 11.15. Assume that in Example 11.14 (a) the actual applied bending moment remains constant, while the torsional moment may vary from zero to failure. (This could occur, for instance, in a horizontal shaft supporting dead weights.) Predict the torsional moment at which failure will occur.

Referring to Fig. 11.27, we find the ultimate value of R_s at the intersection of a horizontal line, at $R_b = 0.5$, with the circle. From Eq. (11.41)

$$R_s = \sqrt{1 - R_b^2} = \sqrt{1 - 0.50^2} = 0.866$$

This means that the tube will be able to develop 86.6 percent of its strength for pure torsion.

$$M_{s,\text{ult}} = 0.866 \times 10,000 = 8,660 \text{ in.-lb}$$

* Refers to fraction by which actual strength exceeds required strength (Sec. 15.5).

Note that, even though one-half of the tube's ultimate bending strength is utilized, the effect of the bending moment is to reduce the tube's torsional strength by only 14 percent. This is typical of combined-loading conditions involving axial and transverse (shear) stresses.

When three loading conditions act simultaneously, the condition of failure can be represented by an *interaction surface*. Figure 11.29 shows the outline of such a surface for a case of combined axial load, bending,

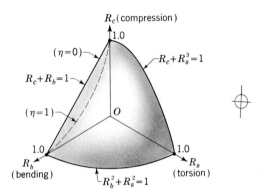

Figure 11.29. Interaction surface for combined axial load, bending, and torsion.

and torsion. Tests under the triple-loading condition will determine the shape of the surface.

It is possible to derive an interaction equation that will reduce to the proper two-term equation when any one of the three loading conditions is absent. For typical applications of this method see Ref. 39.

PROBLEMS

11.1. (See also Prob. 11.2.) Figure P11.1a shows a mechanism consisting of two pinned bars, each assumed to be absolutely rigid except for the motion permitted by the pins. A horizontal spring is attached at the midpoint. The spring is assumed to have zero force when the column is "absolutely straight," and it has a spring constant K. Using an *equilibrium analysis* similar to that for the Euler column (Sec. 11.1) find the critical load P at which the system is in equilibrium in a slightly deflected configuration. *Suggestion:* Consider equilibrium of the pin at the midpoint of the column for a small deflection of the system (Fig. P11.1b).

11.2. For the column of Prob. 11.1, use an *energy analysis* to determine the critical load P; that is, apply the law of conservation of energy by equating the loss of potential energy, associated with axial displacement of the external load P during buckling, to the gain in internal strain energy of the system (spring energy in this case). *Suggestion:* For the deflected system shown in Fig. P11.1*b*, cos α may be replaced by its series

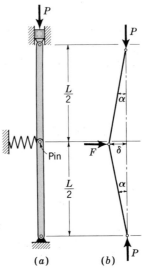

Figure P11.1

representation

$$\cos \alpha = 1 - \frac{\alpha^2}{2!} + \frac{\alpha^4}{4!} - \frac{\alpha^6}{6!} + \cdots$$

For small deflections, only the first two terms of this series need be considered. Furthermore, for small deflections $\alpha \doteq \delta/(L/2)$. (*Note:* In general, the critical load found by use of an energy analysis will not be exact unless the assumed deflected shape is the correct one; otherwise the calculated value of P_{cr} will be too high.

11.3. For an assigned tube size from Table B.3 and an assigned material from Table A.1, determine an actual column length such that $L/\rho = 70$.

(*a*) Calculate the elastic buckling stress and corresponding buckling load for the end conditions shown in cases a to d of Fig. 11.4.

(*b*) Modify answers in Part a by assuming the material to have an elastoplastic compressive stress-strain diagram in which the stress is "cut off" at the value of σ_y given in Table A.1.

11.4. *Alternate to Prob.* 11.3. Same as Prob. 11.3 except that a wide flange section is to be assigned from Table B.4, using properties computed with respect to the y axis (axis of smaller I).

11.5. Design a wood column, of square cross section, to transmit a compressive force of 10,000 lb over a length of 12 ft. Use $E = 2.0 \times 10^6$ psi.

Assume the compressive stress-strain diagram to be elastoplastic, with $\sigma_y = 6{,}000$ psi. A factor of safety of 2.0 is to be developed (that is, design the column to buckle at 20,000 lb). Design (determine minimum cross-sectional dimensions) for two different conditions of end constraint:

(*a*) Pinned-pinned.

(*b*) Elastically supported at each end, such that the effective-length coefficient is estimated to be 0.70. (*Note:* End fittings not to be designed.)

11.6. Use the column curve of Fig. 11.7*b* to design a column which must transmit an assigned compressive load P over the actual length L, from the accompanying table. The effective length coefficient is estimated to be 0.60 (nearly fixed). Stress (P/A) must not exceed 45,000 psi. A factor of safety of 1.5 is to be used, that is, column must not buckle or exceed the above stress before the load reaches 1.5P. Here "design" means to select a suitable tube size from Table B.3. (*Note:* Try to find the tube which will do the job with minimum cross-sectional area, among those listed.)

TABLE P11.6

	1	2	3	4	5	6	7
P, lb	9,200	20,000	50,000	65,000	21,000	10,000	4,500
L, in.	60	65	52	85	42	20	16

11.7. *Alternate to Prob.* 11.6. Same as Prob. 11.6 except that a thin-walled square tube is to be used. Find the mean width b and the thickness t, with the restriction that b/t must not exceed 30. *Note:* Use the "thin-walled" approximation, $I = \frac{2}{3}tb^3$. (See Prob. 7.2.) Ignore local buckling.

11.8. For an assigned tube size (larger than 2 in. OD) from Table B.3, determine an actual length such that $L/\rho = 60$.

(*a*) Determine the critical load (pounds) for pinned ends, using the column curve of Fig. 11.7.

(*b*) Repeat for completely fixed ends.

(*c*) Calculate the critical load by *erroneously* assuming that the effect of fixed ends is to multiply the pinned-end load by the coefficient of fixity of 4.0, as in the elastic case. Assume that this erroneous result had been used in actual design, together with a factor of safety of 1.5, applied to the maximum expected load. At what fraction of the maximum expected load would the column buckle?

11.9. A test of an actual column resulted in a buckling load of 38,000 lb. The length was 6 ft. Another column has a cross section of identical proportions, but all its dimensions, including length, are 20 percent greater than the tested column. At what load may the second column be expected to buckle, under similar testing conditions? (*Suggestion:* First show why the buckling stresses will be identical, then compute the ratio between cross-sectional areas.)

11.10. Assume that a compressive-stress-strain diagram has a value of $E = 29 \times 10^6$ psi, up to a stress of 36,000 psi, after which the inelastic range is approximated by a straight line having a slope corresponding to $E_t = 10 \times 10^6$ psi. Plot the Euler-Engesser curve approximately to scale.

11.11. A column is constructed from seven solid round steel bars of length L and diameter D (six are nested closely around a central bar). The bars are bound together by straps, but are not otherwise constrained as to relative motion. The ends of each bar are rounded, to simulate pinned ends. (Each bar may buckle individually.) Friction between the bars is, for safety, assumed to be zero. Derive a formula which gives the elastic buckling load P_{cr} for the entire column in terms of L, D, E.

11.12. (*a*) Express the tangent-modulus formula (11.6) in terms of the parameters used in the Ramberg-Osgood empirical stress-strain equation (1.16a), that is, E, B, and n. (*Suggestion:* First determine $d\epsilon/d\sigma$.)

(*b*) Modify Eq. (11.7) accordingly, and use it to plot the column curve for an assigned material in Table 1.1 (Sec. 1.8).

11.13. A 3-in.-OD aluminum-alloy tube ($E = 10 \times 10^6$ psi), with a wall thickness of 0.120 in., is to be used as a vertical antenna mast 40 ft high. Three equally spaced guy wires are attached to the top. Each wire makes an angle of 30 degrees with the mast. Each wire has a diameter of 0.15 in. As a preliminary design step, assume that the wires are all stressed to 20,000 psi and find the compressive load in the mast (neglect weight, wind loads, etc.). Using this load, find the spacing required (from the top) for attaching a second set of wires to prevent buckling of the top segment. Assume that the effective length coefficient is 1.0. (*Note:* In the complete design it would be necessary to include wind loads and weight of antenna and structure. Other sets of wires would also be needed.)

11.14. A 2-in.-OD aluminum-alloy tube having $t = 0.065$ in. acts as a vertical pinned-end beam of length $L = 72$ in. A compressive force $P = 1,750$ lb is being transmitted and a horizontal wind load produces a line force $q = 0.5$ lb/in. over the entire length. Calculate the maximum stress (axial plus bending) and the lateral deflection at mid-span, including secondary bending. ($E = 10 \times 10^6$ psi.)

11.15. A steel wide-flange beam, 8 by 8 by 40 (see Table B.4), with $L = 20$ ft, is simply supported at the ends and loaded with a constant line force $q_0 = 1,100$ lb/ft, acting along the y axis. (The beam bends about the x axis and is laterally supported.) Find the maximum compressive load P that can be transmitted before actual failure occurs. (Add beam weight to q_0.) Use a value of $\sigma_y = 36,000$ psi to represent column "cut-off" stress, and also the modulus of rupture in pure bending. $E = 29 \times 10^6$ psi. Use Fig. 11.19 to solve problem.

11.16. For an assigned tube size from Table B.3 made from an aluminum alloy for which the column curve is given by Fig. 11.7, find the length at which the tube will develop a buckling stress of 40,000 psi, with ends pinned. Calculate the buckling load. Then find the maximum compressive load that could be transmitted by the same column with a constant eccentricity $e = 0.20D$ (D = outside diameter). Use Fig. 11.20, with a modulus of rupture of 50,000 psi for pure bending.

11.17. Plot the Engesser column curve of Fig. 11.11b (to a larger scale) and then reduce it to represent the effect of a constant eccentricity having a value equal to one-half the core radius. Use 50,000 psi for the bending modulus of rupture σ_{b_0}. Follow the method represented by Table 11.3 and plot the eccentric column curve.

11.18. For an assigned tube size from Table B.3 assume that the basic column curve is that of Fig. 11.7b and that the modulus of rupture in bending is 50,000 psi. The column is pinned-pinned and the length is such that a buckling stress of 35,000 psi is developed (calculate L, using Fig. 11.7b). If this column is to develop a factor of safety of 1.5 with respect to actual failure, find the maximum load P that may be applied (divide P_{cr} by FS). Now assume that the tube is found to have a sinusoidal eccentricity (crookedness), the maximum value of which is given by $e = 0.25D$ (where D is the outside diameter). Determine the reduced value for the maximum axial load that may be applied, if the 1.5 factor of safety is to be maintained.

11.19. (a) For an assigned wide-flange section from Table B.4, calculate the local buckling stress of the web when the member is used as a column. Assume $E = 29 \times 10^6$ psi for steel. For simplicity, assume that b is the depth of the section, ignore the edge constraint afforded by the flanges, and assume elastic action. The answer should show that the elastic buckling stress is well above the yield point for structural steel.

(b) Using the same assumptions, find the web thickness at which the local buckling stress (elastic) will be equal to a yield stress of 36,000 psi.

(c) Determine the elastic buckling stress for the web of case b above, when the edges of the web are assumed to be completely fixed.

11.20. (a) Derive an equation for the buckling load of thin-walled square steel tubes having the same wall thickness t_1 but having different widths b.

(b) Assume $E = 29 \times 10^6$ psi, up to $\sigma_y = 36,000$ psi (elastoplastic), $K = 3.62$, $t_1 = 0.020$ in. Plot a curve of local failing load P (lb) against b, for a range of b up to 12 in. (The failure curve will be the lower of two curves, one for buckling and one for $\sigma = 36,000$ psi.)

(c) Plot a failing-load curve for square tubes of the same width, $b_1 = 4.0$ in., but having different thicknesses. Plot P against t.

11.21. For the flat-sided corrugation of Example 11.10, assume that the material is carbon steel, for which $E = 29 \times 10^6$ psi, $\sigma_y = 36,000$ psi (elastoplastic).

(a) Find the value of b/t at which $\sigma_{cr} = \sigma_y$; this determines b.

(b) Calculate the maximum value of L_e/ρ at which $\sigma_E = \sigma_y$.

(c) Calculate ρ in terms of b; that is, evaluate k in the equation $\rho = kb$. (ρ will be the same as for a square tube, $b \times b$, treating b as the mean width.)

(d) Let $L = 10$ ft. Design a corrugation that will develop a buckling stress equal to σ_y ($= 36,000$ psi), both as an Euler column (pinned end) and in local buckling. Assuming that a factor of safety of 2.0 is required, determine the allowable compressive load per inch (q).

11.22. A built-up steel I beam has a web 8 in. deep and 0.080 in. thick. Assuming elastic shear buckling and simply supported edges, calculate the critical shear stress (use $K_c = 4.8$ from Table 11.4). At what actual transverse-shear load (V) will the web begin to buckle? $E = 29 \times 10^6$ psi. Repeat, assuming all edges fixed.

11.23. A thin-walled round steel tube has a mean diameter of 6 in. and a wall thickness of 0.020. Find the buckling stress for pure bending, and calculate the bending moment at which the tube will buckle. Assume elastic action ($E = 29 \times 10^6$ psi). Use formulas for thin-walled tubes (Table B.1).

11.24. A tube of aluminum alloy has a mean diameter of 4 in. and a wall thickness of 0.20 in. Calculate the torsional moment at which it can be expected to buckle, using the upper curve of Fig. 11.24.

11.25. A 12- by 1-in. wooden plank is set up edgewise as a simple beam, 9 ft long. The ends are compelled to remain vertical, but there is no other constraint.

(a) Find the value of the uniformly distributed load q (lb/in.) at which the beam will buckle laterally. (Assume that $E = 1.5 \times 10^6$ psi, $\nu = 0.30$.)

(b) Find the total concentrated load that can be applied at the center (neglect dead weight).

11.26. For an assigned tube from Table B.3, assume that the material is steel (elastoplastic) with $E = 29 \times 10^6$ psi, $\sigma_y = 36,000$ psi, and $\nu = 0.30$. Assume that $\tau_y = 0.6\sigma_y$.

(a) Determine the allowable buckling stresses from Eqs. (11.32) and (11.34), for bending and torsion, respectively, using $K = 0.60$ in each case.

(b) Calculate the failing moments for pure bending (M_{b_0}) and pure torsion (M_{t_0}), respectively.

(c) Using a circular interaction curve, find the values of M_b and M_t at which the tube will fail, if a combined loading of $M_t = 0.40 M_b$ is acting.

Note: The values of D/t in Table B.3 are for outside diameter. Check the difference in buckling stress obtained by using mean diameter.

11.27. Using the interaction curve of Fig. 11.28, predict the simultaneous values of compressive load P and torsional moment M at which a certain thin-walled cylinder will fail, for the following conditions (the material is stainless steel):

$$M = 0.212P \qquad \frac{D}{t} = 800$$

$$D_{av} = 16 \text{ in.} \qquad E = 28 \times 10^6 \text{ psi}$$

$$t = 0.020 \text{ in.} \qquad \sigma_y = 75,000 \text{ psi}$$

Use Eqs. (11.32) and (11.34) for buckling stresses in compression and torsion, respectively, with $K = 0.6$ in each case.

Chapter 12

Joints and Fittings

12.1 Classification of joints

The types of joints used in structures can be roughly classified as follows:

1. Riveted, bolted, pinned, screwed, nailed
2. Bonded (glued, brazed, soldered)
3. Welded (fusion, spot, seam, diffusion)

In class 1, the forces are transmitted through intermediate members (such as bolts, rivets, and pins) by compression on the contacting surfaces. Such joints require holes through the primary members; these cause a loss of efficiency (unless material is added locally).

In class 2, the members are joined by means of a bonding agent, without the necessity of drilling holes.

In class 3, the bond is made by applying heat and pressure sufficient to establish true interatomic bonding; that is, the metal itself is joined.

The detailed analysis and design of joints are largely governed by codes and accepted practices, which vary considerably between industries, cities, states, and countries. Therefore no attempt will be made to include such information here, except by way of illustration.

12.2 Strength of rivets, bolts, and pins

The primary function of these elements is to transmit shear forces. Rivets and pins are not usually intended to transmit tension forces; *bolts* are generally used for this purpose.* (See Fig. 12.3.)

The *shear strength* of rivets, bolts, and pins is based directly on tests in which the conditions of a joint are closely simulated. The ultimate shear stress for a rivet, bolt, or pin is defined as

$$\tau_{\text{ult}} = \frac{P_s}{A} \tag{12.1}$$

where P_s is the maximum transverse force developed (in a test) by a cross section, and A is the nominal cross-sectional area of rivet, bolt, or pin. A typical test setup for *double shear* is shown in Fig. 12.1. In this case

Figure 12.1. Double-shear test of rivet.

$P_s = P/2$. The shear stress determined in such a test is, from Eq. (12.1), the average value. It is somewhat affected by the details of the test setup. (For example, the test fixture should be made with close clearances, from a material harder than that of the specimen.)

The transverse-shear strength is found by multiplying the cross-sectional area of the element by this shear stress:

$$P_s = \tau_{\text{ult}} A \tag{12.2}$$

The tensile strength of rivets depends on the size and perfection of the rivet head. Since this can vary considerably in practice, rivets are not generally used to transmit direct tension loads.

The actual *tensile strength of bolts* depends on the ultimate tensile strength of the material and the minimum cross-sectional area at the root of the thread:

$$P_t = \sigma_{\text{ult}} A_{\min}$$

* An exception is made (in building codes) for rivets in shelf angles and brackets used in building construction.

In some cases the head or nut may not be capable of developing the full tensile strength of the bolt; that is, the head may "shear off" if too thin.

For design purposes, tables of bolt strengths have been compiled in various specifications and handbooks. Most of these tables (except for aerospace design) are based on reduced allowable stresses obtained by dividing the ultimate tensile and shear stress by an arbitrary factor of safety, which may have a value in the order of 2 to 4. Because of this, rather large discrepancies may be found between various specifications.

Since this text is concerned primarily with the *actual* strength of elements, the bolt strengths of Appendix Table A.4 have been based on

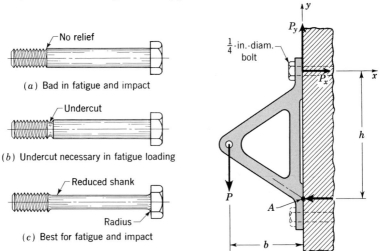

(a) Bad in fatigue and impact

(b) Undercut necessary in fatigue loading

(c) Best for fatigue and impact

Figure 12.2. Design of tension bolts.   *Figure 12.3. Example of combined shear and tension on bolt.*

actual material properties. To comply with any particular specification, the values must be reduced to correspond to the reduced allowable or working stress specified. Figures 12.2 and 12.3 show typical bolts and a typical application.

The nominal tensile strength of bolts is based on unidirectional (static) loading and is therefore not safe for varying loads. For fluctuating or dynamic loading conditions, special bolts should be used, in which stress concentration is reduced to a minimum, as shown in Fig. 12.2b. The fatigue strength of bolts can be estimated by the methods of Chap. 14.

For combined shear and tension, a circular interaction curve can be used:

$$R_a{}^2 + R_s{}^2 = 1$$

where $$R_a = \frac{\text{tension load}}{\text{ultimate tension load}}$$

and $$R_s = \frac{\text{shear load}}{\text{ultimate shear load}}$$

EXAMPLE 12.1.   The nominal cross-sectional area of a $\frac{1}{4}$-in.-diameter bolt is given in Appendix Table A.4 as 0.0491 in.[2] For low-carbon steel the ultimate shear stress given in this table is 35,000 psi. Therefore the shear strength of the bolt is

$$P_s = \tau_{ult}A = 35,000 \times 0.0491 = 1{,}718 \text{ lb}$$

The tensile strength of the $\frac{1}{4}$-in. bolt is determined in Appendix Table A.4 as

$$P_t = \sigma_{ult}A_{min} = 55,000 \times 0.0326 = 1{,}793 \text{ lb}$$

EXAMPLE 12.2.   For the fitting shown in Fig. 12.3, predict the load P at which the bolt will fail, if $b = 6$ in. and $h = 4$ in. Assume $\sigma_{ult} = 55,000$ psi, $\tau_{ult} = 35,000$ psi. The fitting is shown as a free body.

The lower bolt will be neglected entirely, since it will not resist any of the compression load and is statically indeterminate with respect to vertical (shearing) load. The center of resistance of the compressive force is conservatively assumed to be at A, as indicated.

Taking moments about A (positive clockwise), for $\Sigma M_A = 0$,

$$-Pb + P_x h = 0$$

$$P_x = P\frac{b}{h} = P\frac{6}{4} = 1.5P$$

and for $\Sigma P_y = 0$,

$$P_y = P$$

The failing values for these axial and shear loads are found from the previous example as

$$P_t = 1{,}793 \text{ lb} \qquad P_s = 1{,}718 \text{ lb}$$

Using a circular interaction curve, we obtain

$$\left(\frac{1.5P}{1,793}\right)^2 + \left(\frac{P}{1,718}\right)^2 = 1$$

from which,

$$P = 982 \text{ lb}$$

Let us (erroneously) find the failing load by considering each loading condition as independent of the other. For tensile failure of the bolt, $P_x = P_t$ and

$$P = \frac{P_t}{1.5} = \frac{1,793}{1.5} = 1{,}195 \text{ lb}$$

For shear failure,

$$P = P_s = 1{,}718 \text{ lb}$$

Note that the lower of these two values would overestimate the strength by a factor $\frac{1195}{982}$, or about 22 percent.

If a factor of safety of 2.0 were required against failure, the maximum load that could actually be applied would be $\frac{982}{2} = 491$ lb. (See Sec. 15.5.)

12.3 Analysis of single-pin joints

Several types of single-pin joints are shown in Fig. 12.4. The *single shear* type (*a*) is so designated because the pin or rivet would have to be sheared off through only one plane. In the *double-shear* type (*b*), two shear planes are available, thus doubling the shearing strength of the joint. In type *c*, a still larger number of shearing planes is involved. Type *a* has an eccentric loading and will tend to bend so as to align the loads when in tension. This causes additional bending stresses which are generally alleviated by plastic action before failure occurs. This situation is

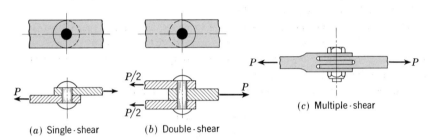

Figure 12.4. Types of single-pin joints.

bad for fatigue, however (see Chap. 14). In compression, this type of joint tends to cause local buckling unless it is well supported. The double-shear and multiple-shear joints shown are noneccentric.

EXAMPLE 12.3. In Fig. 12.4*c* assume that the bolt is $\frac{1}{4}$ in. in diameter and is made from steel having an ultimate tensile stress of 125,000 psi. Calculate the load P at which the bolt will fail in shear.

From Appendix Table A.4, the single-shear strength is found to be 3,680 lb. Failure of the bolt would require shearing along four different cross-sectional planes. Therefore

$$P = 4 \times 3,680 = 14,720 \text{ lb}$$

Figure 12.5 indicates the types of failure that can occur in a bolted or riveted joint. In elementary fitting analysis, stress-concentration factors are neglected (assumed to have been alleviated by plastic flow). Typical formulas for the failing strength P are as follows:

For *tension failure* (*a*),

$$P_t = (b - D)t\sigma_{\text{ult}} \qquad (12.3a)$$

For *shear failure* (*b*),

$$P_s = \frac{\pi}{4} D^2 \tau_{\text{ult}} \qquad (12.3b)$$

For *bearing failure* (c),

$$P_{br} = Dt\sigma_{br} \tag{12.3c}$$

For *tear-out failure* (d),

$$P_{to} = 2a\tau_{ult} \tag{12.3d}$$

where σ_{ult} = ultimate tensile stress for fitting material

σ_{br} = ultimate bearing stress

σ_{ult} = ultimate shear stress for bolt, rivet, or pin, in Eq. (12.3b)

= ultimate shear stress for fitting material, in Eq. (12.3d)

The bearing ("crushing") type of failure is actually a form of plastic flow under compression. The value of σ_{br} is generally obtained from

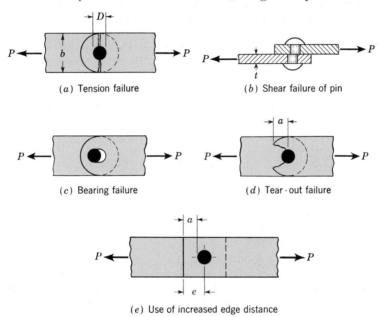

(a) Tension failure   (b) Shear failure of pin

(c) Bearing failure   (d) Tear-out failure

(e) Use of increased edge distance

Figure 12.5. Types of joint failure.

tests. In steel construction the allowable bearing stress for pins, power-driven rivets, and close-fitting bolts is on the order of 24,000 psi for single shear and 30,000 psi for double shear, as compared with an allowable stress of 20,000 psi for tension and 13,500 psi for shear. In aerospace construction the ultimate bearing stress is specified in detail for each material and is also affected by the edge-distance ratio. Tests have shown that the ratio of rivet diameter to sheet thickness also affects bearing failure, high values of D/t tending to reduce the allowable bearing stress.

In view of the rather arbitrary nature of specified ultimate bearing stresses, an accurate analysis is not possible. For approximate design purposes, the ultimate bearing stress may be assumed to be 50 percent greater than the ultimate tensile stress.

Equation (12.3d) is a semiempirical formula that represents a complex (tear-out) type of failure. The value of a to be used should be based on tests; it will usually be somewhat greater than the distance from the edge of the hole to the end of fitting. This type of failure can be avoided by using an edge distance of 1.75D or greater (see Fig. 12.5d). When smaller edge distances are used, the value of a may be safely taken as the distance from the edge of the hole to the edge of the sheet, as indicated in Fig. 12.5e.

For multiple-shear connections, the above formulas must be modified to account for the greater number of elements involved in failure. For example, the tension load from Eq. (12.3a) is multiplied by 2 when applied to the joint shown in Fig. 12.4c, because two lugs must fail in tension. The shear-failing load from Eq. (12.3b) is multiplied by 4.

EXAMPLE 12.4.   A joint such as that shown in Fig. 12.5e has the following dimensions:

$$b = 1.0 \text{ in.} \qquad D = \tfrac{1}{4} \text{ in.} \qquad t = \tfrac{1}{8} \text{ in.} \qquad e = \tfrac{7}{16} \text{ in.}$$

Assume the following values for material properties for both sheet and rivet:

$$\sigma_{\text{ult}} = 60{,}000 \text{ psi} \qquad \tau_{\text{ult}} = 36{,}000 \text{ psi} \qquad \sigma_{\text{br}} = 90{,}000 \text{ psi}$$

The load that will cause failure will be the lowest of the following values:

$$P_t = (b - D)t\sigma_{\text{ult}} = (1 - 0.25) \times 0.125 \times 60{,}000 = 5{,}625 \text{ lb}$$

$$P_s = \frac{\pi}{4} D^2 \tau_{\text{ult}} = \frac{\pi}{4} \times 0.25^2 \times 36{,}000 = 1{,}770 \text{ lb}$$

$$P_{\text{br}} = Dt\sigma_{\text{br}} = 0.25 \times 0.125 \times 90{,}000 = 2{,}810 \text{ lb}$$

$$P_{\text{to}} = 2a\tau_{\text{ult}} = 2 \times (0.438 - 0.125) \times 36{,}000 = 22{,}500 \text{ lb}$$

The joint can therefore be expected to fail at an applied load of approximately 1,770 lb, by shearing the rivet. Obviously, the joint could be made stronger by increasing the rivet diameter. This would reduce the value of P_t. In this case, the optimum diameter would be reached when $P_t = P_s$ (see next section).

12.4 Analysis of continuous joints

Structures made from plates or sheet metal employ continuous joints, three types of which are shown in Fig. 12.6. The analysis can be made on a unit-width basis, but it is more convenient to use a base width b representing the distance within which the rivet pattern repeats itself. (In single-row joints this is equal to the *pitch* p, as shown in Fig. 12.6a.)

Equations (12.3) can be applied to continuous joints by treating P as the load over the base width ($P = qb$). In multiple-row joints, the load per row can be estimated by assuming that each rivet resists a load proportional to its diameter or to its bearing area, whichever gives the lower load per rivet. In the staggered joint (Fig. 12.6c), the diagonal distance d must be great enough to prevent tension failure along a diagonal line through the rivet holes. (Various codes have arbitrary requirements of this type.)

The *efficiency of a joint* can be expressed as

$$\eta = \frac{\text{failing load of joint}}{\text{failing load of base element}} \qquad (a)$$

For a sheet-metal joint, this value is found by using the *smallest* load determined from Eqs. (12.3). For the base element, the failing load, in tension, will be equal to

$$P_0 = bt\sigma_{\text{ult}} \qquad (b)$$

where t is the thickness of the thinner sheet.

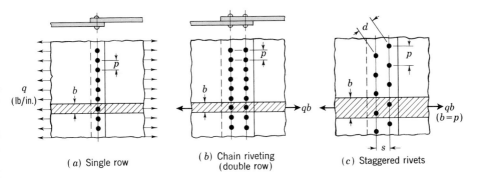

(*a*) Single row   (*b*) Chain riveting (double row)   (*c*) Staggered rivets

Figure 12.6. Different types of continuous joints.

For example, if failure of a single-row joint were to occur by tensile failure between rivets [Eq. (12.3a)], the efficiency would be

$$\eta = \frac{P}{P_0} = \frac{p - D}{p} = 1 - \frac{D}{p} \qquad (c)$$

Obviously, the tensile efficiency is improved by using smaller rivets or by placing them farther apart. In either case, a limit is reached when the rivets begin to fail in shear or the sheet fails in bearing. This indicates that there must be an *optimum design* in which maximum possible efficiency is obtained. The optimum proportions between p, D, and t can be found by making P equal for all three types of failure. (Tear-out is omitted, because it can be avoided by allowing sufficient edge distance.) This type of design is sometimes referred to as *balanced*.

To determine the optimum proportions, let us start with Eqs. (12.3b) and (12.3c), representing shear failure of rivets and bearing failure of the sheet.

Equating the values of P gives

$$\frac{\pi}{4} D^2 \tau_{ult} = Dt\sigma_{br}$$

from which,

$$\left(\frac{D}{t}\right)_{opt} = \frac{4}{\pi} \frac{\sigma_{br}}{\tau_{ult}} \qquad (d)$$

The allowable stresses specified for bearing are generally two to three times the value specified for shear. This means that the optimum rivet diameter will be in the range of about 2.5 to 4.0 times the thickness of the (thinner) sheet.

Now equate tension strength [Eq. (12.3a)] to bearing strength [Eq. (12.3c)]:

$$(p - D)t\sigma_{ult} = Dt\sigma_{br} \qquad (e)$$

from which,

$$\left(\frac{p}{D}\right)_{opt} = 1 + \frac{\sigma_{br}}{\sigma_{ult}} \qquad (f)$$

Since σ_{br} is usually specified as having a value from 1.5 to 2.0 times the ultimate tensile stress, the above formula indicates that the optimum rivet spacing (for a single-row joint) is between 2.5 and 3.0 times the rivet diameter.

If optimum rivet spacing is assumed, as in Eq. (f), the maximum possible efficiency for a single-row joint is found by substituting expression (f) in Eq. (c), giving

$$\eta_{max} = \frac{1}{1 + \sigma_{ult}/\sigma_{br}} \qquad (g)$$

This shows that for a single-row joint the maximum possible efficiency will generally lie between 60 and 67 percent.

For a given value of q (load per inch), the required thickness of the optimum joint will be

$$t_{min} = \frac{q}{\eta\sigma_{ult}} \qquad (h)$$

Such a joint will require an increase in the weight of the sheet, over the theoretical minimum, by 50 to 67 percent. This is unacceptable where weight reduction is important, as in aerospace structures. Various ways of improving riveted-joint efficiency are used, the two most important being the use of multirows (two or more) and local thickening (or upsetting) of the sheet or member.

For the *two-row joint* (Fig. 12.6b or c), the load may be assumed to be divided equally between the two rows. Although the total tension load must pass between rivets of the first row [Eq. (12.3a)], the load to be carried by the rivets in shear and bearing is cut in half. In Eqs. (12.3b) and (12.3c) the value of P is therefore changed to $P/2$.

In deriving the optimum proportions, Eq. (c) is unchanged, but Eq. (f) becomes

$$\left(\frac{p}{D}\right)_{opt} = 1 + 2\frac{\sigma_{br}}{\sigma_{ult}} \qquad (i)$$

Substituting this in Eq. (*c*) gives, for the double-row joint,

$$\eta_{max} = \frac{1}{1 + \frac{1}{2}(\sigma_{ult}/\sigma_{br})} \tag{j}$$

For a range of σ_{br}/σ_{ult} of from 1.5 to 2.0, the best possible efficiency will be between 75 and 80 percent.

Many other arrangements of rivets are possible, and the above figures can be improved somewhat, but in general they represent typical values for actual efficiencies of riveted or bolted joints in ductile material.

If upsetting, machining, or chemical milling is possible (and economical), the problem can be solved by increasing the thickness at the point where the holes

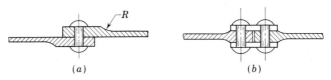

(*a*)   (*b*)

Figure 12.7. Method of improving joint efficiency.

must be drilled. Two examples are shown in Fig. 12.7. If fairly large fillets are used, such joints can be made 100 percent efficient, for relatively little extra weight.

EXAMPLE 12.5. Using the same material properties as in Example 12.4, find the optimum rivet diameter D and spacing p for a single-row, single-shear joint such as that shown in Fig. 12.6. Determine the joint efficiency. Let $t = \frac{1}{8}$ in. for both sheets. Assume that failure by tear-out is prevented by use of adequate edge distance.

From Eq. (*d*),

$$\left(\frac{D}{t}\right)_{opt} = \frac{4}{\pi}\frac{\sigma_{br}}{\tau_{ult}} = \frac{4 \times 90,000}{\pi \times 36,000} = 3.18$$
$$D_{opt} = 3.18 \times 0.125 = 0.398 \text{ in.}$$

From Eq. (*f*),

$$\left(\frac{p}{D}\right)_{opt} = 1 + \frac{\sigma_{br}}{\sigma_{ult}} = 1 + \frac{90,000}{60,000} = 2.5$$
$$p_{opt} = 2.5 \times 0.398 = 0.995 \text{ in.}$$

From Eq. (*g*),

$$\eta_{max} = \frac{1}{1 + \sigma_{ult}/\sigma_{br}} = \frac{1}{1 + \frac{2}{3}} = 0.60$$

EXAMPLE 12.6. A double-row, single-shear continuous joint is to be designed to transmit an actual distributed tension force $q = 2,800$ lb/in. Assume that, in order to provide a factor of safety of 3.0, the joint must not fail at less than $3 \times 2,800 = 8,400$ lb/in. Using the same material properties as in Example 12.4, find the required sheet thickness, rivet diameter, and rivet spacing for maximum efficiency.

From Eq. (j),

$$\eta_{max} = \frac{1}{1 + \frac{1}{2} \times \frac{2}{3}} = 0.75$$

From Eq. (h),

$$t_{min} = \frac{q}{\eta \sigma_{ult}} = \frac{8,400}{0.75 \times 60,000} = 0.187 \text{ in.}$$

From Eq. (d),

$$\left(\frac{D}{t}\right)_{opt} = \frac{4 \times 90,000}{\pi \times 36,000} = 3.18$$

$$D = 3.18 \times 0.187 = 0.595 \text{ in.}$$

From Eq. (i),

$$\left(\frac{p}{D}\right)_{opt} = 1 + 2 \times \frac{90,000}{60,000} = 4.0$$

$$p = 4.0 \times 0.595 = 2.38 \text{ in.}$$

In actual design the sheet thickness would be selected as the closest (larger) gauge available. The optimum diameter would then be recomputed and the closest actual rivet size chosen. The required pitch would be computed and rounded off to a practical dimension. As a final check, the strength of the redesigned joint should be computed for each mode of failure, using the actual dimensions.

The foregoing methods of analysis are applicable to highly ductile materials and "static" loading. In the elastic range, a hole or notch will cause *stress concentration*, which increases the local stress considerably above the average value. Such effects are alleviated by plastic action. For materials having relatively low elongation (roughly less than 10 percent) the effects of stress concentration must be taken into account (see Chap. 13).

If the loading fluctuates or reverses during service, the effects of *fatigue* must be introduced in the analysis (Chap. 14). *A combination of stress concentration and fatigue may greatly lower the failing strength.*

12.5 *Load distribution in riveted and bolted joints*

When more than two rivets (or bolts) are in line with the load, the distribution of loads is quite complex. If the members being joined were "infinitely stiff," a given relative displacement δ would cause an equal displacement of each pair of holes (Fig. 12.8a). It would then be satisfactory to divide the loads equally between rivets (if all are of the same size) or to proportion the loads by rivet areas (assuming that rivets yield in shear).

If the stresses remain in the elastic range and if deflections are considered, the situation will be similar to that of Fig. 12.8b. Because of the loads transferred by the rivets, the stresses in each portion will decrease from one end to the other (σ_1 is the highest stress in the sketch). But the highest-stressed segments will be opposite the lowest-stressed ones, as indicated. Consequently the relative motion (slip) is greatest at the end rivets. This means that the end rivets must transmit shear loads greater than the average, while those near the center transmit loads lower than the average.

If sufficient plastic strain of sheets or rivets (or both) can take place before failure occurs, the distribution of loads will approach that for case *a* of Fig. 12.8. This is usually a safe assumption for unidirectional loading of ductile materials, but it can be unsafe for relatively brittle materials or for repeated loading

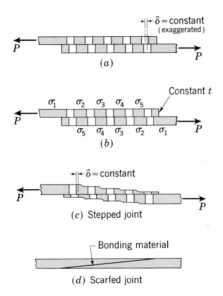

(a)

(b)

(c) Stepped joint

(d) Scarfed joint

Figure 12.8. Distribution of loads in multiple-row joints.

(fatigue). One way to equalize the stresses is to reduce the sheet thickness in steps, as shown in Fig. 12.8c. (Adequate fillets must be used at the steps.) The *scarfed joint* (*d*), widely used in timber construction, is ideal from this viewpoint.

An analysis to determine the elastic stress distribution in the type *b* joint can be made by writing the equations for the relative deflections as a function of the loads transmitted by the rivets. (See Ref. 19, Ex. 28.7.) This is a statically indeterminate problem involving the solution of several simultaneous equations. High ductility of the material tends to eliminate any need for such analysis for unidirectional loading.

12.6 Strength of rivet (or bolt) groups

Figure 12.9 shows a fitting consisting of two steel plates which transmit a force P to a wood beam through three bolts of equal size. In Fig. 12.9a the line of action of the force goes through the centroid of the bolt cross-sectional area. If the relatively small deformation of the fitting plates is neglected, each bolt will produce the same amount of deformation in the wood. The load transmitted by each bolt will therefore be the same, and the center of resistance will fall on the line of loading. Actually, the resistance offered by the wood will tend to be proportional to the projected area of the bolt, which is proportional to the bolt diameter. Therefore, if the bolts are not all the same size, the center of resistance should be determined by the centroid of bolt diameters, so far as bearing is con-

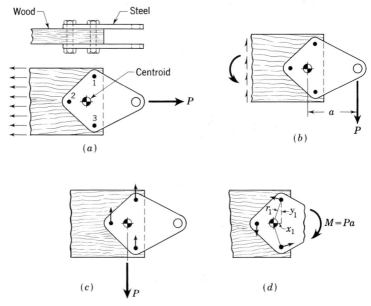

Figure 12.9. Analysis of bolt or rivet groups.

cerned. The failing load for bolt shear should be based on the bolt cross-sectional areas. For maximum efficiency, the fitting should be designed so that the line of action of the applied load goes through the center of resistance.

In Fig. 12.9*b* the line of loading is displaced from the center of resistance by an eccentricity *a*. The displacement of the fitting may be represented by two separate types of deformation, *translation* and *rotation*, as shown in Fig. 12.9*c* and *d*. The bolt loads corresponding to translation may be found as described for case *a*. For rotation, the fitting is assumed to rotate about some point such that the resulting forces represent a pure moment. This point is usually taken as the centroid determined for translation. If deflections of the fitting itself are again neglected, the displacement of each bolt will be proportional to its radial distance from the center of rotation and will be normal to the radius line.

For angular rotation ϕ (radians) about a given point, the displacement δ_i of each bolt will be proportional to its radius r_i from that point. The bolt force P_i will be assumed to be proportional to the displacement and to the bolt cross-sectional area:

$$P_i = CA_i\delta_i \tag{a}$$

Substituting $\delta_i = \phi r_i$ gives

$$P_i = C\phi A_i r_i \tag{b}$$

Therefore

$$M_i = C\phi A_i r_i^2$$

The total moment is

$$M = C\phi\Sigma A_i r_i^2$$

from which

$$\phi = \frac{M}{C\Sigma A_i r_i^2}$$

Substituting ϕ in (b),

$$P_i = M\frac{A_i r_i}{\Sigma A_i r_i^2} \tag{12.4}$$

If all areas are equal, A_i cancels out.

Since $r_i^2 = x_i^2 + y_i^2$ (see Fig. 12.9d), the following equation can be used to simplify the calculations:

$$\Sigma A_i r_i^2 = \Sigma A_i x_i^2 + \Sigma A_i y_i^2$$

The forces computed from Eq. (12.4) will act normal to the radius r_i, as shown in Fig. 12.9d. The total force on each rivet is then found by vector addition of the forces from the axial load (Fig. 12.9c) and the moment (Fig. 12.9d). Note that, for a fitting such as that shown in Fig. 12.9b, the bolts closest to the line of action of the force will be the most heavily loaded.

If rivets were used and ideal plastic action were to be assumed, every rivet might be expected to develop a certain (limit) load before complete failure of the fitting occurred. The most logical way to account for plastic action is to start with the elastic analysis and, after finding the load on the most highly loaded rivet, increase the external loading until this load reaches its limiting value. At this point the rivet reaction can be replaced by its *limit load*, after which the external loading is again increased, and so on until maximum loading is attained.

EXAMPLE 12.7.   In Fig. 12.9b. assume that the two vertically spaced bolts are 5 in. apart and that the third bolt is 3 in. to the left of the other two. All bolts have the same diameter. Let $a = 6$ in. and $P = 1,000$ lb. Find the load in each bolt.

The centroid of the three bolt areas can be found by determining the centroid of the first two bolts (on the center line) and then locating the centroid between this point (having a value of $2A$) and the third bolt (value of A).* It will lie on the center line, 1 in. to the left of the vertical line joining the two end bolts. In

---

* This simple method can be applied progressively to any number of bolts, each time locating the centroid by inverse proportion between the "weight" of the two centroids being connected.

Fig. 12.9d, $x_1 = 1$ in., $y_1 = 2.50$ in. Then

$$r_1 = \sqrt{1^2 + 2.5^2} = 2.69 \text{ in.} \qquad r_2 = 2 \text{ in.} \qquad r_3 = 2.69 \text{ in.}$$

For direct loading (Fig. 12.9c),

$$P_1 = P_2 = P_3 = 333 \text{ lb}$$

For rotational loading (Fig. 12.9d),

$$M = Pa = 1{,}000 \times 6 = 6{,}000 \text{ in.-lb}$$

Since areas A_i are all equal, Eq. (12.4) becomes

$$P_i = M \frac{r_i}{\Sigma r_i^2}$$

$$\Sigma r_i^2 = 2.69^2 + 2^2 + 2.69^2 = 18.50$$

$$P_1 = 6{,}000 \times \frac{2.69}{18.50} = 872 \text{ lb}$$

$$P_2 = 6{,}000 \times \frac{2}{18.50} = 650 \text{ lb}$$

$$P_3 = P_1 = 872 \text{ lb}$$

These three forces (from moment M) must be added vectorially to those determined for the force P. For bolt 2, direct algebraic addition is possible:

$$P_2 = 333 - 650 = -317 \text{ lb} \qquad \text{(acting down)}$$

For bolts 1 and 3 the resultant load will be equal in magnitude, although not the same in direction.

From similar triangles, the horizontal component of the M load for bolt 1 is

$$P_{1x} = 872 \times \frac{y_1}{r_1} = 872 \times \frac{2.5}{2.69} = 810 \text{ lb} \qquad \text{(to left)}$$

$$P_{1y} = 872 \times \frac{x_1}{r_1} = 872 \times \frac{1}{2.69} = 324 \text{ lb} \qquad \text{(up)}$$

The total components of P_1 are therefore

$$P_{1x} = 810$$
$$P_{1y} = 333 + 324 = 657$$

from which, $\qquad P_1 = \sqrt{810^2 + 657^2} = 1{,}043 \text{ lb}$

From this result, it can be seen that bolt 2 is considerably underloaded. For the most efficient use of the bolt strength, this bolt should be moved farther to the left until its loading becomes equal to that of the other two.

12.7 Strength of bonded joints

The term "bonded," as used here, includes joints in which the force is transmitted through a bonding agent consisting of a material that is different from the base material. The most common example is the *glued joint* in wood. Metal members are bonded together by such techniques as *soldering, brazing,* and nonmetallic *adhesives.*

The basic principle common to all such joints is the transmission of the force primarily by shearing action, through a thin layer of the bonding material. The materials used may be much weaker than the base material, but if sufficient contact area is provided, the shearing strength will be adequate. The nature of the bond developed in such joints is chemically complex and will not be discussed here. Various kinds of bonded joints are illustrated in Fig. 12.10.

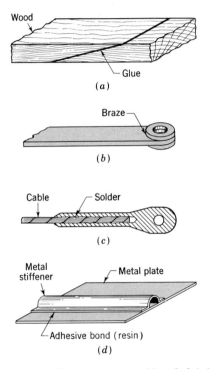

Figure 12.10. Various types of bonded joints.

In the *mitered, or scarfed, joint* (a) shear stress is low because of the flat angle used. As previously noted, this type of joint is ideal with respect to stress concentration. If properly made, such a joint will be 100 percent efficient; that is, failure will occur through the base material.

The *brazed joint* shown in Fig. 12.10b illustrates one way of increasing the bearing area of a fitting. *Soldered joints* are identical in principle to brazed joints. Figure 12.10c shows how a cable can be efficiently attached to a fitting by soldering. Figure 12.10d shows an application of *adhesive bonding* in which a stiffener is attached to a thin plate.

In calculating the strength of a bonded joint (of the types shown in Fig. 12.10), the procedure is simply to determine the area that would have to be sheared if failure were to occur in the bonding material. This is multiplied by the ultimate shear stress of the bonding material, as obtained from tests (preferably simulating the particular application involved).

For eccentric loading on a bonded joint, the centroid and polar moment of the bonded area are determined and used in the manner described for riveted joints (Sec. 12.6).

Bonded joints exhibit a tendency to develop increased stresses at the two ends of the joint, as described for rivets in Sec. 12.6. Theoretically, the elastic stress distribution tends to look approximately like that shown in Fig. 12.11a (see Ref. 38).

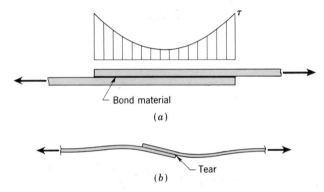

Bond material

(a)

Tear

(b)

Figure 12.11. Stresses in bonded joints.

Eccentric joints, like that shown in Fig. 12.11, will tend to bend and thereby produce a tensile stress at the edges of the joint. This can cause a progressive (tearing) failure.

The use of nonmetallic bonding agents in metal joints has many attractive features, but because of the various secondary factors involved and the difficulty of inspection, tests of full-sized parts should be conducted, adequate factors of safety should be used, and quality-control procedures and tests should be required.

12.8 Welded joints

The welding of metals involves bringing two surfaces into contact at such temperature and pressure that interatomic bonds are established, thereby forming a continuous metallic path for the transmission of forces. The blacksmith welds iron by heating it to a temperature somewhat short of the melting point and then supplying the necessary pressure by means of hammer blows. In *fusion welding* (gas or thermit), arc welding, and electron-beam welding, the metal is actually melted. Spot (resistance) welding requires pressure, but the primary action is thermal. *Diffusion bonding* is a process in which two metals become welded under relatively low pressure and temperature. If the surfaces are extremely clean (no oxides or other impurities) the surfaces in contact virtually disappear, and a solid metallic joint results. *Molecular deposition* gives similar results.

Because of the long history of welding, a tremendous amount of information is available. (For detailed information, see publications of the American Welding Society, American Society for Testing Materials, and American Society for Mechanical Engineers, welding magazines, publications of equipment manufacturers, and so on.)

The general principles involved in calculating the strength of welds are quite simple: Use the minimum cross-sectional area through which failure can occur, together with the specified value for the allowable stress (or load per spot). For types *a* and *b* of Fig. 12.12, the minimum cross-sectional area is arbitrarily specified as that corresponding to the thickness of the thinner sheet.

For fillet welds in shear, the minimum cross-sectional area is arbitrarily measured as shown in Fig. 12.13 (throat = 0.707 weld size). For structural steel, the

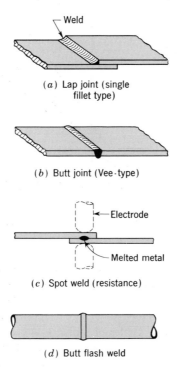

(*a*) Lap joint (single fillet type)

(*b*) Butt joint (Vee-type)

←—Electrode

←—Melted metal

(*c*) Spot weld (resistance)

(*d*) Butt flash weld

Figure 12.12. Various types of welds.

allowable shear stress is specified by various building and civil-engineering codes as ranging from approximately 13,000 to 15,000 psi.

In aerospace design, where the factor of safety is included in the applied loads, the ultimate shear and tensile stresses are specified as approximately twice as great as in civil practice. (A typical value for allowable shear stress, from Ref. 39, is 32,000 psi for low-carbon steel.)

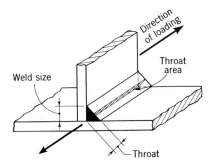

Figure 12.13. Shear strength of a fillet weld.

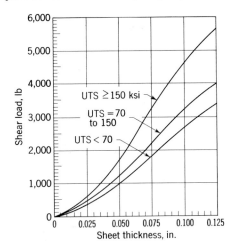

Figure 12.14. Shear strength of individual spot welds in steel sheets. (Data from Ref. 39.)

The shearing strength of *spot welds* can be estimated by multiplying the shearing area of the spot by a specified shear stress. However, the size of the spot depends on the thickness of the thinner sheet, and failure may also involve tearing of the sheet. It is therefore customary to specify the strength per spot in terms of the sheet thickness. Tables of strength per spot, based on tests, are available in various specifications. Some values for steel sheets are plotted in Fig. 12.14. These are based on the aircraft system and should therefore be divided by a factor of approximately 2 for civil-engineering use.

Seam welds are formed by overlapping spot welds, usually produced by roll welding. The strength in shear can be estimated from the fusion area of the weld. Allowable stresses should be based on tests simulating the actual construction.

Improper design or fabrication in welding can produce very severe *stress concentrations*. Whether these concentrations will seriously affect the strength of the joint depends primarily on the ability of the material to alleviate the peak stresses through plastic action. For this reason, welding has been highly successful in those structures which are made from structural (low-carbon) steel and carry primarily static loads. The use of a less ductile material or the application of repeated or fluctuating loads requires much more attention to stress-concentration effects (see Chaps. 13 and 14).

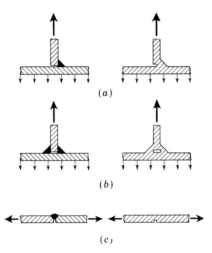

Figure 12.15. Visualization of stress concentration in welded joints.

The degree of stress concentration to be found in welded joints can be visualized by the simple process of viewing the structure as a monolithic (solid) unit, which it actually is. For example, Fig. 12.15 shows three different joints, viewed in this manner. For loading of the type shown, joint *a* obviously develops a very high stress concentration as compared with joint *b*.

Thermal strains of considerable magnitude occur in welding, because of the large changes in temperature that must take place. For a value of $\alpha = 6.5 \times 10^{-6}$ (per degree F), a strain corresponding roughly to the yield stress of structural steel (at room temperature) will be produced by a temperature change of only 150°F. Therefore, if the last portion of a weld occurs between two portions that have already cooled down, it is possible that a residual tensile stress of the order of the yield stress will be present. This occurs when a small hole in a relatively large part is "plugged" by welding; also when a small lug is welded to a thick plate.

Residual stresses, like stress concentrations, are not likely to reduce the failing strength in tension, provided that the material is ductile and not subjected to fatigue loading. But they can be very dangerous if these conditions are not fulfilled. They also cause undesirable warping in some cases.

Probably the most insidious combination that can be obtained involves stress concentration, residual tension stresses, repeated loading, and triaxial stresses. All shear stresses become zero when *equal* triaxial loading is reached (fortunately, this is practically impossible to achieve). Any degree of triaxial loading will tend to reduce the apparent ductility. One more unfavorable factor is *low temperature*. For some materials, the ductility is greatly decreased at low temperature.

These unfavorable conditions, if recognized by the designer, can usually be reduced to a satisfactory degree. Various techniques have been developed for minimizing residual stresses (preheating, annealing after welding, and so on). The important point is to realize that no mysterious unknown properties or behavior of materials are involved.

12.9 Special types of joints and connectors

Various ideas have been developed for improving joint efficiency. One example is found in the common use of *bushings*. When a joint is to be made in a relatively soft material, the bearing strength may be the con-

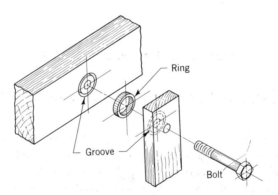

Figure 12.16. Example of connector for wood truss.

trolling factor. By inserting a bushing, the bearing area is increased without the necessity of using a larger bolt. Bushings are also desirable when relative motion takes place, in order to reduce wear and to provide a means of replacement.

Antifriction bearings (ball bearings, roller bearings) represent a type of bushing. Detailed strength analysis of such bearings is a subject for advanced strength of materials and will seldom have to be done by the designer who uses the bearings. Strengths, rated loads, and other data, are obtainable from the manufacturers and in various handbooks.

Wood connectors have proved to be highly efficient. The basic principle involved is to use a bolt only to clamp members together, the major force transmission being done by other elements that provide high shearing and bearing strength. One popular form of wood connector is shown in Fig. 12.16. In this type the shear force is transferred primarily by the ring insert, which provides a large bearing area.

PROBLEMS

12.1. In Fig. P12.1, for an assigned value of θ between 15° and 45°, predict the axial load P at which the bolts will fail, given the following values for failing loads:

$$P_t = 1{,}486 \text{ lb (tension)} \qquad P_s = 1{,}717 \text{ lb (shear)}$$

Solve both analytically and graphically.

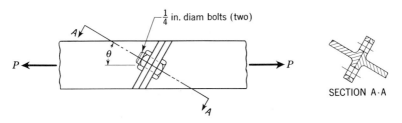

Figure P12.1

12.2. The two hollow shafts are to be joined by a riveted fitting of the type shown in Fig. P12.2. (The tube ends are upset to form a flange.) Assume that the diameter of the rivet circle is 3.25 in.

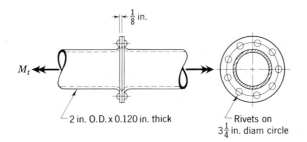

Figure P12.2

Determine the number and spacing of $\frac{1}{8}$-in. rivets required to develop the full torsional strength of the tube, if the tube fails in torsion at a shear stress of 20,000 psi and the rivets fail in single shear at 35,000 psi. [*Note:* Specify the number of rivets to the next highest integer (i.e., no fractions) and determine the spacing accordingly.]

12.3. For an assigned design in the following table, predict the failing load P for a joint like that shown in Fig. P12.3, checking four possible types of failure.

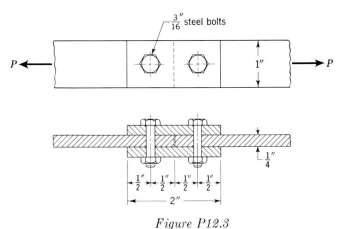

Figure P12.3

TABLE P12.3

	1	2	3	4	5	6
Plate, σ_{ult}, ksi	50	72	65	85	105	150
Plate, τ_{ult}, ksi	30	56	40	65	60	80
Plate, σ_{br}, ksi	90	110	105	125	150	200
Bolt, τ_{ult}, ksi	35	65	40	60	65	75

12.4. A multiple-shear fitting, such as that shown in Fig. 12.4c, must transmit a tension force P of 18,000 lb. Design a fitting that will provide a factor of safety of 2.0 against failure. Use a steel bolt, from Table A.4. The following values apply to the fitting material:

$$\sigma_{ult} = 60,000 \text{ psi}$$
$$\tau_{ult} = 36,000 \text{ psi}$$
$$\sigma_{br} = 90,000 \text{ psi}$$

Note: The design involves the selection of bolt size, number of lugs, and size and thickness of lugs. Check strength for four types of failure.

12.5. Estimate the actual failing load in terms of line force q (load per inch of joint width) for a single-row lap joint, such as that shown in Fig. 12.6a, assuming that the sheet thickness is $\frac{1}{16}$ in., the rivet diameter is $\frac{3}{16}$ in., the overlap of sheets is $\frac{3}{4}$ in., and the bolt or rivet spacing is $\frac{3}{4}$ in. Material properties to be assigned from the table in Prob. 12.3. Check four possible types of failure. Calculate joint efficiency.

12.6. Same as Prob. 12.5 except that two rows of rivets, $\frac{3}{4}$ in. apart, are used. The edge distance remains the same as it was in Prob. 12.5 (see Fig. 12.6b).

12.7. A lap joint is designed with three rows of rivets. The center row is the same as in Prob. 12.5 (pitch $= \frac{3}{4}$ in.), but the two outer rows have a pitch of $1\frac{1}{2}$ in. The rows are $\frac{3}{4}$ in. apart. Using assigned properties from the table of Prob. 12.3, calculate the value of q at which the joint can be expected to fail. Also determine the efficiency.

Notes: (*a*) This type of joint is sometimes used when high efficiency is desired. The greater spacing of the outer rows of rivets allows less material to be removed from the sheet. The load transmitted by the outer rows of rivets can be subtracted from the total load, to find the load across the middle row.

(*b*) Neglect the possibility of edge failure, but consider all other combinations of failures. It may be assumed that each element of the joint will be stressed to its individual failing load when overall failure takes place.

(*c*) The following modes of failure must be considered independently: (1) plate failure through outer row of rivets; (2) failure of outer rows of rivets by shear or bearing (whichever is lower), together with plate failure through center row; (3) simultaneous failure of all three rows of rivets, in shear or bearing, whichever is lower.

12.8. Find the optimum rivet diameter and pitch (disregarding practical sizes) for a single-row lap joint in two sheets $\frac{1}{8}$ in. thick, using a set of material properties from the table of Prob. 12.3. Assume that failure by tear-out will not occur.

12.9. Same as Prob. 12.8 except that a double row of rivets is used.

12.10. Design an efficient double-row single-shear continuous joint that must transmit a line force of $q = 4,000$ lb/in. with a factor of safety of 2.0. Select a set of material properties from the table of Prob. 12.3 and determine t, D, and p. Also indicate the joint efficiency obtained.

12.11. In Fig. 12.9, assume that the arrangement of the three bolts is reversed; i.e., the single bolt is placed near the end of the beam and the pair of bolts takes the place of the single bolt. (Draw a sketch.) Find the loads in the three bolts, using dimensions from Example 12.7.

12.12. Determine the magnitude and direction of load on each bolt for the fitting shown in Fig. P12.12. Also calculate the maximum bearing pressure exerted by a bolt on the wood. Bolts are $\frac{1}{4}$ in. in diameter. (P is divided between plates.)

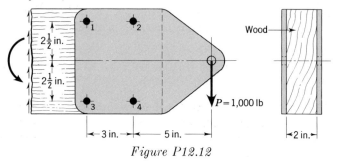

Figure P12.12

12.13. Calculate the load P at which the attachment bolts for the fitting shown in Fig. P12.13 could be expected to fail. Use an assigned set of material properties from Prob. 12.3.

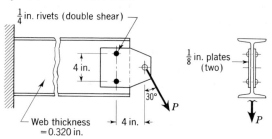

Figure P12.13

12.14. A lug is to be attached to a cable, as shown in Fig. 12.10c, by soldering. The diameter of the cable is $\frac{1}{8}$ in., and its ultimate tensile strength is approximately 2,000 lb.

(a) Using a value $\tau_{ult} = 6,000$ psi for the solder, calculate the contact length required in order to develop the full strength of the cable, with a factor of safety of 2.0 (with respect to failure of solder).

(b) Repeat for silver solder ($\tau_{ult} = 15,000$ psi).

(c) Repeat for brazing ($\tau_{ult} = 30,000$ psi).

12.15. The "fish-mouth" weld shown in Fig. P12.15 is sometimes used to obtain improved joint efficiency. Two tubes are to be assigned from

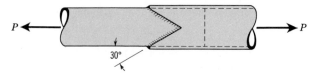

Figure P12.15

Table B.3 such that one will fit over the other, with a small clearance. (Tubes are to be not less than 1 in. OD.)

(a) Calculate the ultimate load (P) that could be transmitted by the weaker tube if there were no joint, assuming that the steel has an ultimate tensile stress of 90,000 psi.

(b) To allow for the effects of welding, reduce the load to 80 percent.

(c) Calculate the load (P) at which the weld material will fail in shear, assuming that the thickness of the weld is equal to that of the thinner tube and using an ultimate shear stress of 32,000 psi.

12.16. Assuming an ultimate shear stress of 32,000 psi for the weld material, find the length L (shown in Fig. P12.16) required to develop the

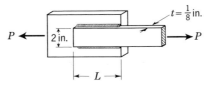

Figure P12.16

full tensile strength of the smaller member. Assume $\sigma_{t_{ult}} = 55,000$ psi for this member, with no reduction for welding (see Fig. 12.13).

12.17. Use the properties of Prob. 12.16 to determine the weld lengths *a* and *b* in Fig. P12.17, assuming that *P* is applied at the centroid of area of the one angle. [*Note:* Adjust the weld lengths so that the center of

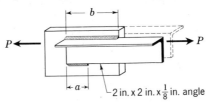

Figure P12.17

resistance of the weld areas has the same vertical location as the line of action of the applied load. Neglect the effect of eccentricity in the direction normal to the plate. (It will be offset by the presence of a second angle, shown by dashed lines.)]

Chapter 13

Stress Concentration

13.1 Nature of stress concentration

Whenever actual material failure occurs in a structure, the phenomenon of *stress concentration* is almost certain to play an important role. The term *stress concentration* is applied to a condition in which high localized stresses are produced as a result of the geometry (shape) of the structure. In dealing with axial loading, bending, and torsion, it was possible to make certain general assumptions regarding the internal behavior of the structure (plane cross sections remain plane, and so on). However, it was pointed out that these assumptions were satisfactory only when Saint-Venant's principle could be applied; that is, when the sections being analyzed were not close to a point of local-load application or an abrupt change in cross section. For example, in the vicinity of a notch, plane cross sections will not remain plane. Even though the average tensile stress (P/A) may be low, the stress at the tip of the notch may be very high, perhaps many times the average value.

The analytical determination of the elastic-stress distribution in the region of a hole or notch is an advanced problem in the theory of elasticity. Because of the difficulty of solving the problem for arbitrary shapes of notches or holes, various experimental methods have been developed. Since these are described in detail in texts and papers on experimental stress analysis, they will be mentioned only briefly. In the *photoelastic method*, a visible pattern is obtained from a model in which the intensity and direction of the principal stresses can be determined (see Fig. 7.3). Many types of stress concentration have been investigated by this method. Results are available in various publications (Refs. 11, 40, 67, 84).

In the *photostress method* a piece of photoelastic material is bonded directly to the actual structure. By viewing this with suitable equipment, the stress distribution can be determined.

Another method consists in applying a *brittle coating* to the actual member and then loading it in the desired manner. The coating will start to crack when the strain in the member reaches a certain value. The direction and number of cracks formed indicate the direction and magnitude of the principal tension strain. Small *strain gauges* can be applied at various points over the stress-concentration

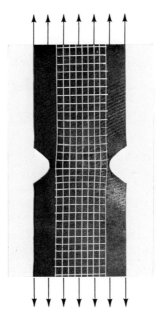

Figure 13.1. Rubber model showing increase in local strain at root of notch.

area. *Flexible models* are useful in instruction and in rough design work. Such models can be purchased or can be made by scribing a network of lines on a piece of rubber having the desired shape. The increase in the local strain at the root of a notch is easily seen, as indicated in Fig. 13.1.

Various other methods have been employed successfully, some of them based on electrical or hydrodynamic analogies (see Refs. 4, 67).

13.2 Stress-concentration factors

The stress-concentration factor is defined as the ratio between the maximum local stress and the nominal stress. The effect of the "stress raiser" in reducing the net area is usually taken into account in calculating the nominal stress. Thus in Fig. 13.2a the nominal tensile stress is P/A, where A is the minimum cross section. Similarly, the nominal stress in bending is computed as if the bar were of uniform depth h (Fig. 13.2b):

$$K_t = \frac{\sigma_{\max}}{\sigma_{\text{nom}}} \quad \text{or} \quad \frac{\tau_{\max}}{\tau_{\text{nom}}} \tag{13.1}$$

where K_t is the theoretical (elastic) stress-concentration factor and $\sigma_{\max}$ and σ_{nom} are defined as shown in Fig. 13.2.

A convenient fact to remember is that *the theoretical stress-concentration factor for a round hole in an infinitely wide plate is* 3. As the plate becomes narrower, the factor drops off, as indicated in Fig. 13.3a (Ref. 40).

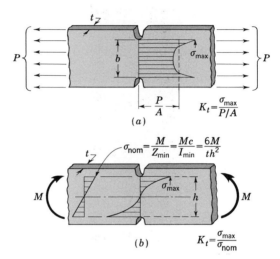

Figure 13.2. Definition of stress-concentration factor.

The same factor of 3 applies to an infinitely wide plate in tension, having a semicircular groove on each edge, and to a round shaft in bending, with a circular hole drilled through it (normal to the neutral plane). For a plate having a row of holes normal to the line of tension, the theoretical upper limit is again 3 for infinitely wide spacing of holes. In all these cases, the factor drops off as the actual width (or hole spacing) becomes less.

Any value of K_t from 1.0 to infinity, can theoretically be obtained by notches of varying geometry, the value approaching infinity as the ratio of notch radius to depth approaches zero. Although the theory must be modified for very small radii, it does show that sharp notches can have a disastrous effect for "brittle" (low ductility) materials and in fatigue of ductile materials (Chap. 14).

Figure 13.3 shows stress-concentration factors for a few typical cases. Values of K_t for various types of stress raisers likely to be encountered in design are available in textbooks and handbooks prepared specially for this purpose (see Ref. 40).

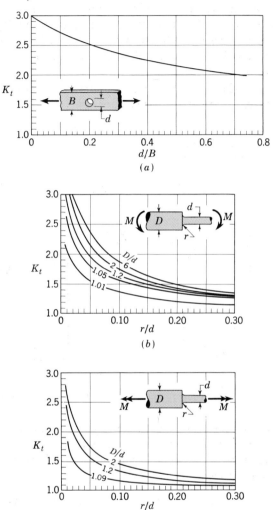

Figure 13.3. Stress-concentration factors. (After Peterson, Ref. 40.)

13.3 Streamline analogy

The effects of stress concentration can be visualized by a "streamline" analogy. Figure 13.4a shows a flat plate with edge notches. A uniformly distributed force q_1 is applied at the ends, which are some distance away from the notches. The width B_1 is arbitrarily divided into a number of equal segments ΔB_1. The same force ΔP will act over each segment.

Assume that it is desired to have a uniform force distribution over the material between the two notches. To represent this, divide the width B_2 into the same number of elements of width ΔB_2 (shown by Fig. 13.4b). Since the same force ΔP acts over each of these elements, the value of q_2 will be increased over q_1 in the ratio B_1/B_2 and will be constant over the section. (The nominal stress is, of course, equal to q_2/t and is also uniformly distributed.)

Now connect the corresponding elements by means of straight lines, as shown. In fluid dynamics, such lines are called *streamlines*. For the

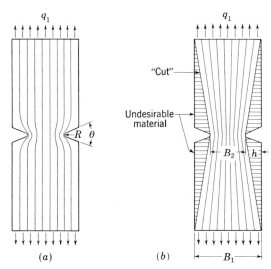

Figure 13.4. Stress-concentration analysis by lines of constant force.

present purpose, they can be thought of as *forcelines*. They describe paths over which the force being transmitted is constant.[*]

If the "undesirable material" is now removed, there will be only a negligible stress-concentration effect.

To obtain an idea of the effect of this undesirable material, imagine that it has first been cut away along the lines labeled "cut." The tensile force is now applied, and the plate is elongated. Assume that the wedge of material is now to be attached in its original position. In order to do so, it would have to be stretched out along the cut line so as to coincide with the elongated member. This adjustment requires tensile forces, the magnitude of which will depend greatly on the width of the wedge, that is, the *depth of the notch h*. These relatively high tensile forces are transmitted around the root of the notch and therefore cause a high local increase in stress. In Fig. 13.4a this effect is shown approximately by the narrowing of the forcelines adjacent to the notch. (The stress is

[*] The effects of stresses acting normal to the forcelines are neglected in this analogy.

inversely proportional to the width of a forceline.) It is important to note that, in the actual specimen, high *shear* forces must exist along the "cut" section. Any plastic slip in this region will have the effect of alleviating the stress concentration at the root of the notch.

This analogy explains why it is possible to relieve stress concentration by cutting slots or drilling holes, as indicated in Fig. 13.5. The objective is obviously to remove or weaken the undesirable material.

The analogy also indicates the effects of the three variables that control the shape of the notch. The magnitude of the additional force flow is controlled

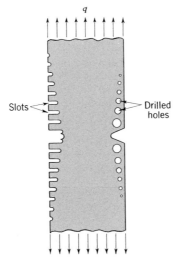

Figure 13.5. Two ways of relieving stress concentration.

primarily by the *notch depth* (Fig. 13.4). The *notch angle* θ has the effect of removing undesirable material as θ increases. The *notch radius* determines the intensity of the stress over a very small area at the root of the notch. It affects the *gradient* of stress in this region. The highest concentration will be obtained when the notch depth is large, the notch radius small, and the notch angle small. A fine saw-cut or a fatigue crack represents such a situation.

13.4 Combined stresses caused by stress concentration

Figure 13.6 shows how the curvature of the forcelines causes radial tensile stresses in the cross section at the root of a groove in a round specimen. The radial stress increases from zero at the surface to a maximum value at the center (Ref. 5). The effect of this triaxial loading is to decrease the shear stress in the interior of the specimen (see Sec. 2.8).

Tests of specimens with machined grooves of various depths (Ref. 44) have shown an apparent increase in net ultimate tensile stress. This is explained by the fact that, because of the radial tensile stress, a higher average stress over the notched region is required to produce slip (see Sec. 5.2).

Another example is found in the distribution of stress around a round hole (Fig. 13.7). In *compression* the curvature of the force lines causes a lateral *tensile*

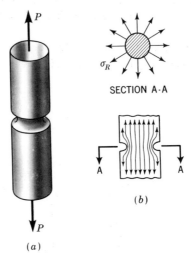

SECTION A-A

(b)

(a)

Figure 13.6. Radial stresses caused by a groove in a cylindrical specimen.

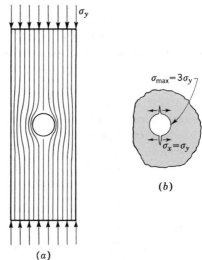

(a)

Figure 13.7. Lateral stresses near a round hole, in compression loading.

stress at the upper and lower edges of the hole. For the ideal case of an infinitely wide specimen, this lateral tensile stress is equal to the nominal compressive stress. When the loading is compressive, the tensile stresses thus produced can cause longitudinal cracking of a brittle material, as indicated in sketch *b*.

The stress-concentration factor for holes is reduced by elongating the hole in the direction of loading. The width of the hole has the same general effect as the depth of a notch. A narrow crack directly across the tensile force field causes K_t to be very high.

By combining the results for pure tension and compression (Fig. 13.8), it is found that the value of K_t for *pure shear* is 4.0 for a round hole. This means that a tensile stress equal to four times the shear stress will act at the edges of the hole.

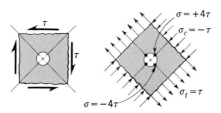

Figure 13.8. Stress concentration in pure shear (round hole in infinite plate).

13.5 Inelastic effects in stress concentration

The inelastic stress distribution at a stress raiser can be approximated by the following method: the elastic stress distribution can be converted into a *strain* distribution by dividing the stress values by E. The factor K_t then becomes a *strain-concentration factor*. To find the stress distribution, plot the strain-distribution curve and read the corresponding stresses from the stress-strain diagram. The results of such an analysis are indicated roughly in Fig. 13.9. The high peaks on the elastic stress-distribution diagram are rounded off by the inelastic effect.

To find the approximate value of the *inelastic stress-concentration factor* enter the stress-strain diagram at the required value of the average stress and then multiply the corresponding strain by K_t. The maximum stress is then read from the stress-strain diagram, at this new value of strain. The inelastic stress-concentration factor is found by dividing the maximum stress by the average stress P/A. The value of K obtained in this way will be somewhat on the low side, because no correction has been made for the fact that the reduction in maximum stress will also lower the mean stress. (For a more accurate method, see Ref. 43.)

Although plastic action may greatly reduce the stress-concentration factor, it does not eliminate the combined-stress condition that must exist whenever stresses are being transmitted "around a curve." For example, the circumferential notch shown in Fig. 13.6 will require radial stresses to be present, even if ideal plasticity (constant stress) were assumed. In order to maintain constant shear stress over the cross section, the longitudinal tensile stress must increase by the same amount that the radial stress increases. As a result, the tensile stress is not uniformly distributed over the cross section, but has a maximum value at the center. This value is greater than the so-called "true" stress (see Ref. 5).

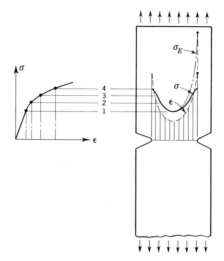

Figure 13.9. Inelastic effects in stress concentration.

13.6 Residual stresses caused by stress concentration

Whenever the stresses near a stress raiser enter the inelastic range, some residual stresses will remain after unloading. The method of estimating

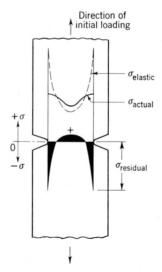

Figure 13.10. Residual stresses caused by stress concentration.

such effects is the same, in principle, as that used for residual stresses in inelastic bending (Sec. 7.7). As shown in Fig. 13.10, it is only necessary to subtract from the actual stress distribution an equivalent elastic distribution (representing the same axial load). After tension loading, the residual stress at the root of a notch will be compressive. If the value of K_t is high, the residual compressive stress will itself enter the inelastic range in compression and will therefore have a value on the order of the compressive yield stress for the material. Compression of a notched member will produce tensile residual stresses at the root of the notch. This phenomenon is dangerous in connection with fatigue.

PROBLEMS

(*Note:* Additional problems involving stress concentration are included in Chap. 14.)

13.1 Assume that in Fig. 13.2 the thickness is 0.25 in. and the width (unnotched portion) is 1.0 in. The notches are semicircular, with a depth of 0.125 in. The material is brittle and can be expected to fail when the stress at any point reaches 20,000 psi (elastic). Using a value of $K_t = 3.0$, calculate the values of P and M (independently) for failure. Compare these values with those for a similar member with no notches.

13.2. A solid round shaft has a nominal diameter (D) of 2 in. but is reduced to a diameter (d) of $1\frac{1}{2}$ in. at a certain point (see Fig. 13.3b). Two different designs have been drawn up: (a) fillet radius $r = \frac{1}{4}$ in. and (b) fillet radius $r = \frac{1}{16}$ in. Using Fig. 13.3b, estimate the theoretical (elastic) stress-concentration factor K_t for each case. Also calculate the ultimate bending moments for the following cases, assuming that failure will occur when the tensile stress reaches 50,000 psi: (c) shaft without reduction in diameter ($D = 2$ in.), (d) shaft with reduction in diameter but without stress-concentration effect ($d = 1.5$ in., $K_t = 1.0$), and (e) shaft with stress-concentration factor calculated above, for the $\frac{1}{16}$ in. fillet radius.

Note: For a material with a large degree of ductility, the effective value of K_t would approach 1.0 (no stress concentration), provided that the loading is applied only once; that is, fatigue effects are not involved.

13.3. A round shaft is to be made from heat-treated steel having an ultimate tensile stress of 230,000 psi. A torque $M_t = 18,000$ in.-lb is to be transmitted. At a particular point it is necessary to change the diameter in the ratio $D/d = 1.2$ (see Fig. 13.3c). A fillet radius r of 0.10 in. is to be used. Ignoring possible fatigue effects (Chap. 14), find the diameter d at which failure would occur in torsion. [*Note:* To estimate the ultimate shear stress, use the octahedral shear stress theory, for which $\tau_{\text{ult}} = 0.577\,\sigma_{\text{ult}}$ (see Example 5.3).]

13.4. A large flat plate, constructed of material having an elastoplastic uniaxial stress-strain diagram, has been designed to transmit a pure shear (for example, the web of a plate girder) such that no yielding will occur below an average shear stress of 30,000 psi. A small hole is now drilled in the center of the plate. Using the octahedral shear-stress theory, determine the magnitude of the average shear stress that may be applied without causing yielding in the material at the edge of the hole.

13.5. A ductile tension member containing a round hole is stressed well into the inelastic range, after which the load is removed. Explain why there will be compressive residual stresses along the edges of the hole. If the material has a flat-topped (elastoplastic) stress-strain diagram, with a yield stress of 20,000 psi, estimate the maximum value of the residual stresses.

Chapter 14

Fatigue and Brittle Fracture

14.1 Fatigue

Metals and other materials may fail at relatively low values of the applied stress if this stress is repeated or reversed a sufficient number of times. The nature of the loading history of a structure or part depends on its function. For example, the framework of a large building carries primarily static loads; repeated or alternating loads are relatively quite small. Fatigue failures are unlikely under such conditions. On the other hand, a rapidly rotating shaft that transmits a bending moment will undergo a complete reversal of bending stress during every revolution, as shown in Fig. 14.1a. If the shaft is to have a long service life, it must be designed primarily on the basis of fatigue strength.

Figure 14.1 also shows some other types of loading.* Type *b* would occur if a forced vibration of constant amplitude were to be applied to a structural part already transmitting a constant load. Type *c* is typical of an airplane wing in level flight. The average stress in this case represents the effect of supporting the weight of the airplane; the fluctuations represent the effects of gusts and maneuvers.

The fatigue problem, from the design viewpoint, can be stated as follows:

> *The designer or structural engineer must ensure that the structure can withstand the expected loadings throughout its entire service life without developing cracks that have a significant effect on strength.†*

---

* The time history of loading is often referred to as the *loading spectrum*.
† The probability of a fatigue-induced failure must be very small.

14.2 The S–N diagram

Many thousands of fatigue tests have been made. Yet there has been no clear understanding of the phenomenon, and designers have had to rely almost entirely on test data, supplemented by empirical rules and formulas. The following facts are generally agreed on, as a result of experimental observations (see Refs. 45, 46, 47, 77).

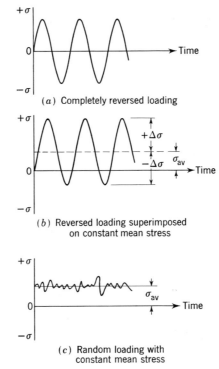

(a) Completely reversed loading

(b) Reversed loading superimposed on constant mean stress

(c) Random loading with constant mean stress

Figure 14.1. Some types of load fluctuation.

If a member is subjected to completely reversed (cyclic) stress of sufficient magnitude (Fig. 14.1a), a crack will eventually be observed; this will usually grow until sudden failure of the remaining cross section occurs. The region of crack growth can be seen on the fractured specimen as a relatively smooth surface, often showing rings similar to the growth rings of a tree. The surface involved in final failure will usually have a crystalline appearance, as demonstrated in Fig. 14.2. (This does not mean that the metal has "crystallized," as is sometimes supposed.) The phenomenon is complicated by the high stress concentration effect of the fatigue crack.

If specimens are tested at different stress amplitudes, the fatigue life N

(number of cycles to failure) will be found to vary with stress in a manner such as that indicated by Fig. 14.3. This curve (often called the *S–N diagram*) shows that, when the applied stress ($\pm\sigma$) is high, the specimen fails after relatively few reversals. On the other hand, at lower stress levels the "life" becomes very long. For some structural materials (at room temperature), there appears to be a stress σ_0 below which the life is infinite, at least for all practical purposes. This stress is called the *endurance limit*. It is of great importance in the design of rotating machinery

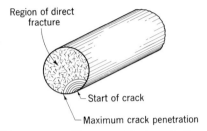

Region of direct fracture

Start of crack

Maximum crack penetration

Figure 14.2. Nature of fatigue failures.

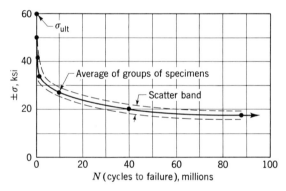

Figure 14.3. Typical fatigue curve, 2024-T4 aluminum-alloy rotating beam. (Data from Ref. 48.)

and other members that must withstand millions of cycles of repeated loading.

In order to condense the N scale, it has become customary to plot fatigue curves against log N. Two kinds of plot are in common use: *log-log* and *semilogarithmic*. In the former, log σ is plotted against log N; in the latter, σ is plotted against log N. Figures 14.4 and 14.5 show the curve of Fig. 14.3 plotted in these two ways.

This type of plotting greatly distorts the true picture and does not give a clear idea of the rate at which fatigue life drops off with increasing stress. However, it is useful for presentation of fatigue data, particularly for determining the value of the endurance limit.

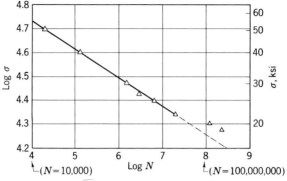

Figure 14.4. Log-log type of fatigue curve.

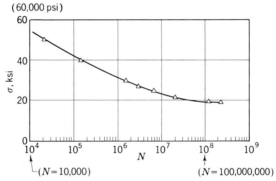

Figure 14.5. Semilogarithmic type of fatigue curve.

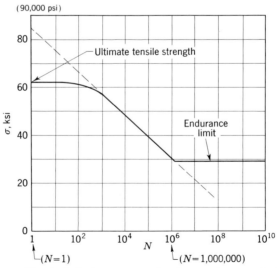

Figure 14.6. Typical fatigue curve for low-carbon steel (completely reversed bending stress).

Materials which have a sharp knee in the tensile stress-strain diagram (such as low-carbon steel) tend to show an abrupt break in the *S–N* diagram when log *N* is used for plotting.* This is clearly indicated in Fig. 14.6.

If the *N* scale is extended back to *N* = 1, the fatigue curve should coincide with the ultimate tensile stress. (To be exact, *N* = ¼ for a tensile test, because loading in one direction represents only one-quarter of the complete loading cycle.) This causes the diagram to curve to the left, as indicated in Fig. 14.6, when either σ or log σ is plotted against log *N*.

14.3 Stress concentration and fatigue

It was previously shown that for ductile materials stress concentration is relieved by inelastic behavior to such an extent that it may often be entirely neglected in design. But in fatigue the repeated stresses required to cause failure can be well below the value at which such alleviation could be expected. This suggests that the full theoretical (elastic) stress-concentration factor K_t should be used in designing to prevent fatigue failure. Tests have shown that this procedure will generally be on the safe side; that is, the effective value of K_t in fatigue is usually lower than the theoretical value.

The drastic effect of notches has been proved by thousands of tests involving all types of stress raisers and many different materials. Figure 14.7*a* shows results for SAE 4130 steel bars, of 0.335-in. diameter, tested as rotating beams (completely reversed bending). Figure 14.7*b* shows curves obtained from tests of aluminum-alloy sheets with edge-cut notches (Ref. 49). A mean stress (σ_{av}) of 10,000 psi was maintained. Instead of the maximum stress, the *stress increment* $\Delta\sigma$ has been plotted (see Fig. 14.1*b*). This must be added to the mean stress to obtain the maximum value. The values of K_t listed are the theoretical (elastic) values for the notches.

Examination of the curves in Fig. 14.7*b* will show that the fatigue-stress increment $\Delta\sigma$ does not vary inversely as the theoretical stress-concentration factor K_t, as might be expected. Increasing the latter factor (by using a sharper radius) has less and less effect. It has been found experimentally that there is a limiting small value of the notch radius below which there is no additional stress-concentration effect in fatigue (Ref. 62). The ratio between the apparent increase in local stress in fatigue and the increase predicted by the elastic theory of stress concentration has been defined by Peterson as *notch sensitivity*. (See Ref. 40 and other references listed therein.) The *notch-sensitivity factor* is given by

$$q = \frac{K_f - 1}{K_t - 1} \tag{14.1}$$

* Figures 14.4 to 14.6 also show different ways of designating the scales. All are found in the literature.

where K_t = theoretical (elastic) stress-concentration factor

K_f = fatigue stress-concentration factor obtained from tests

$$= \frac{\text{stress amplitude for failure (with notch)}}{\text{stress amplitude for failure (no notch)}}$$

This definition of q provides a scale of notch sensitivity varying between $q = 0$ (no notch effect) and $q = 1$ (full theoretical effect).

Figure 14.8 (from Ref. 40) shows how q tends to vary with notch or hole radius.

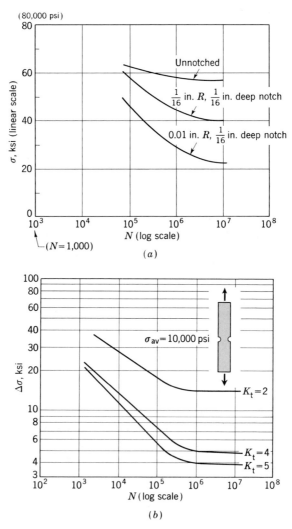

Figure 14.7. Effect of notches in fatigue tests. (a) Notched steel bars in rotating bending; (b) aluminum-alloy sheet in axial loading (σ_{av} = 10,000 psi).

Such information is useful in estimating a value of K_f in the absence of actual fatigue data for the type of stress concentration involved. However, the *actual depth* of notch, or size of hole, usually has a more important effect in fatigue than the geometrical relationships involved. These phenomena are commonly classed under the general heading of "size effect." Fatigue-test data obtained from small specimens with stress raisers may be unsafe to use for considerably larger specimens having exactly the same proportions.

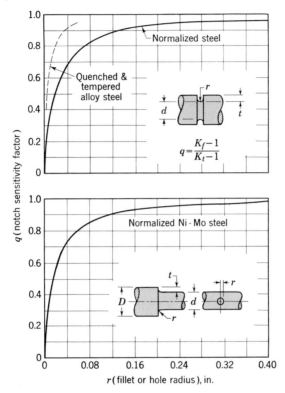

Figure 14.8. Notch sensitivity in fatigue. (After Peterson, Ref. 40.)

EXAMPLE 14.1. Assume that a round shaft of low-carbon steel has dimensions as follows (refer to Fig. 13.3b):

$$D = \tfrac{3}{4} \text{ in.} \qquad d = \tfrac{1}{2} \text{ in.} \qquad r = \tfrac{1}{16} \text{ in.}$$

It must have an indefinitely long service life, rotating at high speed under an applied bending moment of 250 in.-lb (that is, the direction of bending rotates relative to the shaft). Assume that the other stresses involved are small enough to be neglected. Determine the approximate *factor of safety* against fatigue failure, based on stress.*

* *Factor of safety* is further discussed in Sec. 15.5.

The maximum theoretical applied bending stress is found by multiplying the nominal bending stress by the stress-concentration factor. In Fig. 13.3b, $D/d = 1.5$, $r/d = 0.125$, $K_t = 1.59$.

The maximum bending stress is therefore

$$\sigma = K_t \frac{M}{Z} = 1.59 \times \frac{250}{0.0123} = 32{,}300 \text{ psi}$$

Z for a $\frac{1}{2}$-in.-diameter shaft is found from Appendix Table B.2.

From Fig. 14.6, the endurance limit for low-carbon steel in completely reversed bending is approximately 29,000 psi. The factor of safety is defined as

$$FS = \frac{\sigma_{\text{allowable}}}{\sigma_{\text{applied}}} = \frac{29{,}000}{32{,}300} = 0.90$$

A factor of safety greater than unity is desirable; the shaft must be redesigned. The radius r will be increased to $\frac{1}{8}$ in., to reduce the stress-concentration factor. In Fig. 13.3b, $D/d = 1.5$, $r/d = 0.25$, $K_t = 1.34$.

$$\sigma = 1.34 \times \frac{250}{0.0123} = 27{,}200 \text{ psi}$$

$$FS = \frac{29{,}000}{27{,}200} = 1.06$$

This indicates that very few fatigue failures would be likely to occur in service. A more precise interpretation of the factor of safety for fatigue can be made only if probability data have been obtained from fatigue tests.

14.4 Effect of mean stress on fatigue

When an alternating stress is superimposed on a constant mean stress, the maximum value of the stress is, of course, increased. The mean stress has the effect of reducing the fatigue life below that for a mean stress of zero. There are various ways of plotting fatigue curves to show the effect of mean stress. Three will be illustrated here.*

Figure 14.9 shows the results of testing sheet specimens having a theoretical stress-concentration factor $K_t = 4.0$. The stress increment $\Delta\sigma$ has been plotted (on a log scale) against log N. The top curve represents a mean stress equal to zero. Increasing the mean stress has the effect of lowering the allowable value of $\Delta\sigma$. For some materials (such as high-strength steel), the mean stress has relatively little effect on the allowable value of $\Delta\sigma$. In general, the variable portion of the stress ($\Delta\sigma$) has more effect in fatigue than the average value σ_{av}.

* Data of this type are often plotted in terms of σ_{max}, by using the parameter $R = \sigma_{\text{max}}/\sigma_{\text{min}}$. Such a plot conceals the effect of mean stress.

For cases in which test data are not available, various formulas have been suggested by which the effects of mean stress may be predicted. In the *Goodman diagram*, Fig. 14.10a, the *maximum* stress is plotted against the *mean* stress, *for some particular value of N*. The points for these curves were obtained from tests. The relation to $\Delta\sigma$ is indicated in the figure.

The curves can be expected to go through the value of the ultimate tensile stress, because when the average stress reaches this value there will be failure without any cyclic loading. However, it is not rational to extend the curves in this manner for a high value of N; consequently the upper portions of the curves are shown by dashed lines.

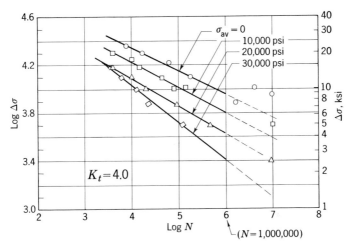

Figure 14.9. Fatigue data for notched aluminum-alloy 7075-T6 sheet, $K_t = 4.0$. (From Ref. 49.)

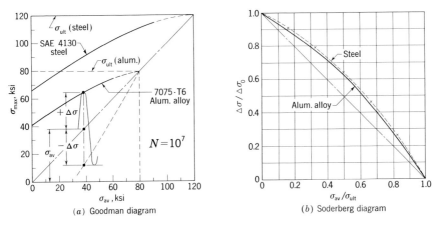

Figure 14.10. Two methods of showing effect of mean stress.

Goodman's original suggestion was that a straight line be used for this curve and that the left end of this line could be located at a value of one-third of the ultimate tensile stress (for very high values of N). This will be on the safe side for most materials and can be used as a conservative approximate design method, in the absence of any fatigue data.

An alternative (Soderberg) method of presenting the same data is to plot the variable stress $\Delta\sigma$ against the mean stress. If a straight line is used in Fig. 14.10a, this alternative method will also produce a straight line. Both methods can be reduced to dimensionless form. If the Soderberg method is used, the dimensionless form will appear as in Fig. 14.10b. This is a normalized interaction curve. Note that the straight line gives conservative results. If adequate test data on the effects of mean stress are available, as shown in Fig. 14.9, neither the Goodman nor the Soderberg diagram is needed. These diagrams are useful, however, in estimating the probable effects of mean stress and in extrapolating from inadequate test data.

EXAMPLE 14.2.   Assume that a notched tension member in a structure has been analyzed for the loading conditions expected in service. At the most critical section it is found that the loading can be represented by a steady (mean) stress of 20,000 psi, on which is superimposed an alternating stress of $\pm 4,000$ psi. It is estimated that there will be a maximum of 100,000 cycles of alternating stress imposed during the service life. The material is the same as that of Fig. 14.9, and the theoretical stress-concentration factor is assumed to be 4.0. Find the factor of safety with respect to the alternating stress increment $\Delta\sigma$.

From Fig. 14.9, the allowable value of $\Delta\sigma$ is determined at $\sigma_{av} = 20,000$ psi and $N = 100,000$ ($\log N = 5$). This indicates an allowable value of 7,000 psi. The factor of safety with respect to fatigue is therefore

$$\text{FS} = \frac{7,000}{4,000} = 1.75$$

This would indicate that the probability of fatigue failure during the service life of the structure would be extremely low.

EXAMPLE 14.3.   In the previous example it was possible to refer directly to curves obtained from test results. An example will now be given in which nothing is known about the material except its ultimate tensile stress. The results will, of course, be only approximately correct but can be used as a safe basis for design in most cases.

Assume that the loading is tensile and that the stress increment $\pm \Delta\sigma$ is always 20 percent of the mean stress σ_{av}. The part is to be designed for "infinite" life. Assume that the ultimate tensile stress for the material is 120,000 psi. Find the allowable mean stress σ_{av}, without regard to a factor of safety and assuming no stress-concentration effects.

If no fatigue-test data on the endurance limit are available, Goodman's original assumption of one-third the ultimate stress may be adopted. (This is generally on the safe side.) This gives a value of 40,000 psi for the endurance limit in completely reversed loading.

Referring to Fig. 14.10*b*, assume that the interaction curve is a straight line. From the prescribed loading conditions, $\Delta\sigma = 0.20\sigma_{av}$. From the Goodman assumption, $\Delta\sigma_0 = \sigma_{ult}/3$. Therefore, $\Delta\sigma/\Delta\sigma_0 = 0.60\sigma_{av}/\sigma_{ult}$. In Fig. 14.10*b* this condition can be represented by a straight line from the origin to the value of 0.60 on the right edge of the chart. The intersection of this line gives the allowable value for σ_{av}/σ_{ult}. It can be read from the chart or computed as follows. The equation of the straight-line interaction relationship is

$$\frac{\Delta\sigma}{\Delta\sigma_0} + \frac{\sigma_{av}}{\sigma_{ult}} = 1.0 \qquad (a)$$

Substituting $\Delta\sigma/\Delta\sigma_0 = 0.6\sigma_{av}/\sigma_{ult}$ gives

$$1.6\,\frac{\sigma_{av}}{\sigma_{ult}} = 1.0$$

$$\frac{\sigma_{av}}{\sigma_{ult}} = \frac{1}{1.6} = 0.625$$

Therefore the nominal average stress, for infinite life, is

$$\sigma_{av} = 0.625 \times 120,000 = 75,000 \text{ psi}$$

This would have to be reduced by an appropriate factor of safety, unless the latter has been incorporated in the applied loading.

If a hole happened to be located in the critical section, a rough method of allowing for the stress-concentration effect would be to assume that a value $K_t = 3.0$ is applied to the alternating stress only. (This method was suggested by Peterson, in Ref. 40, and appears to be satisfactory for ductile materials.)

Then
$$\Delta\sigma = 3 \times 0.20\sigma_{av} = 0.60\sigma_{av}$$

Still assuming that $\Delta\sigma = \sigma_{ult}/3$, the following relationship is obtained:

$$\frac{\Delta\sigma}{\Delta\sigma_0} = 1.8\,\frac{\sigma_{av}}{\sigma_{ult}}$$

Substituting this in Eq. (*a*),

$$2.8\,\frac{\sigma_{av}}{\sigma_{ult}} = 1.0$$

$$\frac{\sigma_{av}}{\sigma_{ult}} = \frac{1}{2.8} = 0.357$$

The allowable average stress (for FS = 1.0) is therefore

$$\sigma_{av} = 0.357 \times 120,000 = 42,800 \text{ psi}$$

Although based on a number of assumptions, the above method shows that it is possible to account for the effects of repeated loading, mean stress, and stress concentration in a simple manner. Further refinement would permit some reduction in material, but in most cases it is far more important to ensure against fatigue failure than to save a relatively small amount of material.

14.5 Torsion, combined loading, and other effects

Tests under alternating torsion reveal that fatigue cracks can form and cause failure. The relationship between life and stress amplitude can be plotted as an *S–N* diagram, using the nominal shear stress. Most failures of this type start at stress concentrations. A solid round bar with a small hole drilled transversely will usually crack along 45° lines radiating out from the hole. (Note that in Sec. 13.4 it was shown that the round hole causes a theoretical stress-concentration factor K_t of 4, with respect to the principal tensile stress.) Keyways and sharp re-entrant fillets are common causes of fatigue cracking in torsion.

For *combined bending and torsion,* experiments show that a circular interaction curve fits test data reasonably well at the endurance limit (Ref. 1, p. 381). The interaction equation is

$$\left(\frac{\sigma}{\sigma_e}\right)^2 + \left(\frac{\tau}{\tau_e}\right)^2 = 1 \qquad (14.2)$$

In a general survey of fatigue under combined loading, Sines (Ref. 47) has proposed that the critical fatigue stress (at a given value of life *N*) is a function of the octahedral shear stress and the mean normal stress (both of these quantities are invariants, in a general state of stress).

Corrosion fatigue occurs when a member is surrounded by a corrosive medium during cyclic loading. For some materials, ordinary tap water will cause a large reduction in fatigue resistance (lowering of the *S–N* curve), especially for members having stress concentrations. On the other hand, the absence of oxidizing or contaminating agents (as in outer space) appears to extend fatigue life.

Surface preparation plays an important part in fatigue. Longest life is obtained when surfaces are extremely smooth. *Shot-peening, nitriding,* and other processes that produce a residual compressive stress in the surface can have a very helpful effect, if not overdone.

As previously shown (Fig. 14.3), there is a considerable amount of scatter in fatigue-test data. If a sufficient number of tests are made, with "identical" specimens, this scatter can be analyzed statistically. It then becomes possible to assign a probability value to each of a family of *S–N* curves (see Ref. 19, p. 704; also Ref. 47, Sec. 3.6).

14.6 Variable-amplitude loading

When the amplitude of loading varies, as in Fig. 14.1c, it is not possible to use directly the *S–N* diagram obtained by conducting fatigue tests at constant amplitude. The expected loadings can be approximated by a chart such as shown in Fig. 14.11, which represents the *loading spectrum*. Two different ways of attacking this problem have been developed. One is based on *prediction of fatigue life under variable-amplitude loading;* the other is based on prediction of an *equivalent stress of constant amplitude* that would have the same effect (on life) as the variable-amplitude loading spectrum.

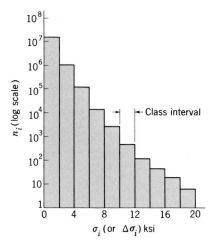

Figure 14.11. Loading spectrum.

In the first method (Palmgren, Langer, Miner; Refs. 51, 52, 53) the postulate is that the fractions of life "used up" at any given stress amplitude will add up to unity at failure. The resulting *cumulative-damage equation* is

$$\frac{n_1}{N_1} + \frac{n_2}{N_2} + \cdots \frac{n_n}{N_n} = 1$$

or
$$\sum_{i=1}^{n} \frac{n_i}{N_i} = 1 \qquad (14.3)$$

where n_i is the number of cycles applied at stress σ_i (or $\Delta\sigma_i$), and N_i is the number of cycles to failure at stress σ_i (or $\Delta\sigma_i$). If the summation (sometimes called the *Miner fraction*) is less than unity, the total life can be predicted by dividing the "applied" life (in cycles, hours, etc.) by this quantity.

In the second method, an *equivalent stress* can be found by entering the *S–N* diagram at the value of N predicted by Eq. (14.3). This stress represents an "allowable" stress for fatigue. The stress corresponding to the predicted life can be thought of as the "applied" stress. This method has the advantage of indicating how much material is required to prevent fatigue failure.

The above ideas represent an oversimplification of this complex problem but can be used as a basis for design.

The "flatness" of the *S–N* curve at low stress values (long life) was illustrated by Fig. 14.3. Therefore it is logical to expect a large scatter in experimental values of *N* in the long-life region. On the other hand, when stress is used as a basis for design (that is, when a *required life* is specified) the scatter in "allowable" stress is found to be no worse than for many other types of failure.

The foregoing items include only a few of the known facts about fatigue. The most important lesson to be learned is that *most fatigue failures originate on the drawing board.* Designers should be aware of the danger of small fillets, notches, and holes in parts subjected to cyclic loading. Usually a small increase in material at critical locations is sufficient to reduce a high stress-concentration factor to an acceptably low value. *A small reduction in operating-stress level will, in general, cause a large increase in fatigue life.*

For additional design information, see Ref. 50, which contains many helpful suggestions.

14.7 Brittle fracture

Brittle behavior of a material generally means rupture without appreciable prior plastic deformation. A *brittle material* is commonly defined as one which exhibits brittle behavior at "room" temperature. (For example, glass is brittle at room temperature but is extremely ductile at the temperatures used in glass-blowing.) The tensile stress-strain diagram representing brittle behavior is a straight line terminating in failure.

There is obviously a range of behavior between "extremely brittle" and "extremely ductile." Figures 5.3 and 5.4 showed, for example, that the elongation of a metal tends to decrease as the ultimate tensile stress is increased by alloying or cold-working (or a combination of both).

In a ductile material the attainment of the ultimate tensile stress does not actually represent rupture. Brittle failure, on the other hand, starts by highly localized rupture. It is therefore not surprising that tests of brittle materials usually reveal a relatively large scatter in strength. The analytical prediction of behavior of brittle materials is difficult, and there is much uncertainty about methods of design with such materials. The engineer avoids these problems, so far as possible, by *not using* brittle materials in structures. However, it is often necessary to use materials of very low ductility, for special reasons (for example, electrical insulators, glass doors, structures that must withstand extremely high temperatures).

Following is a brief summary of facts and theories concerning brittle behavior. (For a more complete discussion see Timoshenko's summary in Ref. 1, pp. 358–362, Refs. 50, 54, or recent papers on this subject.)

1. *Behavior of a brittle materials is greatly affected by the state of stress.* By superimposing a state of high triaxial compression, brittle materials can be caused to behave in a ductile manner.

2. *A ductile material will behave in a brittle manner if the maximum shear stresses are sufficiently reduced relative to the maximum tensile stresses.* This reduction occurs when the state of stress approaches that of equal triaxial tension. If such an extreme state could be produced, there would be no internal shear stresses; theoretically, *any* material would then behave in a brittle manner.

3. *Surface defects and surface environment may have a powerful effect on brittle behavior.* Small cracks or sharp notches normal to the direction of maximum tensile stress are particularly harmful.

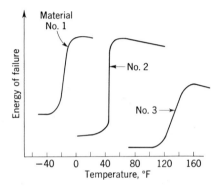

Figure 14.12. Transition-temperature phenomena in impact testing of notched specimens. (After Jonassen, Ref. 46.)

4. *Brittleness greatly reduces energy-absorption capacity.* This explains why a ceramic plate will fracture when dropped on a hard surface, whereas a similar metal plate will not.

5. *Some materials show a rather abrupt transition from brittle behavior (low energy absorption) to ductile behavior as the temperature is increased, as shown in Fig. 14.12.*

6. *There is a critical crack length, corresponding to a given applied tensile stress, at which a material will become unstable with respect to crack propagation.*

For an extremely brittle material, Griffith (Ref. 55) showed analytically that the critical crack length for a plate under uniform axial tension, with a central crack, is given by the formula

$$L_{cr} = \frac{4SE}{\pi\sigma^2} \tag{14.4}$$

where L_{cr} = crack length at which the crack will grow without further increase in stress (*Note:* For surface cracks L is twice the depth of the crack.)

S = surface energy per unit of crack area

E = Young's modulus

σ = mean stress = P/A_{net}

The surface energy S used by Griffith is the surface tension, obtained by experiments.

The Griffith formula predicts rather accurately the failing stress in tests of glass at room temperature but cannot be used directly when any appreciable amount of plastic deformation accompanies crack growth. Various modifications have been proposed, but the analytical prediction of behavior of actual structures made from relatively brittle materials is not yet in a satisfactory state of development, from the engineering viewpoint. Tests of actual structures are desirable.

Ductile materials will behave in a brittle manner under certain combinations of stress concentration, stress level, rate of loading, and environment. Full scale tests should be made to determine the critical crack length at which crack growth becomes unstable.

PROBLEMS

14.1. Assume that a round shaft of low-carbon steel is to be designed for infinite life under a completely reversed (alternating) bending moment of 3,600 in.-lb. For low-carbon steel, the endurance limit shown in Fig. 14.6 is approximately 29,000 psi. To provide for material variations, dimensional tolerances, corrosion effects, etc., an arbitrary factor of safety of 1.5 is to be used, *based on stress.*

(*a*) Find the required shaft diameter, to the nearest $\frac{1}{16}$ in.

(*b*) Assume that the shaft has an enlarged portion in which the diameter is increased to 1.2 times that of the smaller shaft ($D/d = 1.2$) and that the fillet radius is $\frac{1}{8}$ in. Determine the elastic-stress-concentration factor from Fig. 13.3 and find the required diameter, assuming that the factor K_t applies fully in fatigue. (*Note:* This involves several trials, since K_t depends on r/D.)

14.2. Design the shaft of Prob. 14.1 by using Fig. 14.8 to estimate the fatigue-stress-concentration factor K_f, using curves for normalized steel.

14.3. A solid round aluminum-alloy shaft must withstand a completely reversed (alternating) bending moment of 8,000 in.-lb for an estimated 10 million cycles ($N = 10^7$). Assume that the material is the same as that for which Figs. 14.3 and 14.4 were obtained. A factor of safety of 1.25 is to be used, with respect to the *average* test data.

(*a*) Find the required shaft diameter.

(*b*) Assume that the previous estimate of the service life is *doubled*, that is, $N = 20,000,000$. Find the new diameter required, and calculate the percentage increases in diameter and volume of shaft.

Note: This will show that it actually costs little to stay on the safe side in design for prevention of fatigue failures.

14.4. The sheet which forms the lower surface of an airplane wing structure (box beam) is subjected to a constant mean tensile stress (representing level flight) on which is superposed an alternating stress of variable amplitude, due to gusts and maneuvers. To illustrate a rough method of design, assume that the calculated value of the mean distributed tension load is $\bar{q} = 750$ lb/in. in level, unaccelerated flight. Assume also that the lifetime integrated effect of the variable loadings has been found to be equivalent to a completely reversed loading $\Delta q = \pm 250$ lb/in., applied 800,000 times. The effect of holes, joints, etc., is known (from tests) to be represented roughly by a value of K_t on the order of 4.0.

Using this information, together with Fig. 14.9, find the sheet thickness required to provide a factor of safety of 1.25 with respect to the variable stress increment $\Delta \sigma$.

Suggestions: Assume some arbitrary value of t to start with, such as 0.10 in. Then calculate σ_{av} and $\Delta \sigma$. Enter Fig. 14.9 at the required value of N and find the value of $\Delta \sigma$ at which failure would occur. Divide this by the applied value to find the factor of safety. If the latter exceeds 1.25, try lower values of t, until FS $= 1.25$.

14.5. For completely reversed loading in combined bending and torsion, use the dimensionless interaction curve of Eq. (14.2) to calculate the factor of safety for a case in which $\tau/\tau_0 = 0.50$, $\sigma/\sigma_0 = 0.60$.

Note: If the material does not have a well-defined endurance limit, it is necessary to specify a required value of N and to determine τ_0 and σ_0 accordingly.

14.6. Assume that nothing is known about a particular material except that its ultimate tensile stress is 150,000 psi. It is necessary to check, in some manner, the possibility of fatigue failure for a member in which the average (mean) stress is calculated to be 50,000 psi, on which is superposed an alternating stress of $\pm 25,000$ psi. The estimated required life is $N = 10,000,000$ cycles.

(*a*) Determine whether the part is likely to fail before reaching the required service life.

Suggestion: Use the Goodman assumptions that the endurance limit (or the fatigue stress at $N = 10^7$) is one-third of the ultimate tensile stress and that the interaction curve is a straight line. Check answers by drawing both the Goodman and Soderberg diagrams (Fig. 14.10).

(*b*) Use the Soderberg diagram, with a straight-line interaction curve, to estimate the factor of safety developed.

14.7. The values shown in the table represent the estimated lifetime stress spectrum for a particular portion of an airplane structure. The values of $\pm \Delta \sigma$ are superimposed at random on an average tension stress of 20,000 psi.

STRESS INCREMENT* $\pm \Delta \sigma$, PSI	NUMBER OF CYCLES ΔN (OR n_i)
1,550	8×10^5
4,650	1×10^5
7,750	1×10^4
10,850	2×10^3
13,950	4×10^2
17,050	1×10^2
20,150	3×10
23,250	12
26,350	5
29,450	3

* Mean value in class interval of 3,100 psi.

Sum up all values of ΔN to determine the required (lifetime) value of N, and determine the factor of safety, with respect to $\Delta \sigma$, by means of Eq. (14.3) and Fig. 14.9 (based on $K_t = 4.0$).

14.8. Fig. P14.8a shows an element of a flexure pivot which provides a limited amount of angular displacement by bending. In a certain applica-

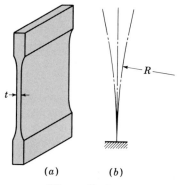

(a) (b)

Figure P14.8

tion the maximum degree of curvature $(1/R)$ required is found to correspond to $R = 30$ in. The steel used has an endurance limit of 80,000 psi. ($E = 29 \times 10^6$ psi.) For additional safety, it is desired to limit the bending stress to $\pm 60,000$ psi. In the initial design the thickness is 0.125 in. Is this satisfactory? If not, calculate the thickness that would be required. (*Note:* Omit consideration of any loads that must be transmitted.)

Chapter 15

Elementary Structural Systems

15.1 Introduction

A structural system is created by joining structural components. Examples are the truss, the multistoried building, the airplane structure, and so on. As a class, the system may include the single component which performs a structural function by itself (for example, a baseball bat). Structural systems can be further classified, for convenience, into three categories: the *framed structure*, the *shell structure*, and the *monolithic structure*. Nature tends to follow this breakdown: for example we have the *skeleton* (human body), the *crustacean* (crab), and the *monolith* (mountain). Various combinations of these systems may be employed.

The behavior of a structural system obviously depends on the behavior of its components. Prediction of the behavior of the entire system requires analytical methods and concepts that have not been covered in the foregoing chapters. In particular, the *design* of a structural system, although based on analysis (prediction of behavior), introduces new subjects such as safety and optimization.

15.2 Deflection of trusses (graphical method)

For present purposes a truss is defined as an assembly of slim straight members each of which resists only axial loads (imagine ball-and-socket joints at all junctures of member centerlines). The plane truss transmits forces only in two-dimensional space; the three-dimensional truss represents the general case. We shall now determine the deflection of an elementary truss system from a knowledge of the deflections of the individual components.

355

Figure 15.1 shows a two-member two-dimensional truss (V structure) attached to a rigid base. Plane trusses are composed of such elementary trusses. Member 1 is caused to have an extensional deflection δ_1 (the cause is immaterial; it could be a tensile force, an increase in temperature or a mechanical adjustment). To simplify the analysis we assume first that member 2 undergoes no change in length ($\delta_2 = 0$). If the pin at joint j is removed, each member will be free to rotate about its base fitting. The free ends will describe arcs, as indicated. Imagine that, after member 1 has increased in length, we wish to join the two members again by inserting the pin. Obviously the holes must be brought together at point j' where the two arc lines intersect, as indicated in the figure. If the angular change of position is small, the arcs at the ends of the

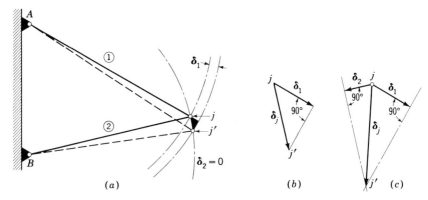

Figure 15.1. Deflection of an elementary truss.

members can be very closely simulated by straight lines normal to the members. To find the deflection at the apex by a graphical method, it is necessary only to draw the small triangle at the apex to a larger scale, as indicated in (*b*), making two sides of the small triangle respectively normal to the centerlines of members 1 and 2. The truss deflection δ_j is thus graphically determined: point j has moved to position j'.

If member 2 is now allowed to change length by the amount δ_2, the graphical method can be extended to give the resultant deflection at the apex as the sum of the partial deflections caused by each member. The graphical procedure differs from the parallelogram method of vector addition in that the auxiliary lines used, instead of being drawn parallel to the vectors, are drawn normal to them, as shown in Fig. 15.1*c*.

Various graphical methods for computing truss deflections have been developed, using the above principles, but such methods are complicated when applied to three-dimensional trusses. Furthermore, they cannot take advantage of high-speed computing facilities. Much simpler methods can be developed on the energy level of abstraction, as shown in the next section.

15.3 Energy methods

Table 15.1 shows, diagrammatically, three of the levels of abstraction involved in structural analysis. The blocks with broken lines represent certain laws of behavior. On the energy level, forces and deflections are combined into a single quantity, *energy*. The fundamental law involved on this level is that of *conservation of energy*. Many of the principles and methods used to predict behavior (analysis) assume a simple form when expressed on the energy level.

TABLE 15.1

Levels of abstraction in structural analysis

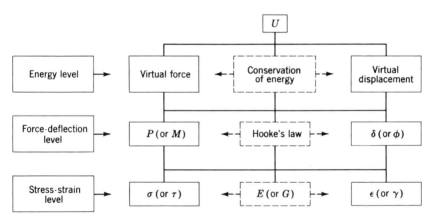

It is not necessary to work with actual energy in order to shift analysis operations to the energy level. Generally it is more convenient to use fictitious energy, that is, *virtual work*. This can be done by either of two imaginary operations:

VIRTUAL-DISPLACEMENT METHOD. Apply a fictitious (virtual) displacement at a point and calculate the virtual work done by the real loads acting through the virtual displacement.

VIRTUAL-LOAD METHOD. Apply a fictitious (virtual) load at a point and calculate the virtual work done by all virtual loads when they move through the real displacements.

Notes:

1. "Displacement" may be either translational or rotational; "load" may be either a force or a moment.

2. During a virtual displacement the real loads (or moments) remain constant.
3. Application of a virtual load causes no real displacements.

If an isolated system, or portion of a system (free body), is in static equilibrium with respect to the forces acting on it, the resultant external force must equal zero. Therefore a virtual displacement of a free body in equilibrium will cause no work to be done on or by the system. It follows that *the real forces acting on a free body in equilibrium must be such that the total virtual work done by the real forces during any virtual displacement is zero.* This statement constitutes the *principle of virtual displacements.*

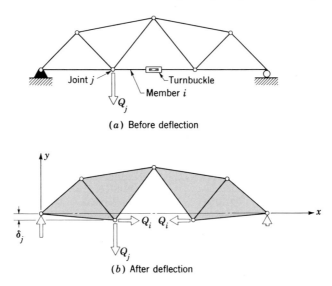

(a) Before deflection

(b) After deflection

Figure 15.2. Calculation of truss deflection.

In the general three-dimensional case it is necessary to apply separately three components of translational displacement and three components of rotational displacement. The virtual displacements must be consistent with any constraints or conditions of support. The equations thus obtained are identical with the general equations of equilibrium ($\Sigma \mathbf{P} = 0, \Sigma \mathbf{M} = 0$).

The *virtual-load method* can be used to determine the geometrical relationships between the deflections of a system and those of its individual members. For example, in Fig. 15.2 we wish to find the vertical movement of joint j caused by an axial deflection δ_i of member i. The deflection δ_i might be caused by a real force in member i, or by thermal expansion, or by mechanical means. To emphasize the geometrical nature of the analysis we shall assume that δ_i is caused by turning a frictionless turnbuckle.

A virtual force Q_j is first applied (in the imagination) at j, in the direction for which the component of δ_j is to be calculated (vertical). The virtual forces in all members may be found by applying the equations of equilibrium, as for real forces, thus determining Q_i in member i. The turnbuckle is now turned, causing member i to lengthen by the amount δ_i. During this operation all other members remain unchanged in length. Therefore the truss can be visualized as two rigid bodies connected by the top pin and by member i, as shown in Fig. 15.2b. As the turnbuckle is turned, the virtual work done by the external force Q_j is equal to $Q_j\delta_j$ (since Q_j remains constant). The virtual work associated with member i is $-Q_i\delta_i$. (This work is negative because the joints at which Q_i acts move in a direction opposite to Q_i.) The Q reactions do no work, nor do the Q forces in all the other members. Therefore the total change in virtual energy is given by

$$\Delta U = Q_j\delta_j - Q_i\delta_i \tag{a}$$

By treating the conceptual model as a closed adiabatic system, we can apply the law of conservation of energy, which requires that there be no change of energy in the closed system. Therefore $\Delta U = 0$ in Eq. (a). Solving for δ_j, we obtain

$$\delta_j = \left(\frac{Q_i}{Q_j}\right)\delta_i \tag{b}$$

We now define a *force-influence coefficient* (for either real or virtual forces) as

$$k_{ij} \equiv \frac{P_i}{P_j}\left[\text{or} \equiv \frac{Q_i}{Q_j}\right]$$

where P_i is the force in member i caused by the force P_j applied at joint j.

Equation (b) shows how the force coefficient can be used in calculating deflections. When there are n members in the truss, the total deflection component at j is found by summation of the individual contributions:

$$\delta_j = \sum_{i=1}^{n} k_{ij}\delta_i \tag{15.1}$$

where δ_j is the component of joint deflection in the direction in which Q_j is applied.

In practice, a value of $Q_j = 1$ is often applied. Then the forces Q_i become numerically equal to the force coefficients. The unit load is called the *dummy load*.

EXAMPLE 15.1. This example shows how the computations for forces and deflections can be organized by using the force-influence coefficient method.

Sketch a of Fig. E15.1 gives the values of k_{ij} when $Q = 1$ is applied at the center. Sketches b and c give the values for application off-center.

Sketch *d* shows a particular loading condition, for which we wish to obtain member stresses, and also the vertical deflections at the three lower joints. Let $E = 29 \times 10^6$ psi, for steel.

In Table E15.1 columns 2, 3, and 4 list the force-influence coefficients for a unit load applied independently at the three lower joints. (Only two sets of calculations are needed, because of antisymmetry.) The (partial) member forces for the given loading conditions are listed in columns 5, 6, and 7 and are added in column 8 to obtain the total member forces. Columns 9 and 10 list the cross-sectional areas and lengths of members. Column 11 gives the stresses, and column 12 gives the (elastic) member deflections. In columns 13, 14, and 15 the member deflections are multiplied by the force-influence coefficients from columns 2, 3, and 4. The respective sums of columns 13, 14, and 15 give the vertical deflections at the three lower joints. (If horizontal deflections are desired, repeat with $Q = 1$ applied horizontally.) Table E15.1 can be used as a basis for a computer program.

The virtual-energy method is not restricted to axially loaded systems.

TABLE

Computation of stresses and

Member (i)	k_{ij} $j = 1$	k_{ij} $j = 2$	k_{ij} $j = 3$	P_i $P_1 =$ 50 kips 50 × (2)	P_i $P_2 =$ 40 kips 40 × (3)	P_i $P_3 =$ 30 kips 30 × (4)	P_i total (5) + (6) + (7)′
(1)	(2)	(3)	(4)	(5)	(6)	(7)	(8)
a	0.75	0.5	0.25	37.5	20	7.5	65
b	−1.06	−0.707	−0.353	−53	−28.3	−10.6	−91.9
c	1	0	0	50	0	0	50
d	0.75	0.5	0.25	37.5	20	7.5	65
e	−0.353	0.707	0.353	−17.6	28.3	10.6	21.3
f	−0.5	−1	−0.5	−25	−40	−15	−80
g	−0.5	−1	−0.5	−25	−40	−15	−80
h	0.353	0.707	−0.353	17.6	28.3	−10.6	35.3
i	0.25	0.5	0.75	12.5	20	22.5	55
j	0	0	1	0	0	30	30
k	−0.353	−0.707	−1.06	−17.6	−28.3	−31.8	−77.7
l	0.25	0.5	0.75	12.5	20	22.5	55
m	0	0	0	0	0	0	0
R_L	0.75	0.5	0.25				
R_R	0.25	0.5	0.75				

Note: 50 kips = 50,000 lb.

For example, the *deflection of an initially curved beam* may be found by applying a virtual force Q_j at the point where the deflection is desired. The beam is then "cut" at a point s on the curved axis, as described in Sec. 9.4. By treating one portion of the cut beam as a closed system in equilibrium under Q forces and moments, we can calculate the change in virtual energy when the cut portion rotates through the real rotational displacement $d\phi$, while Q_j and M_Q remain constant. By setting the change of virtual energy equal to zero and integrating over the whole length we obtain

$$\delta_j = \int_0^{L_s} \frac{M_Q M}{EI} \, ds \qquad (15.2)$$

where M_Q is the virtual moment at s caused by the virtual force Q_j.

When $Q_j = 1$, the value of M_Q is given by the moment arm $(L_y - y)$. Equation (15.2) then reduces to one of the equations (9.3) (Sec. 9.4).

E15.1

deflections of plane truss

A_i (in.²)	L_i (in.)	σ, psi $\frac{(8) \times 1000}{(9)}$	δ_i, in. $\frac{(11) \times (10)}{E}$	$k_{ij}\delta_i$, in. $j = 1$ $(2) \times (12)$	$k_{ij}\delta_i$, in. $j = 2$ $(3) \times (12)$	$k_{ij}\delta_i$, in. $j = 3$ $(4) \times (12)$
(9)	(10)	(11)	(12)	(13)	(14)	(15)
4.5	10	14,500	0.005	0.00375	0.0025	0.00125
6.5	14.14	−14,200	−0.00693	0.00724	0.0049	0.00241
3.5	10	14,300	0.00493	0.00493	0	0
4.5	10	14,500	0.005	0.00375	0.0025	0.00125
2.5	14.14	8,650	0.00422	−0.00129	0.00298	0.00149
6.0	10	−13,300	−0.0046	0.0023	0.0046	0.0023
6.0	10	−13,300	−0.0046	0.0023	0.0046	0.0023
2.5	14.14	14,200	0.00693	0.00241	0.0049	−0.00241
4.5	10	12,200	0.00421	0.00105	0.0021	0.00316
3.5	10	8,600	0.00297	0	0	0.00297
6.5	14.14	−12,000	−0.00586	0.00207	0.00415	0.00621
4.5	10	12,200	0.00421	0.00105	0.0021	0.00316
3.5	10	0	0	0	0	0
		$\Sigma \rightarrow$		0.030 $= \delta_1$	0.035 $= \delta_2$	0.024 $= \delta_3$

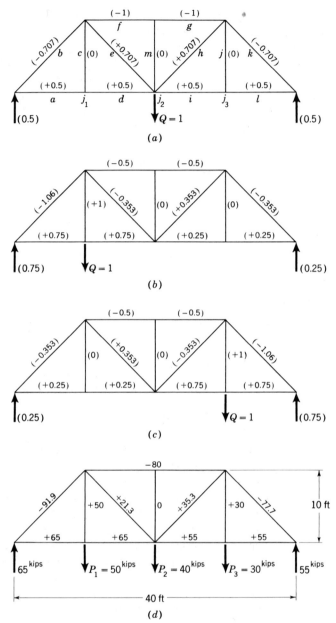

Figure E15.1. Analysis of plane truss, including deflections.

CASTIGLIANO'S THEOREM.   Castigliano's theorem is stated as follows:

$$\delta_1 = \frac{\partial U}{\partial P_1} \qquad\qquad (15.3)$$

This means that *the deflection component at a particular point 1 is equal to the rate of change of total energy (for all members) with respect to the force* P_1, *acting at that point.* The deflection component δ_1 is in the same direction as P_1. If no actual load acts at the point where the deflection is desired, it is necessary to apply a fictitious (virtual) load, which will have no effect on the real deflections.

Assume that an elastic body is acted upon by a system of forces P_i, as shown in Fig. 15.3. Actual deflections have occurred at each of the points

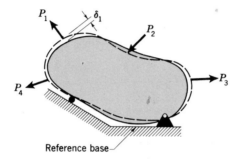

Figure 15.3. Model for Castigliano's theorem.

where a force is applied. These deflections are measured with reference to a base determined by the supports; consequently, there is no deflection at the supporting points. The work done by the applied forces (elastic energy) is

$$U = \frac{1}{2} \sum_{i=1}^{n} P_i \delta_i \qquad\qquad (a)$$

where $\delta_1, \delta_2, \ldots, \delta_n$ are the *components* of deflection along the lines of action of the corresponding forces. (δ_1 is shown in the figure.) No work is done by the reacting forces.

Because of the assumption of elastic action, any component of deflection can be expressed as

$$\delta_i = C_i P_i$$

where C = compliance. Equation (a) can therefore be written

$$U = \frac{1}{2} \sum_{i=1}^{n} C_i P_i{}^2 \qquad\qquad (b)$$

After all forces P_i have been applied, an infinitesimal force dP_1 is applied. The rate of increase of total elastic energy with respect to dP_1 is expressed as $\partial U/\partial P_1$, which can be calculated from (b) if the values of C_i are known. The increase in energy is therefore

$$dU = \frac{\partial U}{\partial P_1} \, dP_1 \qquad (c)$$

Instead of applying dP_1 as above, we may apply it first, after which the forces P_i are applied. The force dP_1 now moves through the finite distance δ_1 (along the line of action of dP_1) and therefore does work equal to

$$dU = \delta_1 \, dP_1 \qquad (d)$$

Since the actual deflections caused by dP_1 are infinitesimal and the corresponding work is proportional to the square of dP_1, this work is omitted in Eq. (d).

The expressions for dU from Eqs. (c) and (d) are now equated, since in elastic action the increase in energy does not depend on the order in which the forces are applied:

$$\delta_1 \, dP_1 = \frac{\partial U}{\partial P_1} \, dP_1 \qquad (e)$$

Since dP_1 cancels, we have derived Eq. (15.3).

If the force P_1 causes bending, torsion, or shear in the members, the energy corresponding to these actions must be included in U, in Eq. (b). If an angular deflection is to be calculated, replace P_1 by M_1 and δ_1 by ϕ_1 (radians).

Many important theorems and useful methods of analysis have been developed on the energy level. (See Ref. 71 or 72 for extensive treatments of energy methods in structural analysis.)

15.4 Dynamic loading

The forces that must be transmitted by structures are dynamic in the sense that there must be a finite rate of loading. In "static" analysis the conceptual model implies that the rate of loading is infinitesimally small. When this assumption is not acceptable, "static" theories of structural behavior can be used by employing *D'Alembert's principle*, which can be stated as follows, for present purposes:

The force with which a body resists acceleration may be treated as a static force.

Application of this principle reduces a dynamic situation to a *pseudo-static* state. For example, when an elevator is accelerating upward, the weight of an occupant is apparently increased. The total downward force on the floor may be treated as a static force.

Engineers often use the term *acceleration factor* to denote a factor by which the weight of an object (or particle) must be multiplied to determine its *apparent weight* in the pseudostatic system.* The factor is defined as

$$n \equiv \frac{W_{app}}{W}$$

In an elevator, for example, the acceleration factor is unity when the elevator is at rest. Therefore, for upward acceleration (or downward deceleration) the acceleration factor is

$$n = 1 + \frac{a}{g}$$

The centrifugal acceleration for a particle describing *uniform circular motion* in a plane, at radius r, is

$$a = \frac{V^2}{r}$$

where a is the magnitude of acceleration (directed inward) and V is the magnitude of tangential velocity. The centrifugal acceleration factor is therefore

$$n = \frac{V^2}{rg}$$

EXAMPLE 15.2. Calculate the acceleration factor n for an airplane flying at constant speed in a perfectly banked turn at angle of bank θ.

For a perfect bank the lift vector (L) must be equal and opposite to the resultant (R) of the vectors representing the pull of gravity (W) and the inertia (centrifugal) force (H). From Fig. E15.2,

$$L = \frac{W}{\cos \theta} \quad \text{and} \quad n = \frac{L}{W} = \frac{1}{\cos \theta}$$

* For space vehicles *mass* should be used instead of weight; that is, Newton's law ($F = ma$) should be used directly.

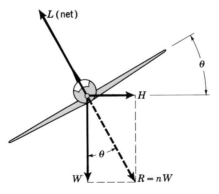

Figure E15.2

For a 30° bank, $n = 1.15$; for a 60° bank, $n = 2.0$; and for a "vertical" bank $n = \infty$. (This means that a vertical bank cannot be performed without obtaining additional "lift" from fuselage or other means.) A passenger in the airplane making the 30° bank actually "feels" 15 percent heavier.

Springs and *shock absorbers* are frequently used to absorb energy of impact. This usually involves reducing the velocity of a moving object to zero. If the object has only horizontal velocity (relative to the earth), the energy to be absorbed is the kinetic energy,

$$U_k = \tfrac{1}{2}mV^2$$

where U_k = kinetic energy
 m = mass = weight/g
 V = velocity
 g = acceleration of gravity = 32.2 ft/sec²

Note that consistent units must be used. If g is used in terms of feet and seconds, V must be in feet per second, and U_k will be in units of foot-pounds. Since material properties are usually given in terms of pounds and inches, it is necessary to convert to consistent units.

EXAMPLE 15.3. A truck weighing 20,000 lb is to be stopped by means of a spring which it will hit at a speed of 30 mph. The maximum horizontal force permitted is 200,000 lb. Find the distance which the spring must deflect and also the required spring constant, $K = P/\delta$.

The velocity is first converted to feet per second:

$$V = 30 \times \tfrac{88}{60} = 44 \text{ ft/sec}$$
$$m = \frac{W}{g} = \frac{20,000}{32.2} = 620 \text{ slugs}$$
$$U_k = \tfrac{1}{2}mV^2$$
$$= \tfrac{1}{2} \times 620 \times 44^2 \times 12 = 7,220,000 \text{ in.-lb}$$
$$U = \tfrac{1}{2}P\delta$$
$$\delta = \frac{2U}{P} = \frac{2 \times 7,220,000}{200,000} = 72.2 \text{ in.}$$
$$K = \frac{P}{\delta} = \frac{200,000}{72.2} = 2,770 \text{ lb/in.}$$

The energy which must be absorbed in order to stop a *freely falling body* can be calculated in the same manner, except that the additional work done by the body in moving through the distance δ must also be included. This is shown in Fig. 15.4, where h is the distance of free fall before the body hits the spring. The potential energy Wh will be converted into kinetic energy during the free fall; however, the former may be used directly in the calculations.

The total energy to be absorbed, including the effects of the additional drop δ, is

$$U = W(h + \delta)$$

The energy which will be absorbed by an elastic member is

$$U = \tfrac{1}{2}P\delta$$

and the relationship between P and δ is given by

$$\delta = \frac{P}{K}$$

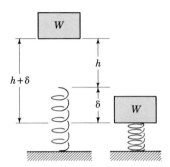

Figure 15.4. Freely falling body.

EXAMPLE 15.4 Freely falling body. In the following example it will be assumed that W, h, and K are known. The maximum impact force will be calculated in general terms, to illustrate the use of the above equations.

The equation representing the conditions at the instant of maximum deflection (and therefore maximum force) is found by equating the total potential energy of the body to the energy stored in the spring:

$$W(h + \delta) = \tfrac{1}{2}P\delta$$

Substituting $\delta = P/K$,

$$W\left(h + \frac{P}{K}\right) = \frac{1}{2}\frac{P^2}{K}$$

from which,

$$P^2 - 2PW = 2KWh$$

Solving for P,

$$P = W + \sqrt{W^2 + 2KWh}$$

or,

$$n = \frac{P}{W} = 1 + \sqrt{1 + 2K\frac{h}{W}}$$

In the special case where $h = 0$, the value of P is equal to $2W$. This represents the situation in which a weight is in contact with an elastic spring but is originally supported by other means. When the support is suddenly removed, the weight will compress the spring to twice the "static" deflection.

15.5 Principles of structural design

Design (synthesis) is directed toward the performance of a function. The structural function is not necessarily the primary function, but it may be an essential function.

The first step in structural design is to *establish criteria for the structural function*. This involves determining the magnitudes and types of forces to be transmitted, and the distances over which this transmission is to be accomplished. It may be necessary also to specify the *environment* (thermal, chemical, and so on) and the *time history* (when creep, rapid loading, or fatigue are involved). Geometric limitations are also included as part of the functional criteria. (For example, width of a bridge, shape of an airplane wing, diameter of a tank.)

The second step is to *establish limitations on behavior*. One quite obvious limitation on behavior is that the structure shall not break or collapse during the maximum expected service life. Another limitation may be that of *deflection*.

The third step in the design procedure is *optimization*. Several different designers, given the same basic functions and limitations on behavior as a starting point, might come up with several different designs, all of which will meet the established requirements. But one design might be much lighter or cheaper than the others. This brings in efficiency and economic aspects.

Another factor that may well play an important role in design is the *limitation of service difficulties* to an acceptable minimum. The *esthetic* aspects of design, although sometimes very important, cannot be treated analytically. However, the most efficient structural configuration is often found to be a pleasing one—the suspension bridge is an example.

In this brief discussion of design philosophy we shall concentrate on the following aspects:

1. *Function* (establishment of the force-time-environment spectrum).
2. *Behavior* (establishment of limitations on behavior).
3. *Optimization* (reduction of cost, weight, service difficulties, or other factors).

The designer must ensure that the required structural functions are accomplished without exceeding certain limitations on behavior. This cannot be done without utilizing, either directly or implicitly, the principles of *probability*. For example, if the designer of an ordinary chair were to use a "design" load of 2,000 lb he would have confidence that the probability of collapse would be very small, *provided* that the probability of serious defects in material or fabrication is also very small. The word "safe" implies that the probability of failure is very small. We would like to reduce this probability to zero. Usually this is not possible, but in most cases the probability of failure must be so low as to be "virtually zero."

The example of the chair showed that two basically different types of probability enter into the over-all probability of failure; one has to do with *function*, the other with *behavior*. More specifically we must consider:

1. The probability that certain loads will be applied. (This includes magnitude, direction, distribution, duration, and so on.)
2. The probability that the structure will "fail" (by collapse, yielding, or some other mode) under such loading conditions.

For example, in bridge design the "dead loads" represented by the weight of the bridge can be predicted quite accurately. It is more difficult to predict the maximum "live loads" represented by the weight and motion of the vehicles that will utilize the bridge.

We now consider the factors that can affect the *actual behavior* of the structure under load, as compared with predicted behavior. Some of these factors are

1. Variations in material properties.
2. Variations in actual dimensions of cross sections (tolerances).
3. Variations in fabrication, particularly in joints.
4. Effects of loading history (fatigue, creep, and so on).
5. Environmental effects, such as corrosion, high or low temperature.
6. Inaccurate analysis methods, that is, failure to predict correct internal stresses, buckling loads, or other factors.

The designer must do something to provide for all of these uncertainties. The usual procedure is to introduce a general *factor of safety*, which is currently used in two different ways.

In *civil engineering* the factor of safety (for buildings, bridges, and other structures) is used to reduce typical strength properties (such as the yield stress), to obtain an *allowable stress*, that is,

$$\text{Allowable stress} = \frac{\text{typical stress}}{\text{factor of safety}}$$

The "typical stress" includes, for example, predicted buckling stresses. The value of the factor of safety varies considerably with type of structure, mode of failure, and even with the agency which promulgates the requirements. On the average the civil factor of safety is in the neighborhood of 2.0 (it is seldom less). See Ref. 68 for examples.

In *aeronautical and aerospace engineering* the factor of safety is used to multiply the maximum values of the expected loads. The allowable stresses are based on actual material properties (or buckling stresses). For example, the load required to be sustained is usually called the *design load* and is given by

> Design load* = factor of safety × maximum expected load

A typical value for the "ultimate" factor of safety in aeronautical engineering is 1.5 (Ref. 69). For missiles and some aerospace applications the value may be less (Ref. 70). For complicated fittings, pressure vessels, and other structures, the required value may exceed 2.0.

Even in the factor-of-safety system we cannot escape probability considerations entirely. For example, how are "typical stresses" or "maximum expected loads" defined? These matters are quite complex and therefore cannot be taken up in detail in this text. However, it is important to realize that a particular system of design criteria usually has been developed on the basis of many years of experience, including actual service failures. Such experience must not be ignored in replacing the factor-of-safety approach by direct probability analysis. (See Appendix Figs. A.10 to A.13 for statistical data on material properties.)

The term *margin of safety* (MS) is sometimes used in design. Generally this does not have the same meaning as factor of safety. In aircraft design, for example, a margin of safety of 20 percent means that the particular member has 20 percent more strength than that actually required for the particular design condition being considered. The following relationship expresses this interpretation.

$$MS = \frac{\text{actual (or predicted) strength}}{\text{required strength}} - 1$$

A negative margin of safety indicates that the member is not acceptable.

In general it is necessary to consider all combinations of load and direction in establishing the force-transmission function. The concept of *load envelopes* aids in clarifying the picture. Figure 15.5a shows an *applied-load envelope* in two-dimensional space. (In reality the applied-load envelope is three-dimensional.) In design work it is customary to select a few "design conditions" out of the infinite number that are possible.

Fig. 15.5b shows a two-dimensional *allowable-load envelope*, or *strength envelope*. The strength envelope is found graphically by drawing lines through the ends of the strength vectors, parallel with the center lines of the members. *Any loading within this envelope will not cause failure.* The *margin of safety* for a given load P_i is indicated. The direction and magnitude of the *minimum strength* are also determined by this construction. This is an important feature.

---

* Design loads may be further classified with respect to the behavior of the structure; that is, there may be different values of the factor of safety against yielding, against fatigue, or against ultimate failure (complete collapse).

A model of a *three-dimensional strength envelope* for a tripod is shown in Fig. 15.6. This is obtained by passing planes through the ends of the strength vectors, each plane being parallel with the plane of the other two members involved.

Strength envelopes can be determined for conditions of torsion, bending, or other loading conditions.

A general mental picture of structural-design criteria can be obtained by visualizing the applied-load envelope and the strength envelope in

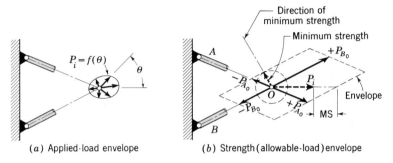

(a) Applied-load envelope   (b) Strength (allowable-load) envelope

Figure 15.5. Load envelopes for a V structure.

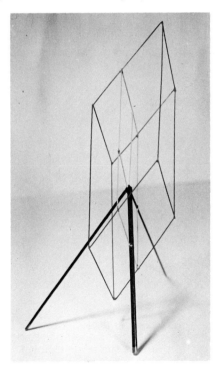

Figure 15.6. Model of strength envelope for a tripod.

terms of *probability*. This is indicated schematically in Fig. 15.7, for the two-dimensional case. A strength probability line indicates the probability that the structure will fail at a value of applied force equal to or greater than that determined by the intersection of the loading vector with that line. An applied-load probability line indicates the probability of occurrence of a load of given magnitude and direction. The probability of failure of the structure is a function of both types of probability and

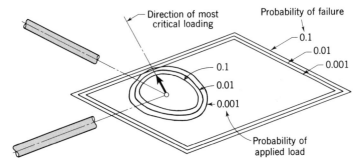

Figure 15.7. Schematic illustration of probability-load envelopes.

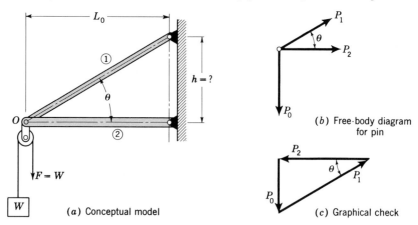

Figure 15.8. Design of an elementary plane truss.

can be computed by the laws for probability of combined events. The factor of safety can be thought of as establishing a suitable separation of the applied- and allowable-load envelopes, in lieu of a direct probability analysis.

15.6 Design of a plane truss element

The V structure (bipod) represents the basic element in all plane trusses constructed from axially loaded members. Figure 15.8 shows a situation calling for the design of a V structure which must transmit forces horizontally to a vertical base. The only fixed dimension is the length L_0. It is required that member 2 be horizontal. This two-dimensional model implies that there are no loads applied normal to the plane of the members. It would be realistic only for a structure that is intended to pivot about a vertical axis, or which is adequately supported in the third direction.

FUNCTIONAL REQUIREMENTS. The maximum expected load W is estimated to be about 5,000 lb. (The cables are shown vertical, but usually other angles for force F would have to be considered.)

INTERNAL FORCES. $P_0 = 10,000$ lb (from two cables). The forces in members 1 and 2 can be found by drawing a free-body diagram for the pin at joint O, as in sketch b (showing all forces as tension) and applying the equations of equilibrium:

$$[\Sigma P_x = 0] \qquad\qquad P_2 + P_1 \cos \theta = 0$$
$$[\Sigma P_y = 0] \qquad\qquad 0 + P_1 \sin \theta - P_0 = 0$$

from which

$$P_1 = \frac{P_0}{\sin \theta} \qquad \text{(tension)}$$

$$P_2 = -\frac{P_0}{\tan \theta} \qquad \text{(compression)}$$

(A graphical check is shown in sketch c.)

OPTIMIZATION OF CONFIGURATION. A further abstraction will be made, in order to concentrate on the design of member 1. Assume that member 2 is already available and is strong enough. Since we cannot change the size (or cost) of this member, we have only the problem of selecting the angle θ and designing member 1. Let us optimize the angle θ on the basis of *volume of material* in member 1:

$$A_1 = \frac{P_1}{\sigma_{\text{allow}}} = \frac{P_0}{\sigma \sin \theta}$$

$$L_1 = \frac{L_0}{\cos \theta}$$

$$V_1 = A_1 L_1 = \frac{P_0 L_0}{\sigma \sin \theta \cos \theta} \qquad (a)$$

The minimum volume will occur when $\sin \theta \cos \theta$ is a maximum. By differentiation, or plotting, the optimum value of θ is found to be 45°. Figure 15.9 shows how the volume varies as θ departs from the optimum value. *Note that small deviations from the optimum configuration have relatively little effect.* Equation (a) can be written as

$$V_1 = k_v \frac{P_0 L_0}{\sigma} = k_v V_0 \qquad (b)$$

Where
$$k_v = \frac{1}{\sin \theta \cos \theta} \qquad \text{(member 2 not included)}$$

and V_0 is the volume of a member of length L_0, transmitting the same force axially at the same stress.

The factor k_v indicates the penalty paid in transmitting the force horizontally instead of axially. At $\theta = \theta_{opt} = 45°$, the value of $k_v = 2.0$. Also,

$$P_1 = 2P_0 = 20,000 \text{ lb}$$

SELECTION OF MATERIAL AND WORKING STRESS. If cost is the primary criterion, the most likely choice, for a metal, is ordinary (low-carbon) structural steel. Referring to Appendix Table A.1, we find the yield stress for low-carbon

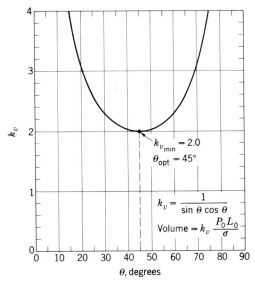

Figure 15.9. Effect of angle on volume required for diagonal member only.

structural steel to be about 36,000 psi, and the ultimate tensile stress about 55,000 psi.

For this type of steel there is a sudden large increase of plastic strain at the yield stress. Therefore a logical limitation on behavior would be that the structure should not yield.

Let us select an arbitrary factor of safety of 2.0 against yielding. Using the civil engineering system, we divide the yield stress (36,000 psi) by this factor, giving an *allowable stress* of 18,000 psi. The required cross-sectional area is

$$A_{req'd} = \frac{P_1}{18,000} = \frac{20,000}{18,000} = 0.9 \text{ in.}^2$$

The corresponding diameter of a solid round rod is

$$D = \sqrt{\frac{4 \times 0.9}{\pi}} = 1.07 \text{ in.}$$

The above result does not necessarily mean that we can use a rod of this diameter. The fittings must also be designed. If a fitting of 100 percent efficiency were designed (as by enlarging the cross-sectional area at the ends), the calculated diameter could be used. In this example the fittings are not designed.

OPTIMIZATION (both members designed).   We now calculate the optimum angle θ for the case in which the horizontal member 2 is also to be designed. The force in this member is compressive; that is, the member must be designed as a column. For simplicity, we shall find the optimum angle when the buckling stress is the same as the yield stress. (This would be nearly true only when the column is short and heavily loaded.)

The required cross-sectional area for member 2 is

$$A_2 = \frac{P_2}{\sigma_2} = \frac{P_0}{\sigma_2 \tan \theta} \quad \text{and} \quad L_2 = L_0$$

The total volume (both members) is therefore

$$V = A_1 L_1 + A_2 L_2$$
$$= \frac{P_0 L_0}{\sigma_1 \sin \theta \cos \theta} + \frac{P_0 L_0}{\sigma_2 \tan \theta}$$

Letting $\sigma_2 = \sigma_1$, we have

$$V = \frac{P_0 L_0}{\sigma} \left(\frac{1}{\sin \theta \cos \theta} + \frac{1}{\tan \theta} \right)$$

The value of k_v is therefore

$$k_v = \frac{1}{\sin \theta \cos \theta} + \frac{1}{\tan \theta}$$

or

$$k_v = \sec \theta \csc \theta + \cot \theta$$

This is shown in Fig. 15.10. Setting the derivative of k_v equal to zero gives $\tan \theta = 2$.

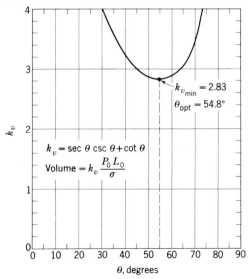

Figure 15.10. Effect of angle on volume (both members designed for same allowable stress).

Therefore $\theta_{opt} = 54.8°$ and $k_v = 2.83$. Note that when $\theta = 45°$, $k_v = 3.0$. The use of $\theta = 45°$ would increase the weight, over the optimum, by about 5 percent.

This highly simplified model can be extended to include the weight of fittings, other directions of loading, and the effect of buckling. Also, the limitation that member 2 must be horizontal can be removed.

A complete two-dimensional truss can be built up by adding one V element to another. For arbitrary locations of the forces to be transmitted, the designer must find a configuration that performs the structural function. The above results can be used as a rough guide toward optimization of trusses, for which the V is the basic element.

15.7 Design of a tripod

The tripod represents the basic element in all three-dimensional structures constructed from axially loaded members and designed to transmit forces in any direction in space. The following example utilizes the concept of the *loading envelope*.

FUNCTION. To transmit a force P to a flat base (such as the ground), from a point of application at a distance h normal to the base, the force P to be applied *in any direction*. (This represents a spherical loading envelope; see Fig. 15.11.)

BEHAVIOR. The axial stress (P/A) in any member must not exceed a specified allowable value of σ_1.

MATERIAL. Aluminum alloy; $E = 10 \times 10^6$ psi. The allowable stress is specified above.

OPTIMIZATION. Find the optimum ratio R/h for minimum volume of material, where R is the radius of the base circle. Derive a formula for volume of material as a function of R/h.

SOLUTION. By applying the laws of equilibrium at the joint, it is possible to find the force in each member as a function of the angles α and β. Then by partial differentiation with respect to each of these angles the direction of loading for maximum compressive load in a member can be determined.

A shorter method is to view the tripod in the position shown in Fig. 15.11a and to treat member 1 as if it were part of a hypothetical V structure. (The other member is represented by the projection of members 2 and 3, hinged at the base.) The strength envelope (Fig. 15.5b) shows that the *greatest load in a member of a V structure occurs when the load vector is normal to the other member*. We therefore apply the load P normal to the plane containing members 2 and 3, as shown in Fig. 15.11b. The closed vector diagram gives the following solution:

$$P_1 = \frac{P}{\sin(\theta + \gamma)}$$

For a given allowable stress σ_1, the volume of material for all three members is

$$V = \frac{3L_1 P_1}{\sigma_1}$$

But

$$L_1 = h \sqrt{1 + \left(\frac{R}{h}\right)^2}$$

Substituting this in the volume equation above gives

$$V = \frac{3Ph}{\sigma_1} \frac{\sqrt{1 + (R/h)^2}}{\sin (\theta + \gamma)} \tag{a}$$

where

$$\tan \gamma = \frac{R}{h} \qquad \tan \theta = \frac{R}{2h}$$

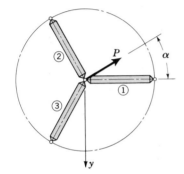

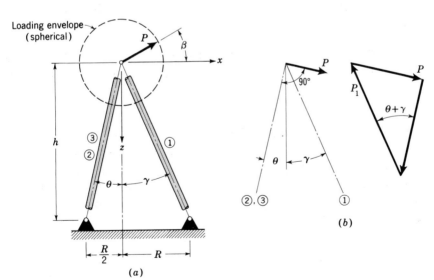

(a)

Figure 15.11. Optimization of tripod structure.

Equation (*a*) can be expressed as

$$V = k_v \frac{Ph}{\sigma_1} \qquad (b)$$

where

$$k_v = 3 \frac{\sqrt{1 + (R/h)^2}}{\sin(\theta + \gamma)} \qquad (c)$$

This coefficient has been plotted in Fig. 15.12. The optimum value of R/h is found to be 0.85. The minimum value of k_v is 4.41. For a given value of R/h the required cross-sectional area of each tube is easily determined.

For column failure the optimum value of σ_1 depends on L_1 and P_1 (see Sec. 15.10). This refinement has not been included here.

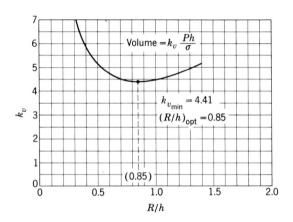

Figure 15.12. Effect of tripod geometry on volume of members (spherical loading envelope).

The k_v curve is relatively flat in the region of optimum design. Therefore the optimum value of R/h will not be strongly affected by minor refinements in the model.

15.8 Design of concrete beams

In the analysis of *reinforced concrete beams*, it is customary to assume that all tensile stresses due to bending are resisted by the steel reinforcing rods, since concrete cracks at low tensile stress. For further simplicity it may be postulated that the concrete itself behaves elastically, although this is not true. (For more accurate methods see Ref. 19.)

The analysis is based on the following postulates, for pure bending.

1. The net axial force must be zero ($\Sigma P = 0$).
2. The moment of the internal stresses in the concrete and steel must be equal and opposite to the external moment M ($\Sigma M = 0$).

3. Initially plane cross sections remain plane; that is, the strain distribution is linear.
4. No tensile stresses exist in the concrete (i.e., it is cracked on the tension side of the neutral axis).

Figure 15.13 shows that the problem would be solved if the location of the neutral axis (the distance y_{con}) could be determined.

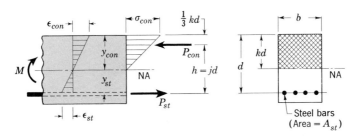

Figure 15.13. Conceptual model for reinforced concrete beam in pure bending.

For the concrete, the average compressive stress is $\sigma_{con}/2$. This stress acts on the cross-sectional area above the neutral axis. Therefore, *for rectangular cross sections:*

$$P_{con} = -\left(\frac{\sigma_{con}}{2}\right) by_{con} \tag{a}$$

For the steel (when all the bars lie at same distance from the neutral axis and therefore have the same stress):

$$P_{st} = \sigma_{st} A_{st} \tag{b}$$

where A_{st} is the cross-sectional area of the steel.

$$[\Sigma P = 0] \qquad \sigma_{st} A_{st} - \frac{\sigma_{con}}{2} by_{con} = 0$$

$$y_{con} = 2\frac{\sigma_{st} A_{st}}{\sigma_{con} b} \tag{c}$$

The values of σ_{st} and σ_{con} are related by the postulate that plane cross sections remain plane. This is expressed by the following equation, which implies that the strain ϵ varies linearly with y.

$$\frac{y_{con}}{\epsilon_{con}} = \frac{y_{st}}{\epsilon_{st}} \tag{d}$$

The effective modulus of elasticity of concrete is taken as the *secant modulus*, $E_{con} = \sigma_{con}/\epsilon_{con}$. From the definition of E_{con} and E_{st},

$$\epsilon_{con} = \frac{\sigma_{con}}{E_{con}} \qquad \text{and} \qquad \epsilon_{st} = \frac{\sigma_{st}}{E_{st}}$$

Substituting these in (d),

$$\frac{y_{con}E_{con}}{\sigma_{con}} = \frac{y_{st}E_{st}}{\sigma_{st}} \tag{e}$$

But $y_{st} = d - y_{con}$. Substituting for y_{st} in Eq. (e) and solving for y_{con},

$$y_{con} = (d - y_{con})\frac{\sigma_{con}}{\sigma_{st}}\frac{E_{st}}{E_{con}} \tag{f}$$

Now substitute for σ_{con}/σ_{st} the value from Eq. (c), giving

$$y_{con} = (d - y_{con})\frac{2A_{st}}{y_{con}b}\frac{E_{st}}{E_{con}} \tag{g}$$

The solution of this equation is

$$y_{con} = \sqrt{\frac{2A_{st}d}{b}\frac{E_{st}}{E_{con}} + \left(\frac{A_{st}}{b}\frac{E_{st}}{E_{con}}\right)^2} - \left(\frac{A_{st}}{b}\frac{E_{st}}{E_{con}}\right) \tag{h}$$

It is customary to reduce this equation to dimensionless form by using the following ratios:

Neutral axis ratio $\qquad k = \dfrac{y_{con}}{d}$ $\qquad\qquad$ (i)

Steel/concrete ratio $\qquad p = \dfrac{A_{st}}{bd}$ $\qquad\qquad$ (j)

Elastic ratio $\qquad n = \dfrac{E_{st}}{E_{con}}$ $\qquad\qquad$ (k)

Equivalent depth ratio $\qquad j = \dfrac{h}{d}$ $\qquad\qquad$ (l)

(Note that the concrete outside of the steel bars is not included in defining d.)
Equation (h) now reduces to the standard form found in most handbooks:

$$k = \sqrt{2pn + (pn)^2} - pn \tag{15.4}$$

The location of the resultant compressive force in the concrete occurs at $y_{con}/3$. The depth of the equivalent two-flange beam is therefore

$$h = d - \frac{y_{con}}{3} \tag{m}$$

This can be written in dimensionless form by letting

$$h = jd \tag{n}$$

then $\qquad\qquad\qquad\qquad j = 1 - \dfrac{k}{3}$ $\qquad\qquad$ (15.5)

The average axial force P_{con} in the concrete was given by Eq. (a). The bending moment is

$$M = Ph = \tfrac{1}{2}\sigma_{con}by_{con}h \tag{15.6}$$

Expressed in terms of the dimensionless parameters, for a given maximum stress in the concrete,

$$M = \tfrac{1}{2}\sigma_{con}jkbd^2 \tag{15.7}$$

For a given bending moment,

$$\sigma_{con} = \frac{2M}{jkbd^2} \tag{15.8}$$

and

$$\sigma_{st} = \frac{M}{jdA_{st}} \tag{15.9}$$

The equivalent moment of inertia (to be used with E_{con} in calculating deflections) can be derived by using the formula:

$$\frac{1}{R} = \frac{\epsilon_{con}}{y_{con}} = \frac{M}{E_{con}I_{equiv}}$$

from which

$$I_{equiv} = \tfrac{1}{2}jk^2bd^3 \tag{15.10}$$

(Compare with $I = \frac{1}{12}bd^3$ for a solid rectangular beam.)

The above formulas were derived for a rectangular cross section. The efficiency can be increased by using a T section, as indicated in Fig. 15.14. If the bending

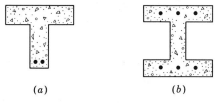

(a)   (b)

Figure 15.14. Types of reinforced concrete beams.

moment can act in either direction, it is necessary to place steel in both upper and lower flanges, as indicated in Fig. 15.14b. (In gravity-loaded horizontal beams, continuous over supports, steel must be placed in the top portion of the beam above the support, in the region of negative bending moment.)

For transverse loading, the distributed shear force can be found by treating the beam as an idealized two-flange beam, with a depth h equal to the effective depth jd,

$$q_s = \frac{V}{jd} \tag{a}$$

To determine the shear stress in the concrete, divide q_s by the width of the beam:

$$\tau_{con} = \frac{q_s}{b} = \frac{V}{bjd} \tag{15.11}$$

The distributed shear force q_s must be transferred from the concrete to the reinforcing bars. This is done by the bond between the concrete and the surface of the bar. The *bond stress* is therefore found by dividing q_s by the surface of a unit length of the bars:

$$\tau_{\text{bond}} = \frac{q_s}{A_r} = \frac{V}{A_r(jd)} \tag{15.12}$$

where A_r is the surface area of the bars, over a unit length (equals the total perimeter of the bars).

For beams that taper in depth or have unusual arrangements of reinforcing rods see Ref. 19.

The allowable shear stresses specified for concrete in various codes are quite low, varying from about 2 percent of the ultimate compressive stress up to about 12 percent, depending on the construction. The allowable bond stress for plain bars may be in the order of 160 psi or less. For *deformed bars* having ridges on the surface, the allowable bond stress is considerably higher.

The shear strength is improved by using either vertical or inclined *stirrups* (Fig. 15.15). In the regions of high shear stress, the maximum tension stress will

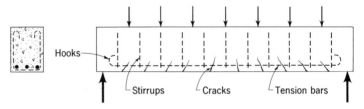

Figure 15.15. Reinforced concrete beam transmitting shear.

occur along lines approaching 45°. The diagonal strips of uncracked concrete are capable of acting as diagonal compression members in a trusslike beam. The stirrups then supply the necessary tension members. The required size and spacing of stirrups are based largely on experience and are specified in various codes and handbooks.

Prestressed concrete beams have been successfully used in buildings and bridges, particularly for long spans. In conventional reinforced concrete beams under loading, the concrete cracks on the tension side. This cracking not only reduces the strength but also reduces the over-all stiffness. Both these effects can be virtually eliminated by *prestressing*, in which the steel bars or wires are installed under tension. (The various ways of doing this will not be discussed here. See any modern textbook or handbook on concrete construction.) The tension load in the wires causes precompression of the concrete; that is, the entire cross section is subjected to a compressive stress before any bending moment is applied to the beam.

Figure 15.16 shows an elementary model in which the precompression is done by a rod located at the centroid of the cross section. Under zero bending moment, the concrete is uniformly stressed to a compressive stress $-\sigma_1$. When the concrete is loaded as a beam, the bending stress is computed as usual, *using the entire cross section of the concrete.* (If the rod or wires are small and are located at the neutral axis, their direct resistance to bending is negligible.) The net stress is

$$\sigma = -\sigma_1 \pm \frac{My}{I}$$

At the top of the beam, the bending stress is compressive, and the initial compressive stress is increased. At the lower edge, the tensile bending stress reduces the compressive stress, as indicated, but does not cause tension unless

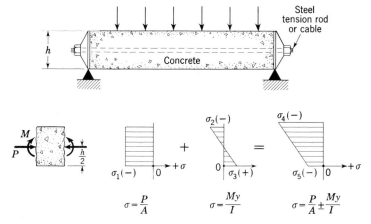

Figure 15.16. Centrally prestressed concrete beam.

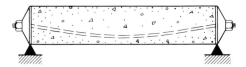

Figure 15.17. Prestressed concrete beam with curved prestressing member.

the bending moment exceeds a certain value. To find this value, let $\sigma = 0$ in the above equation, with $y = c$ (for "tension" fiber):

$$0 = -\sigma_1 + \frac{M_0}{Z}$$

$$M_0 = \sigma_1 Z$$

where σ_1 is the precompression stress, and Z is the section modulus of the entire cross section ($= I/c$).

If the applied bending moment exceeds M_0 appreciably, the concrete will crack, but this will not cause complete failure. The cracks will close when M is decreased. If the applied loads always act in the same direction, greater efficiency can be obtained by locating the prestressing wires eccentrically, on the tension side. The prestressing member may be curved, as indicated in Fig. 15.17. When this member has the same basic shape as the moment diagram, it will have maximum effect in resisting shear.

In practice, wires or cables of very high strength are used (approximately 300,000 psi ultimate tensile stress). This greatly decreases the weight of the steel required. It also makes the load in the wires less sensitive to changes in length caused by creep or temperature effects, because of the much greater elastic strain involved, as compared with ordinary structural steel.

15.9 Dimensional similarity principles in design

If every dimension of a structure (1) is multiplied by a number N the following facts are true for the structure (2) thereby "designed":

$$\frac{L_2}{B_2} = \frac{L_1}{B_1} \qquad \text{All dimensional ratios remain the same} \qquad (a)$$
$$L_2 = NL_1 \qquad L \text{ represents any dimension} \qquad (b)$$
$$A_2 = N^2A_1 \qquad A = \text{cross-sectional area} \qquad (c)$$
$$Z_2 = N^3Z_1 \qquad Z = \text{section modulus} \qquad (d)$$
$$I_2 = N^4I_1 \qquad I = \text{moment of inertia} \qquad (e)$$
$$V_2 = N^3V_1 \qquad V = \text{volume} \qquad (f)$$
$$W_2 = N^3W_1 \qquad W = \text{weight (for same material)} \qquad (g)$$

The above statements may be verified by substituting the proper dimensions in the appropriate formulas.

Assuming that structure 2 is made from the same material as structure 1 (same stress-strain diagram) we may determine the loading that will produce the same stresses in both structures. The student should be able to prove that the following relationships are true:

Pressure	$p_2 = p_1$	Forces	$P_2 = N^2P_1$
Line forces	$q_2 = Nq_1$	Moments	$M_2 = N^3M_1$

If the above loadings are applied to structure 2, the strains will be the same as for structure 1; therefore the relative deflections and energy absorbed will be as follows:

Rotational (angular) deflections	$\phi_2 = \phi_1$
Linear deflections	$\delta_2 = N\delta_1$
Energy	$U_2 = N^3U_1$

If structure 1 fails by buckling at P_1, for example, structure 2 will fail in the same manner when $P_2 = N^2P_1$. Buckling-stress formulas contain only dimensional *ratios*, which remain constant; therefore the buckling stresses are the same for the entire family of structures obtained by the similitude transformation when all structures are of the same material.

In the above statements it is assumed that there are no "size effects" on material properties and that all eccentricities remain proportional to the size (length) of the structure.

The use of similitude principles directly in design can be illustrated by the following example. Column 1, having a length L_1, has been designed so that it will fail at an axial load P_1 (alternatively, the buckling load P_1 may have been determined by a test). *Under what conditions can the same proportions be used to design column 2 which must transmit a greater compressive load P_2 over a greater distance L_2?* Obviously $N = L_2/L_1$ and the buckling load for column 2 will be

$$P_2 = N^2 P_1 \qquad (a)$$

Substituting for N^2 we have

$$P_2 = \left(\frac{L_2}{L_1}\right)^2 P_1 \qquad (b)$$

or

$$\frac{P_2}{L_2{}^2} = \frac{P_1}{L_1{}^2} \qquad (c)$$

The quantity $P_i/L_i{}^2$ is called the *structural index*. It characterizes the relationship between strength and size that is common to an entire family of structures obtained by the dimensional similitude transformation. (The subscript i stands for any member of the family. L_i may be any dimension.) The above index applies to all structures for which the loading is in terms of force. The answer to the question is therefore that *the two structures must have the same structural index*. Also, from Eq. (a), $N = (P_2/P_1)^{\frac{1}{2}}$.

It can be similarly shown that the structural index for loading by bending or torsional moments is $M_i/L_i{}^3$. The required value of N now becomes $N = (M_2/M_1)^{\frac{1}{3}}$. For *line loading* the index is q_i/L_i and for *pressure loading* the index becomes simply p_i. For example, tank 2 can be designed to have the same proportions as tank 1 if the design pressures are the same.

The structural index is a valuable tool in presenting the results of optimization studies, as shown in Sec. 15.10. By putting the results on this basis we show that the optimization applies to an entire class of structures, not only to the particular structure being optimized.

It should be noted that, in the classical treatment of structural similitude, the basic dimensionless parameter is found to be, for force loading, P/EL^2. This means that all dimensionally similar structures having the same value of this parameter, regardless of the material used, will undergo the same *elastic strain* (since P/L^2 is in terms of stress).

15.10 *Elements of optimum* design*

In Secs. 15.6 and 15.7 the geometry of a structural system was optimized on the basis that the allowable stress was unaffected by the length or loading of the members. For components that fail by buckling, this is not true. Before the system can be completely optimized, it is necessary to investigate the optimization of the individual components, that is, to

---

* Also called optimal design. Either designation is correct.

determine the proportions, shape, and size of cross sections so as to achieve the minimum volume (or weight, or cost) of material.

For a given structural function (that is, given certain loads, lengths, etc.), optimization may be accomplished in various ways. One obvious way is simply to design a number of different structures and compare them. However, techniques have been developed which provide a direct solution and which yield important general information regarding the relative efficiency of materials, effects of loading intensity, and other factors.

We shall use as an example a thin-walled tubular column of circular cross section, centrally loaded, with pinned ends. For such members the cross-sectional properties of interest are given, quite accurately, by the following formulas:

$$A = \pi Dt \qquad I = \frac{\pi D^3 t}{8} \qquad \rho = \frac{D}{\sqrt{8}}$$

where D is the mean diameter. For *equilibrium* between external load and internal stresses we have

$$\sigma_{\text{appl}} = \frac{P}{A} = \frac{P}{\pi Dt} \qquad (a)$$

For *column failure* in the elastic range,

$$\sigma_{\text{col}} = \frac{\pi^2 E}{(L/\rho)^2} = \frac{\pi^2 E D^2}{8L^2} \qquad (b)$$

For *local buckling failure* in the elastic range,

$$\sigma_{\text{loc}} = \frac{K_c E t}{D} \qquad (c)$$

From the above equations it is possible to derive equations which represent the cross-sectional area required to prevent each mode of failure, for constant values of P, L, E, and K_c. If we consider A_{reqd} as a function of D, the following equations are easily derived:

$$A_{\text{col}} = \frac{8PL^2}{\pi^2 E D^2} \qquad (d)$$

$$A_{\text{loc}} = \left(\frac{\pi P}{K_c E}\right)^{\frac{1}{2}} D \qquad (e)$$

Equations (d) and (e) are plotted on Fig. 15.18, for the parameters noted. The shaded area under the curves represents a region of unacceptable (understrength) design. The minimum cross-sectional area occurs at the intersection of the curves. This fact reveals that *the optimum design is found by equating the buckling loads for the two independent modes of* *failure.** This is true, of course, only if there are no other modes of failure that require a greater cross-sectional area. If there are, the corresponding curves must be added to the figure to find the lowest possible value of A.

An alternative way of depicting the above situation is shown in Fig. 15.19. Here one design variable is plotted against another. Curves representing different constant values of A are also plotted. The "design space" representing all combinations of t and D that would meet or exceed the loading requirement is the space above the shaded area. Obviously the

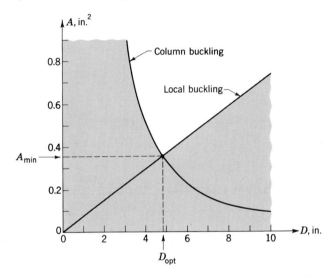

Figure 15.18. Illustration of optimization of a column. (Data from Example 15.5.)

point in design space that lies on the lowest possible curve representing A determines optimum design. This method permits use of formal mathematical techniques for minimizing functions and may be extended to n-dimensional design space involving many variables (see Ref. 74).

Both Figs. 15.18 and 15.19 can be modified to include inelastic effects, but this subject can be more easily handled by optimization on the "structural-index" level, now to be described.

In Sec. 15.9 it was shown that any particular structure belongs to a family of geometrically similar structures obtained by multiplying all original dimensions by the same numerical factor. Since all dimensional ratios then remain constant, the buckling stresses will also remain constant. If the design loading is proportional to the square of a dimension (i.e., if the *structural index* is constant), the applied stresses will remain

---

* In this elementary form, the principle involved is often referred to as the "one-hoss shay" principle, after the famous poem by Oliver Wendell Holmes (see Tuckerman's quotation, Ref. 73).

constant. Therefore, for a column, the basic condition for minimum cross-sectional area can be expressed on the stress level as

$$\sigma_{\text{appl}} = \sigma_{\text{col}} = \sigma_{\text{loc}} \qquad (15.13)$$

The optimum stress can be determined as a function of the structural index (P/L^2 in this case). There are various ways of deriving the necessary equations, but the following method has special advantages.*

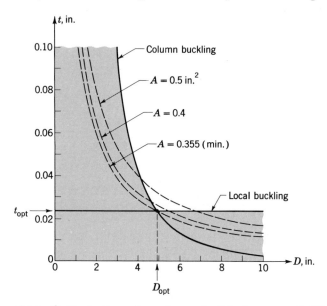

Figure 15.19. Optimization of a column in "design space." (Data from Example 15.5.)

Instead of deriving σ_{opt} directly, in terms of P/L^2, we derive an equation for P/L^2 as a function of σ_{opt}.

For the tubular column, the equilibrium equation (*a*) can be written:

$$P = \sigma A = \sigma \pi D t \qquad (f)$$

To obtain the index, divide both sides of Eq. (*f*) by L^2, giving

$$\frac{P}{L^2} = \frac{\pi \sigma D t}{L^2} \qquad (g)$$

Since $\rho^2 = D^2/8$, multiply the right-hand side by D/D, and substitute for D^2 the value $8\rho^2$. The result may be written in the following form:

$$\frac{P}{L^2} = \frac{8\pi\sigma}{(L/\rho)^2 \, (D/t)} \qquad (15.14)$$

* Originally developed in Ref. 19, page 629.

Assume now that we have a "column curve" which gives σ_{col} as a function of L/ρ, such as Fig. 11.7. A value of σ is selected and the corresponding value of L/ρ is determined. Similarly, the corresponding value of D/t is found from a curve giving σ_{loc} as a function of D/t, as in Fig. 11.23. Substituting the values of L/ρ and D/t in Eq. (15.14), together with the value of σ, we obtain the value of the index, P/L^2. By selecting different values of σ, the entire curve of σ_{opt} can be plotted as a function of P/L^2. This procedure can be used directly with buckling curves obtained

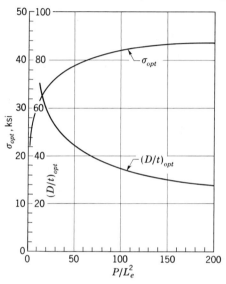

Figure 15.20. Optimum design curves for round tubular columns (aluminum alloy 2024-T3).

from experiment. Figure 15.20 shows optimum design curves obtained in this manner. Note that end constraint is provided for by using the effective column length, L_e.

An equation for σ_{opt} can be derived by substituting in Eq. (15.14) the values of $(L/\rho)^2$ and $(D/t)_{opt}$ obtained from Eqs. (11.6) and (11.33), respectively. The results are, for $L_e = L$,

$$\sigma_{opt} = \left(\frac{\pi}{8}\right)^{\frac{1}{3}} K_c^{\frac{1}{3}} \eta_t^{\frac{1}{2}} E^{\frac{2}{3}} \left(\frac{P}{L^2}\right)^{\frac{1}{3}}$$

For $K_c = 0.40$,

$$\sigma_{opt} = 0.54 \eta_t^{\frac{1}{2}} E^{\frac{2}{3}} \left(\frac{P}{L^2}\right)^{\frac{1}{3}} \qquad (h)$$

An equation for $(D/t)_{opt}$ can be derived by solving Eq. (11.33) for D/t and using σ_{opt} for the local buckling stress. The result is

$$\left(\frac{D}{t}\right)_{opt} = \frac{2K_c^{\frac{2}{3}} E^{\frac{1}{3}}}{\pi^{\frac{1}{3}} (P/L^2)^{\frac{1}{3}}}$$

Since η_t is a function of σ, Eq. (h) should be solved for P/L^2, in plotting. For $K_c = 0.40$,

$$\left(\frac{D}{t}\right)_{\text{opt}} = \frac{0.746E^{\frac{1}{4}}}{(P/L^2)^{\frac{1}{4}}} \tag{i}$$

To obtain an equation for cross-sectional area, divide P/L^2 by σ_{opt}:

$$\frac{A}{L^2} = 1.85\eta_t^{-\frac{1}{4}}E^{-\frac{1}{4}}\left(\frac{P}{L^2}\right)^{\frac{3}{4}} \tag{j}$$

In Ref. 13 various other structural components were optimized (wide column, shear webs, beams, stiffened shells). Many papers have been published in this field. The above brief treatment of one type of component has been presented primarily to emphasize the fact that design need not be a trial-and-error process, but can be put on an efficient mathematical basis. Furthermore, the relative merits of different materials (on a weight basis) cannot be properly evaluated unless the component is optimized for each different material (tension members excepted).

EXAMPLE 15.5. A pinned-end column is to be designed to transmit an ultimate load of 7,000 lb (this includes the factor of safety). The column length is 10 ft. The material is to be aluminum alloy and the cross section is to be circular. The structural index is

$$\frac{P}{L^2} = \frac{7,000}{120^2} = 0.485 \text{ psi}$$

From Fig. 15.20 it is evident that the optimum stress will be in the elastic range. It is therefore possible to use the optimum design formulas directly, with $\eta_t = 1.0$.

For $E = 10 \times 10^6$ psi, Eq. (h) gives

$$\sigma_{\text{opt}} = 0.54(10 \times 10^6)^{\frac{3}{4}}(0.485)^{\frac{1}{4}} = 19,700 \text{ psi}$$

From Eq. (i),

$$\left(\frac{D}{t}\right)_{\text{opt}} = \frac{0.746(10 \times 10^6)^{\frac{1}{4}}}{(0.485)^{\frac{1}{4}}} = 204$$

$$A_{\text{reqd}} = \frac{P}{\sigma} = \frac{7,000}{19,700} = 0.355 \text{ in.}^2$$

Knowing D/t, we can find both D and t from the relationship $A = \pi Dt$.

$$D_{\text{opt}} = \left[\frac{A(D/t)}{\pi}\right]^{\frac{1}{2}} = \left(\frac{0.355 \times 204}{\pi}\right)^{\frac{1}{2}} = 4.78 \text{ in.}$$

$$t_{\text{opt}} = \frac{D}{(D/t)} = \frac{4.78}{204} = 0.0234 \text{ in.}$$

The weight (less fittings) is

$$W = wAL = 0.10 \times 0.355 \times 120 = 4.26 \text{ lb}$$

We have now designed, very quickly, the most efficient column that can be made from a round aluminum-alloy tube for the specified values of P and L.

The optimum wall thickness turned out to be quite small. Let us assume that there is a requirement (constraint) which prohibits the use of a thickness less than a prescribed value t_0. We can now optimize the column again, *subject to this constraint.*

The use of a thicker tube will eliminate local buckling as a design criterion. Equation (15.13) then becomes

$$\sigma_{\text{appl}} = \sigma_{\text{col}} < \sigma_{\text{loc}}$$

Assuming elastic action,

$$\frac{P}{A} = \sigma_{\text{col}} = \frac{\pi^2 E}{(L/\rho)^2}$$

Substituting $A = \pi D t_0$ and $\rho^2 = D^2/8$, and solving for D we obtain

$$D'_{\text{opt}} = \frac{2P^{\frac{1}{2}}L^{\frac{3}{2}}}{\pi E^{\frac{1}{2}} t_0^{\frac{1}{2}}}$$

where the prime indicates the presence of a constraint.

Let $t_0 = 0.125$ in. for this design. Then

$$D'_{\text{opt}} = 2.76 \text{ in.}$$
$$A'_{\text{reqd}} = 1.08 \text{ in.}^2$$

Compared with the original optimized design the relative weight factor is $1.08/0.355 = 3.04$, which is much less than the ratio of thicknesses $t_0/t_{\text{opt}} = 0.125/0.0235 = 5.32$. This example shows how optimization procedures can incorporate and evaluate the effects of various constraints that may be imposed (see also Ref. 75).

15.11 *Introduction to statically indeterminate structures*

A plane statically indeterminate structural system is shown in Fig. 15.21*a*. All members have the same cross-sectional area. From symmetry it is obvious that $\delta_x = 0$.

From the free-body diagram for the pin we have two meaningful equations of equilibrium. ($\Sigma M = 0$ is satisfied because all force vectors pass through a common point.)

$$[\Sigma P_x = 0] \qquad\qquad -P_1 \sin \alpha + P_3 \sin \alpha = 0$$

Therefore
$$P_1 = P_3 \qquad\qquad (a)$$

$$[\Sigma P_y = 0] \qquad P_1 \cos \alpha + P_2 + P_3 \cos \alpha - P = 0$$

Substituting from (a),
$$2P_1 \cos \alpha + P_2 = P \qquad\qquad (b)$$

A *compatibility condition* is required to supply the necessary third equation. This condition is that the common ends of all three members must remain connected; therefore these ends have the same displacement relative to the base to which the members are attached. This base is "rigid." The system deflection is δ_y. (Compatibility with respect to δ_x is satisfied by symmetry.)

For member 2, the axial deflection $\delta_2 = \delta_y$. For members 1 and 3 the axial deflection is found by drawing the deflected configuration (δ_y is exaggerated in

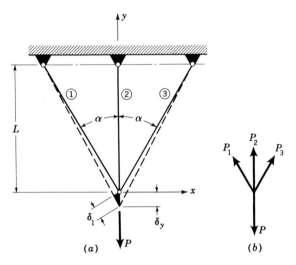

Figure 15.21. Elementary statically indeterminate plane truss (symmetrical).

Fig. 15.21). For small strains the shaded triangle shown at the joint can be treated as a right triangle. (See also Fig. 15.1.) From this triangle

$$\delta_1 = \delta_y \cos \alpha \qquad (c)$$

In the elastic range:

$$\delta_1 = \frac{P_1 L_1}{AE} \quad \text{and} \quad \delta_2 = \frac{P_2 L_2}{AE}$$

Substituting $\delta_y = \delta_2$, $L_1 = L/\cos \alpha$, $L_2 = L$, and cancelling AE (since it is the same for all members) we obtain from (c)

$$P_1 = P_2 \cos^2 \alpha$$

This is the required third equation. Substitution of this value of P_1 in Eq. (b) gives the forces

$$P_2 = \frac{P}{1 + 2 \cos^3 \alpha} \quad \text{and} \quad P_1 = \frac{P \cos^2 \alpha}{1 + 2 \cos^3 \alpha}$$

Substituting the above value of P_2 in the expression for δ_2 gives

$$\delta_2 = \delta_3 = \frac{PL}{AE}\left(\frac{1}{1 + 2\cos^3\alpha}\right)$$

A general method of analysis for an unsymmetrical plane system, shown in Fig. 15.22, will now be described. First we apply the components of the unknown deflection (δ_x, δ_y) separately and calculate the corresponding member deflections. (The geometric analysis of Sec. 15.2 can be used.)

These deflections determine the member forces. For equilibrium the resultant of the member forces must be equal and opposite to the externally applied force. Therefore, the external force **P**, necessary to cause the

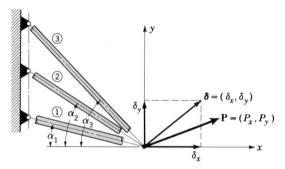

Figure 15.22. General case of elementary statically indeterminate plane truss.

deflection (δ_x, δ_y) is determined by finding the resultant of the member forces. The equations for **P** are then solved simultaneously to determine the deflection of the system as a function of **P**.

Omitting details, we find that

$$P_x = K_{xx}\delta_x + K_{xy}\delta_y$$
$$P_y = K_{yx}\delta_x + K_{yy}\delta_y \tag{15.15}$$

where

$$K_{xx} = \Sigma K_i \cos^2\alpha_i$$

$$K_{xy} = K_{yx} = \Sigma K_i \sin\alpha_i \cos\alpha_i$$
$$K_{yy} = \Sigma K_i \sin^2\alpha_i$$

and

$$K_i = \frac{A_i E_i}{L_i}$$

This represents the application of *Hooke's law*. Since $K_{xy} = K_{yx}$, only three simple calculations are needed to determine the coefficients in Eqs. (15.15).

To find the system deflection (δ_x, δ_y) produced by a force (P_x, P_y), Eqs. (15.15) are solved simultaneously.

These operations can be represented concisely by matrix algebra. Equations (15.15) are written* as

$$\begin{Bmatrix} P_x \\ P_y \end{Bmatrix} = \begin{bmatrix} K_{xx} & K_{xy} \\ K_{yx} & K_{yy} \end{bmatrix} \begin{Bmatrix} \delta_x \\ \delta_y \end{Bmatrix} \tag{15.16a}$$

This procedure represents the behavior of the system by an equation of the same general form as the algebraic equation for a single member:

$$\mathbf{P} = [K]\boldsymbol{\delta} \tag{15.16b}$$

where $[K]$ is the *stiffness matrix*.

To determine $\boldsymbol{\delta}$ as a function of $\mathbf{P}$ we *invert* the K matrix. Then

$$\boldsymbol{\delta} = [C]\mathbf{P} \tag{15.17}$$

where $[C] = [K]^{-1}$. The matrix $[C]$ is the *compliance* (or flexibility) *matrix*.

The K matrix is a *tensor*. It can be *diagonalized* (Sec. 2.10) by a rotation of the base axis system so that Eq. (15.16a) becomes

$$\begin{Bmatrix} P'_x \\ P'_y \end{Bmatrix} = \begin{bmatrix} K'_{xx} & 0 \\ 0 & K'_{yy} \end{bmatrix} \begin{Bmatrix} \delta'_x \\ \delta'_y \end{Bmatrix} \tag{15.18a}$$

This equation can be expressed in ordinary algebra as

$$\begin{aligned} P'_x &= K'_{xx}\delta'_{xx} \\ P'_y &= K'_{yy}\delta'_{yy} \end{aligned} \tag{15.18b}$$

The equations for deflection then become

$$\begin{aligned} \delta'_x &= C'_{xx}P'_{xx} \\ \delta'_y &= C'_{yy}P'_{yy} \end{aligned} \tag{15.19}$$

The x' and y' axis that were found to convert the K matrix to diagonal form represent the *principal axes*. *A force applied along a principal axis will cause a deflection along that axis only.*

Equations (15.16) and (15.17) can be applied to three-dimensional systems, in which case we have

$$\begin{Bmatrix} P_x \\ P_y \\ P_z \end{Bmatrix} = \begin{bmatrix} K_{xx} & K_{xy} & K_{xz} \\ K_{yx} & K_{yy} & K_{yz} \\ K_{zx} & K_{zy} & K_{zz} \end{bmatrix} \begin{Bmatrix} \delta_x \\ \delta_y \\ \delta_z \end{Bmatrix} \tag{15.20}$$

EXAMPLE 15.6. Figure E15.6 shows three members in the same plane. All members are steel ($E = 29 \times 10^6$ psi). Cross-sectional areas are shown on the drawing. The stiffness and compliance matrices will be found.

---

* It is customary, although not essential, to use braces for a matrix which represents a vector.

The first step is to calculate the member lengths and their angles:

$$L_1 = 29.15 \text{ in.} \qquad \alpha_1 = 59.1°$$
$$L_2 = 41.23 \text{ in.} \qquad \alpha_2 = 14.1°$$
$$L_3 = 42.72 \text{ in.} \qquad \alpha_3 = -20.5°$$

$$K_1 = \left(\frac{EA}{L}\right)_1 = \frac{29 \times 10^6 \times 1.25}{29.15} = 1.24 \times 10^6 \text{ lb/in.}$$

$$K_2 = \left(\frac{EA}{L}\right)_2 = \frac{29 \times 10^6 \times 0.75}{41.23} = 0.527 \times 10^6 \text{ lb/in.}$$

$$K_3 = \left(\frac{EA}{L}\right)_3 = \frac{29 \times 10^6 \times 0.50}{42.72} = 0.339 \times 10^6 \text{ lb/in.}$$

For convenience, the term 10^6 will be dropped in subsequent computations. This is equivalent to applying a component of δ equal to 10^{-6}, or 1 μin. (microinch).

$$K_{xx} = \Sigma K_i \cos^2 \alpha_i = 0.327 + 0.497 + 0.297 = 1.121$$
$$K_{xy} = \Sigma K_i \sin \alpha_i \cos \alpha_i = -0.547 - 0.125 + 0.112 = -0.560$$
$$K_{yy} = \Sigma K_i \sin^2 \alpha_i = 0.913 + 0.031 + 0.042 = 0.986$$

Substituting these values in Eq. (15.15) and solving simultaneously give

$$\delta_x = 1.24 P_x + 0.708 P_y$$
$$\delta_y = 0.708 P_x + 1.42 P_y \tag{a}$$

In matrix algebra Eqs. (15.15) become

$$\begin{Bmatrix} P_x \\ P_y \end{Bmatrix} = \begin{bmatrix} 1.121 & -0.560 \\ -0.560 & 0.986 \end{bmatrix} \begin{Bmatrix} \delta_x \\ \delta_y \end{Bmatrix} \tag{b}$$

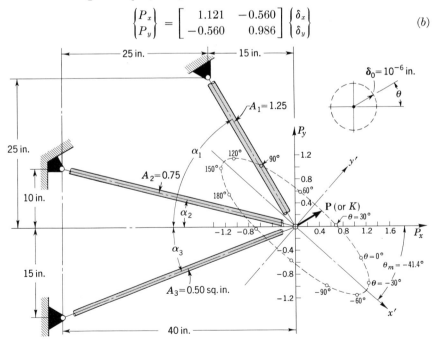

Figure E15.6

Inversion of the K matrix gives the C matrix and Eq. (b) is transformed into

$$\begin{Bmatrix} \delta_x \\ \delta_y \end{Bmatrix} = \begin{bmatrix} 1.24 & 0.708 \\ 0.708 & 1.42 \end{bmatrix} \begin{Bmatrix} P_x \\ P_y \end{Bmatrix} \tag{c}$$

Equation (c) is obviously Eq. (a) in matrix form. When diagonalized, it becomes

$$\begin{Bmatrix} \delta'_x \\ \delta'_y \end{Bmatrix} = \begin{bmatrix} 2.04 & 0 \\ 0 & 0.62 \end{bmatrix} \begin{Bmatrix} P'_x \\ P'_y \end{Bmatrix} \tag{d}$$

The directions of the principal axes x' and y' can be found from the procedures of matrix algebra. However, for this two-dimensional case we can use Eq. (2.14) previously obtained for the two-dimensional stress tensor, since we know that the K and C matrices are tensors. Then

$$\tan 2\theta = \frac{2C_{xy}}{C_{xx} - C_{yy}} = \frac{2 \times 0.708}{1.24 - 1.42} = -7.85 \tag{e}$$
$$2\theta = -82.8° \quad \text{and} \quad +97.2°$$
$$\theta = -41.4° \quad \text{and} \quad +48.6°$$

These values are shown in Fig. E15.6.

By applying a unit deflection δ_0 at various angles θ, the corresponding values of **P** can be determined from Eq. (b). Figure E15.6 shows the resulting polar diagram when $\delta_0 = 10^{-6}$ in. The curve described by the **P** vector is an ellipse. Since $\mathbf{P}/\delta_0 = K$, this curve represents the polar plot of *stiffness* of the system in terms of 10^6 lb/in.

A similar plot of $\boldsymbol{\delta}$ will be determined if Eq. (c) is used, with a constant value of $\mathbf{P}_0$ applied at various angles. This will be an ellipse with its major axis at 90° from the major axis of the stiffness ellipse. It represents the *compliance* (flexibility) of the system in terms of 10^{-6} in./lb (or μ in./lb).

In three dimensions, the stiffness and compliance characteristics of an elastic system are represented by ellipsoids.

15.12 Analysis for ultimate strength (limit design)

In a statically indeterminate system, any inelastic action alters the conditions of constraint. This usually permits the loading to be increased beyond the ultimate loading predicted by elastic theory. The term *limit design*, when used in this sense, applies only to statically indeterminate structures.

As an illustration, consider the three-bar plane truss analyzed elastically in Sec. 15.11, shown in Fig. 15.21. When AE is the same for all members, the forces in members 1 and 2 are given by

$$P_1 = \frac{P \cos^2 \alpha}{1 + 2 \cos^3 \alpha}$$
$$P_2 = \frac{P}{1 + 2 \cos^3 \alpha}$$

The ratio of loading is

$$\frac{P_2}{P_1} = \frac{1}{\cos^2 \alpha}$$

if $\alpha = 45°$, $P_2 = 2P_1$ and $\sigma_2 = 2\sigma_1$.

As the applied load P is increased, member 2 enters the inelastic range and its stiffness (effective value of AE) then decreases. Therefore the above ratio of 2.0 decreases. For a particular stress-strain diagram, the system behavior can be predicted by applying increasing values of δ, calculating δ_1, and δ_2, ϵ_1 and ϵ_2, and the forces P_1, P_2, and P. A load-deflection curve for the system is thus determined.

The analysis is greatly simplified by using the *elastoplastic* approximation. The more highly stressed member (2) reaches the yield stress σ_y before the other two members. From that point on, any increase in the applied load P will cause no further increase in P_2, which will remain at the limit value:

$$P_2^* = \sigma_y A_2$$

Member 2 can now be replaced by a constant force P_2^* applied (upward) at the joint. The system is thereby reduced to a statically determinate system of two members under the applied load $P - P_2^*$. The external force P can be increased until members 1 and 3 also develop the yield stress. Then the system collapses; the deflection δ will increase without further increase in the load P, if changes in geometry are not considered.

Let us now apply the same idea to a *uniformly loaded beam with both ends fixed* (Fig. 15.23b). By using the method of Sec. 7.7 it is possible to determine the inelastic moment-curvature diagram for a beam of given cross section. It will have a shape something like that shown in Fig. 15.23a. We shall use the *ideally plastic* abstraction to simplify the calculations, as indicated in Fig. 15.23a (dashed line).

Figure 15.23c shows the *elastic* moment diagram at the instant the negative moment at the fixed ends reaches the limit value M^*. Note that the positive moment at midspan is only half the limit value. If the applied loading q is now further increased, the ends of the beam will rotate relative to the fixed supports. This phenomenon is implied by the term *plastic hinge*.

The bending moment at each end will remain constant at the limit value during additional loading. When the loading q is increased, the bending moment diagram will increase positively (retaining its parabolic shape) until the maximum positive value reaches M^*, as shown in Fig. 15.23d. The limit (ultimate) value of q is then found by treating the beam as a pinned-end beam having a maximum bending moment equal to twice the limit value:

$$\frac{q^* L^2}{8} = 2M^*$$

$$q^* = \frac{16M^*}{L^2}$$

When the loading reaches this value, a third plastic hinge will be developed at midspan and the beam will collapse.

The limit (ultimate) loading thus determined is one-third greater than that determined from analysis in which failure is assumed to occur when the moment at *any* point reaches M^*.

The limit type of analysis can be applied to systems consisting of continuous beams, frames, interconnected beams and columns, and other forms. The procedure consists in finding the correct location of the plastic hinges that will reduce the structure to a mechanism. The known values of M^* are then applied

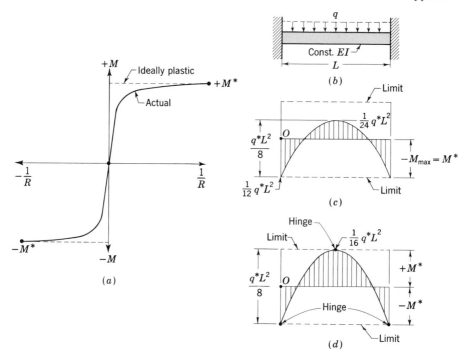

Figure 15.23. Limit analysis of a beam.

at the plastic hinges, and the limit values of applied loading are found from the equations of static equilibrium.

The limit-design method usually gives a realistic estimate of the ultimate loading that can be withstood by the system before complete collapse occurs. However, the stated (and implied) assumptions must be carefully compared with the actual conditions likely to exist in a particular structure. In some cases, the predicted ultimate strength cannot be fully developed because of such phenomena as premature local buckling of flanges, lateral buckling of the beam, inadequate ductility of the material, effects of repeated or reversed loading. The subject is thoroughly treated in modern textbooks on structural systems, in building codes, and similar publications.

EXAMPLE 15.7 Limit design of a beam. In Fig. E15.7 find the value of the limit load P (collapse load) for a 2 in. OD tube with $t = 0.058$ in. Assume that a hinge forms when $\sigma_{max} = \sigma_y = 30,000$ psi; that is, neglecting plastic effect on internal stress distribution.

SOLUTION: From Table B.3, $Z = 0.167$ in.³, $M_P = \sigma_y Z = 30,000 \times 0.167 = 5,000$ in.-lb. This is based on a linear (elastic) distribution. For ideal plasticity the value would be higher (Sec. 7.7).

It is not obvious whether the first plastic hinge will form at B or at C, but there must be hinges at both places for collapse. Let us start with one plastic hinge,

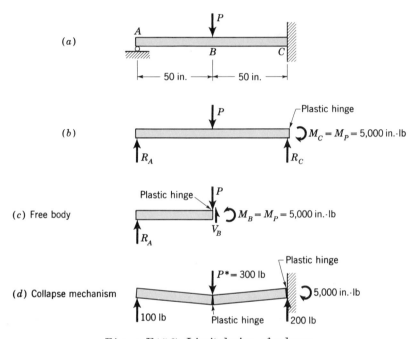

Figure E15.7. Limit design of a beam.

at C. From the free-body diagram we have

$$[\Sigma P = 0] \qquad\qquad R_A + R_C - P = 0$$
$$[\Sigma M_C = 0] \qquad\qquad 5,000 + 100R_A - 50P = 0$$
$$P = 2R_A + 100$$

These equations are not sufficient to determine P. At failure, a plastic hinge develops at B. The free-body diagram for the left half is shown in E15.6c.

$$[\Sigma M_B = 0] \qquad\qquad 50R_A - 5,000 = 0 \qquad R_A = 100 \text{ lb}$$
Therefore $\qquad\qquad\qquad P^* = 200 + 100 = 300 \text{ lb}$

The elastic solution gives $P = 256$ lb. The limit method gives an increase of about 17 percent, without including the inelastic effect on the modulus of rupture. (This effect is relatively small for efficient cross sections.)

PROBLEMS

15.1. *Deflection of plane truss.* Draw a sketch, to scale, for an assigned set of values from Table P15.1. (See Fig. P15.1, drawn for design number 1.) Calculate member loads, P_i. All tension members have cross-sectional

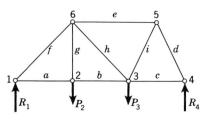

Figure P15.1

areas of 0.20 in.^{2} and all compression members of 0.50 in.^{2}. Find the vertical deflections of joints 2 and 3. Material is steel, with $E = 29 \times 10^6$ psi. Assume that stresses remain in the elastic range and that compression members do not buckle. (Indicate any "zero load" members on the sketch.) Solve by computing force influence coefficients for vertical dummy loads at joints 2 and 3, respectively.

TABLE P15.1

Joint ↓	Joint coordinates, in., for different designs						
	1	2	3	4	5	6	7
1	(0, 0)	(0, 0)	(0, 0)	(0, 0)	(0, 0)	(0, 0)	(0, 0)
2	(40, 0)	(40, 0)	(40, 0)	(30, 0)	(30, 0)	(40, 0)	(50, 0)
3	(80, 0)	(80, 0)	(80, 0)	(60, 0)	(60, 0)	(80, 0)	(100, 0)
4	(120, 0)	(140, 0)	(140, 0)	(120, 0)	(140, 0)	(140, 0)	(160, 0)
5	(100, 40)	(110, 40)	(110, 50)	(90, 50)	(100, 60)	(110, 60)	(130, 60)
6	(40, 40)	(40, 40)	(40, 50)	(30, 50)	(30, 60)	(40, 60)	(50, 60)
	Loadings, lb.						
2	1,000	1,000	2,000	2,000	2,000	3,000	3,000
3	2,000	3,000	2,000	1,000	3,000	3,000	1,000

TABLE P15.2

Member ↓	Length components (L_x, L_y, L_z), ft						
	1	2	3	4	5	6	7
a	$(-2, -1, -6)$	$(-1.5, -1.5, -8)$	$(-1, -1.5, -7)$	$(-2, -1, -6)$	$(-1, -2, -5)$	$(-2, -2, -4)$	$(-3, -1, -5)$
b	$(3, 0, -6)$	$(2, 0, -8)$	$(3, -1.5, -7)$	$(2, -1, -6)$	$(3, 0, -5)$	$(3, 1, -4)$	$(2, 1, -5)$
c	$(0, 2, -6)$	$(-1, 2, -8)$	$(-1.5, 2.5, -7)$	$(1, 2, -6)$	$(-1, 2, -5)$	$(-1.5, 2, -4)$	$(-2, 3, -5)$

TABLE P15.3

Design →	1	2	3	4	5	6	7
P, lb	1,000	1,200	900	1,100	1,500	1,400	1,300
B, in.	(24, 0, 0)	(20, 0, 0)	(18, 0, 0)	(30, 0, 0)	(28, 0, 0)	(26, 0, 0)	(36, 0, 0)
C, in.	(24, 0, 12)	(20, 0, 14)	(18, 0, 20)	(30, 0, 12)	(28, 0, 10)	(26, 0, 12)	(36, 0, 15)
D, in.	(30, 0, 12)	(30, 0, 14)	(32, 0, 20)	(40, 0, 12)	(38, 0, 10)	(36, 0, 12)	(40, 0, 15)

15.2. *Deflection of a tripod.* An unsymmetrical tripod has been designed to transmit a force $P = (2,000, 1,000, 0)$ lb, as shown in Fig. P15.2. For

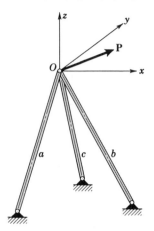

Figure P15.2

an assigned set of dimensions from Table P15.2, calculate the forces in the members and the components of the deflection δ_x and δ_y, in inches (omit δ_z). (All joints are ball-and-socket.) All members have a cross-sectional area of 0.50 in.^{2} Ignore the possibility of column failure.

15.3. *Use of Castigliano's theorem.* In Fig. P15.3 the load **P** (vertical) and the coordinates of the points B, C, and D are to be assigned from Table

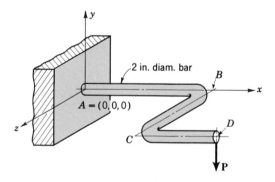

Figure P15.3

P15.3. Assume elastic action, with $E = 29 \times 10^6$ psi, $\nu = 0.30$, and calculate the vertical deflection at point D, with respect to the fixed base, using Castigliano's theorem.

Suggestion: Write expressions for strain energy caused by bending, transverse shear, and torsion, and differentiate total with respect to P. Indicate the portion of deflection caused respectively by each of the above types of force transmission.

Notes: (*a*) The value of A_s, Table B.2, may be used to obtain $\tau_{\max}$ due to transverse shear. For deflections, assume this stress to be uniform over cross section.

(*b*) The structure may be treated as three straight members, ignoring bends.

15.4. *Dynamic loading.* (*a*) An airplane is diving vertically at velocity V and must make a pull-out without exceeding an acceleration factor n_{limit}. Derive a formula for the minimum radius of curvature, R, of the flight path. (Assume V is constant until lowest point of pull-out is reached.) Give two equations, one for V in miles per hour, the other for knots. (One knot = 1.1516 mph.)

(*b*) Evaluate R, in feet, for a case in which $n_{\text{limit}} = 3.0$ and $V = 550$ mph.

15.5. *Optimization of geometry; plane truss element.* Find the optimum values for angles α and β in Fig. P15.5, for two different cases: (*a*) allowable stress equal for both members, (*b*) allowable compressive stress

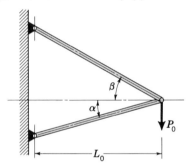

Figure P15.5

σ_c equal to one-half allowable tensile stress σ_t. (*Note:* Actually, the maximum allowable value of σ_c is a function of P_1 and L_1; see Sec. 15.10.) In both cases derive the value of k_v, as defined in Sec. 15.6.)

15.6. *Optimization of geometry; tripod.* (*a*) Derive the optimum value of R/h and the minimum value of k_v for the structure used in Sec. 15.7, except that the force P is to be applied in any direction in a plane parallel with the ground (*not* a spherical envelope).

(*b*) Derive an expression for the deflection δ in the direction of P, in terms of P, h, E and A, where A is the cross-sectional area of each member. The optimum geometry is to be used.

Note: The allowable stress may be assumed the same for each member, but note the comment in Prob. 15.5.

15.7. *Reinforced concrete beam: balanced design.* (*a*) Using relationships developed in Sec. 15.8, derive the following formula for the optimum location of the neutral axis (of a rectangular cross section) at which the allowable stresses for both steel and concrete are developed simultaneously (so-called "balanced" design):

$$k = \frac{1}{1 + (\sigma_{st}/n\sigma_{con})}$$

(b) Derive the following equation for the required value of d, where k is given by the above formula and M is the design bending moment:

$$d = \left[\frac{2M}{k(1 - k/3)\,\sigma_{con}b} \right]^{\frac{1}{2}}$$

The required area of steel bars is then given by Eq. (15.9), with $j = 1 - k/3$.

15.8. *Design of a reinforced concrete beam.* Determine the depth d and required cross-sectional area A_{st} of the steel bars for a *balanced* reinforced concrete beam of rectangular cross section, such as shown in Fig. 15.13; parameters to be assigned from Table P15.8 (see also Prob. 15.7).

TABLE P15.8

Design →	1	2	3	4	5	6	7
M, 10^6 in.-lb	2.0	2.5	2.3	2.4	2.6	1.8	2.1
b, in.	18	20	19	21	22	17	20
σ_{st}, ksi	20	19	18	19	20	18	16
σ_{con}, psi	600	700	650	750	800	600	600
n	15	14	15	14	13	15	15

15.9. *Design of a prestressed concrete beam; extension of Prob. 15.8.* For an assigned design from Prob. 15.8, redesign the beam as a centrally prestressed beam, using the following basis. Let d represent the entire depth of concrete. Concrete is to be prestressed (uniformly) to 300 psi by a steel rod (or cable) at a tensile stress of 250,000 psi. Keeping the same *ratio* of d/b found in Prob. 15.8, calculate the new values of d and b required, and also the cross-sectional area of steel. Calculate also the change of volume for both concrete and steel. (Make no allowance for the change of M caused by change of dead weight of beam.)

15.10. *Column design.* Determine the required cross-sectional dimensions (constant over length) for a column that must transmit an ultimate compressive load P (includes factor of safety) over a length L, with ends pinned. For comparative purposes work up three alternative designs, as follows, for aluminum alloy ($E = 10 \times 10^6$ psi), omitting possibility of inelastic behavior.

Design A: Solid round bar

Design B: A tube selected from Table B.3, using the one which gives minimum cross-sectional area

Design C: An optimized design in accordance with Sec. 15.10 (see Example 15.5)

Omitting considerations of inelastic action and any constraint on minimum wall thickness, compare the relative volumes of designs A, B, and C. Values of P and L are to be assigned from Table P15.10.

TABLE P15.10

Design →	1	2	3	4	5	6	7
P, lb	32,000	40,000	48,000	64,000	72,000	80,000	88,000
L, in.	80	60	72	68	62	64	70

15.11. Derive equations corresponding to Eqs. (f) to (j), inclusive (Sec. 15.10), for the optimum design of a column having a thin-walled square cross section of average width D, using the following assumptions:

(a) Local buckling of entire column will occur when a side buckles locally as a flat plate with simply supported edges.

(b) The inelastic factor for local buckling is given by $\eta = \sqrt{E_t/E}$.

Evaluate constants for Eqs. (h), (i), and (j) for the square tube made from steel ($E = 29 \times 10^6$ psi), for use when σ is in the elastic range. Also calculate the value of the index (P/L^2) above which the yield stress $\sigma_y = 36,000$ psi controls the design.

Plot the curves of σ_{opt} and $(D/t)_{\text{opt}}$ for steel, similar to Fig. 15.20, up to values of $P/L^2 = 10$ psi. Show the entire elastic curve for this range and indicate "cut-off" stress curves for $\sigma_y = 36,000$ and $60,000$ psi, respectively.

15.12. *Statically indeterminate three-bar truss element.* Determine the stiffness matrix for a structural system such as shown in Fig. E15.6, changing only the location of the base joints to conform with an assigned set of values from Table P15.12 (components given in xy system). Also evaluate the compliance (flexibility) matrix and the location of the principal axes of stiffness, as well as the values of the principal stiffnesses, K_{max} and K_{min}.

TABLE P15.12

Joint ↓	Joint locations (x,y), in.						
	1	2	3	4	5	6	7
1	$(-20, 25)$	$(-25, 20)$	$(-18, 20)$	$(-22, 20)$	$(-30, 25)$	$(-27, 30)$	$(-32, 32)$
2	$(-40, 0)$	$(-40, 12)$	$(-40, 2)$	$(-40, 6)$	$(-40, 4)$	$(-40, 8)$	$(-40, 14)$
3	$(-40, -10)$	$(-40, -12)$	$(-40, -14)$	$(-40, -16)$	$(-40, -16)$	$(-40, -18)$	$(-40, -18)$

15.13. *Individual preliminary design project: plane truss, cantilevered.* In this project the designer is given only certain loads and the points at which the loads are applied. These loads are to be transmitted to a vertical rigid wall (see Table P15.13 and Fig. P15.13). The object is to find a stable,

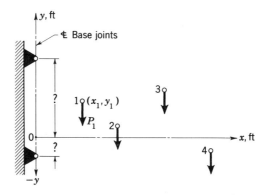

Figure P15.13

statically determinate arrangement of plane truss members that will be relatively efficient, on the basis of the total material volume of members. As a first abstraction (to emphasize the geometrical aspects) compression members need not be designed as columns. Also, the weight of joints is excluded.

TABLE P15.13

Joint ↓	Joint locations, ft						
	a	*b*	*c*	*d*	*e*	*f*	*g*
1	(4, 3)	(4, −1)	(5, 2)	(3, 1)	(5, 1)	(4, −1)	(3, 3)
2	(7, 1)	(8, −1)	(8, 0)	(7, 3)	(9, 2)	(9, 1)	(5, 0)
3	(11, 4)	(11, 2)	(12, −2)	(10, −1)	(13, −1)	(12, 4)	(10, 2)
4	(15, −1)	(15, 0)	(15, −1)	(15, 2)	(15, 0)	(15, 1)	(15, −1)
	Load, kips						
1	6	8	6	8	8	6	9
2	7	7	9	6	7	9	8
3	3	6	5	4	5	3	5
4	2	5	7	2	3	4	2

It is required that the truss be capable of transmitting any or all of the applied forces, in any possible combination.

The allowable stresses (civil engineering system) are to be 20,000 psi for tension members, 10,000 psi for compression members, $E = 29 \times 10^6$ psi, for steel. Density $= 0.29$ lb/in.^{3}

The total material weight is to be computed (results of different student designs may be compared). Also, the deflection at the free end is to be computed *with all loads acting simultaneously.*

Notes: (*a*) All loads must be applied at joints. (*b*) The attachment to the wall must consist of only two pinned joints. (*c*) The truss must be statically determinate. (*d*) Additional members may be added; if this is done, show joint locations on drawing.

Suggestion: After deciding on member centerlines, calculate forces in members by applying, independently, $Q = 1$ at each of the four loading points. Tabulate force coefficients thus obtained. Multiply each load, P_i, by respective force coefficients to obtain partial loads, and tabulate. To find most severe tensile loading in each member, add only the positive partial loads, and vice versa. Find the required area for each member. For full loading, add partial loads algebraically, then calculate δ_i in each member. Use force coefficients for dummy load applied at joint 4 to obtain tip deflection. (This problem can be used as a guide for experimental student projects, using wood, for example. In testing, lateral supports must be provided.)

15.14. Design the structure shown in Fig. P15.14, that is, determine A for member 1 and required cross-sectional dimensions of a tube for member 2 (do not design joints). Ultimate load P, L, and α to be assigned from Table P15.14. Use steel, with $E = 29 \times 10^6$ psi, $\sigma_y = 60,000$ psi (elastoplastic).

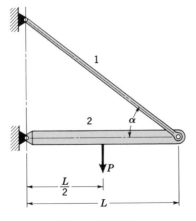

Figure P15.14

Requirements: (*a*) Yield stress not to be exceeded at load *P*. (*b*) Member 2 to be designed as a beam column, using the interaction method for sinusoidal lateral loading (Fig. 11.19).

Note: If a suitable tube size is not available in Table B.3, find required mean diameter, using $D/t = 50$.

TABLE P15.14

Design →	1	2	3	4	5	6	7
P, kips	8	9	7	10	8	9	10
L, in.	60	40	50	70	50	60	70
α, deg	30	35	40	45	50	55	60

15.15. *Continuous beam: elastic.* In Fig. P15.15 the "extra" support makes the structure statically indeterminate; in effect, this is a structural system consisting of two beams which are continuous at joint *B*. The condition

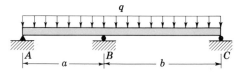

Figure P15.15

of compatibility is that the slopes of both beams, at joint *B*, must be the same. Derive an equation for M_B (selected as the redundant quantity) by figuratively "cutting" the beam at *B* and calculating the difference in slope between the two ends (see Chap. 9). Then calculate the slope caused in each beam by a moment M_B (only) applied at the cut ends, in such a direction as to restore continuity. Express the answer in terms of *q*, *a*, *b*, and *EI* (the latter is constant and equal for both beams). Draw the moment diagrams to scale for the "cut" beam, the beam with internal moment M_B, and the actual beam (the total moment diagram is obtained by superposition). In drawing the diagrams let $q/EI =$ unity and let $b = 1.5a$. (*Note:* Many different methods are available for analyzing continuous beams. The underlying principles are exemplified by this simple problem. See also Prob. 9.11.)

15.16. *Continuous beam: limit design.* (*a*) In Fig. P15.15 for a set of assigned values from the following table, determine the total line load *q* (lb/ft) at which the beam will collapse. In calculating the plastic hinge moment use the value of *Z* from Table B.4.

(*b*) Also calculate the values of the reactions at the collapse loading.

(*c*) Using the result of Prob. 15.15, calculate the maximum total value of *q* if "failure" is defined as the attainment of the yield stress at any point, the rest of the beam remaining elastic.

Notes: (*a*) If ideal plasticity were assumed, the effective ("plastic") section modulus *Z* would be increased somewhat (see Ref. 68 for tabulated values). The collapse load would be increased proportionately.

(*b*) Omit the dead weight of the beam in calculating *q*. The collapse value of the "live" loading is found by subtracting the beam weight (per foot) from the total *q* at collapse.

(*c*) No factor of safety is to be used in calculating the collapse loading (more exactly, let $FS = 1$).

TABLE P15.16

Design →	1	2	3	4	5	6	7
WF Section (Table B.4)	$8 \times 8 \times 58$	$10 \times 8 \times 33$	$10 \times 10 \times 89$	$12 \times 8 \times 40$	$8 \times 8 \times 35$	$12 \times 12 \times 85$	$12 \times 10 \times 53$
a, ft	20	22	32	36	40	38	40
b, ft	30	30	28	30	42	44	48
σ_y, ksi	33	36	42	46	50	90	120

Mechanical Properties of Materials

The information contained in this section is provided for educational purposes, and, because it was drawn from several different sources, discrepancies may be present. For actual design work refer to pertinent codes and specifications.

TABLE A.1

Mechanical properties of structural metals*

Material	Modulus of elasticity $E \times 10^{-6}$, psi	Shear modulus of elasticity $G \times 10^{-6}$, psi	Ultimate tensile strength σ_u, psi	Yield strength (0.002 offset) σ_y, psi	Ultimate shear stress (pins, rivets, etc.) τ_u, psi	Density w, lb/in.³	Coefficient of expansion $\alpha \times 10^6$, strain/°F
Steel:							
AISI 1025	29.0	11.0	55,000	36,000	35,000	0.283	6.8
AISI 4130							
(normalized)	29.0	11.0	90,000	70,000	55,000	0.283	6.3
AISI 4130	29.0	11.0	125,000	103,000	82,000	0.283	6.3
AISI 4140	29.0	11.0	180,000	163,000	109,000	0.283	6.3
17-7PH stainless	30.0	11.7	180,000	150,000	120,000	0.276	6.3
18Ni250 maraging							
(typical)	26.5	10.2	255,000	245,000	145,000	0.289	5.6
Aluminum:							
2024-T3	10.5	4.0	60,000	44,000	32,000	0.100	12.6
2014-T6	10.5	4.0	64,000	58,000	37,000	0.101	12.5
7075-T6	10.3	3.9	81,000	72,000	45,000	0.101	12.9
Magnesium:							
M1A	6.5	2.4	30,000	17,000	14,000	0.064	14
AZ61A	6.3	2.4	38,000	20,000	19,000	0.065	14
Titanium (6Al-4V)	16.0	6.2	130,000	120,000	80,000	0.160	4.6
Cast iron (typical)	14.0	5.6	20,000	....	30,000	0.261	6.0
Soft solder (approx.)	....	....	....	....	6,000		
Silver solder (approx.)	....	....	....	....	15,000		
Brazing metal (approx.)	....	....	....	....	20,000		

* Values given are minimum, except as noted.

TABLE A.2

Mechanical properties of timber* (typical values†)

Species	Grain direc- tion	Modulus of elas- ticity‡ $E \times 10^{-6}$, psi	Ultimate com- pressive strength σ_u, psi	Propor- tional limit σ_p, psi	Shear strength τ_u, psi	Den- sity, lb/in.^{3}	Coeffi- cient of expan- sion $\alpha \times 10^6$, strain/°F
Birch.........	W	2.1	8,300	6,200	2,000	0.0255	1.1
	X			1,300		0.0255	
White oak.....	W	1.6	7,000	4,400	1,900	0.0278	2.7
	X			1,400		0.0278	
Douglas fir....	W	1.9	7,400	6,500	1,100	0.0208	3.0
	X			900		0.0208	
Southern pine.	W	2.0	8,400	6,100	1,500	0.0230	3.0
	X			1,200		0.0230	

* R. J. Roark, "Formulas for Stress and Strain," 3d ed., p. 372, Table XIX, McGraw-Hill Book Company, New York.

† Based on clear, seasoned wood of 12 percent moisture content.

‡ $G = \frac{1}{16}E$ (approx.).

TABLE A.3

Mechanical properties of concrete, plastics, and ceramics (typical values)

Material	Modulus of elas- ticity $E \times 10^{-6}$, psi	Ultimate tensile strength σ_u, psi	Ultimate com- pressive strength σ_u, psi	Ultimate shear strength τ_u, psi	Den- sity w, lb/in.^{3}	Coeffi- cient of expan- sion $\alpha \times 10^6$, strain/°F
Concrete:*						
Low strength	2.5	.....	1,000	200	0.09	6.0
Medium strength	3.4	.....	5,000	1,000	0.09	6.0
High strength	4.5	.....	10,000	2,000	0.09	6.0
Ceramics:						
Soft brick	1.5	.....	2,000	1,000	0.070	3.0
Hard brick	3.5	.....	5,000	2,500	0.070	3.0
Sewer pipe	6.0	2,000	20,000	10,000	0.16	3.0
Glass	9.4	1,300	13,000	7,000	0.15	4.0
Alumina†	50.0	40,000	400,000	20,000	0.14	9.0
Plastics:						
Cellulose acetate	2.0	4,000	26,000	13,000	0.047	120
Polyethylene	1.9	1,300	......	2,200	0.033	170

* Properties vary with mix ratios and age. The values given are approximate.

† Ref. 81.

TABLE A.4

Areas, shear and tensile strengths of bolts

Bolt size*	Cross-sec-tional area, in.²	Area at thread root, in.²	Shear, lb			Tension, lb	
			UTS 55,000 psi	UTS 100,000 psi	UTS 125,000 psi	UTS 55,000 psi	UTS 125,000 psi
$\frac{3}{16}$	0.0276		966	1,794	2,070		
$\frac{1}{4}$	0.0491	0.0326	1,717	3,190	3,680	1,795	4,080
$\frac{5}{16}$	0.0767	0.0520	2,684	4,984	5,750	2,860	6,500
$\frac{3}{8}$	0.1105	0.0808	3,868	7,183	8,280	4,450	10,100
$\frac{7}{16}$	0.1503	0.1088	5,261	9,770	11,250	5,980	13,600
$\frac{1}{2}$	0.1963	0.1480	6,871	12,760	14,700	8,150	18,500
$\frac{9}{16}$	0.2485	0.1889	8,697	16,152	18,700	10,390	23,600
$\frac{5}{8}$	0.3068	0.241	10,740	19,940	23,000	13,270	30,100
$\frac{3}{4}$	0.4418	0.352	15,460	28,720	33,150	19,400	44,000
$\frac{7}{8}$	0.6013	0.480	21,050	39,080	45,050	26,400	60,000
1	0.7854	0.645	27,490	51,050	58,900	35,500	80,700
$1\frac{1}{8}$	0.994	0.693	34,800	64,600	74,600	38,200	86,600
$1\frac{1}{4}$	1.227	0.890	42,900	79,800	92,100	49,000	111,200
$1\frac{3}{8}$	1.485	1.054	52,000	96,600	111,500	58,000	131,800
$1\frac{1}{2}$	1.767	1.294	61,800	114,900	132,500	71,300	161,800
$1\frac{5}{8}$	2.074	1.515	72,600	135,000	155,500	83,300	189,300
$1\frac{3}{4}$	2.405	1.745	84,100	156,500	180,500	96,000	218,000
$1\frac{7}{8}$	2.761	2.049	96,700	179,700	207,000	112,800	256,000
2	3.142	2.300	110,000	204,500	236,000	126,500	288,000
$2\frac{1}{4}$	3.976	3.021	139,100	258,000	298,000	166,000	378,000
$2\frac{1}{2}$	4.909	3.716	171,900	319,000	368,000	204,000	463,000
$2\frac{3}{4}$	5.940	4.620	208,000	386,000	446,000	254,000	577,000
3	7.069	5.428	247,000	460,000	530,000	298,000	678,000

* Bolt sizes from $\frac{3}{16}$ to $1\frac{1}{2}$: fine threads; from $1\frac{1}{4}$ to 3: coarse threads.

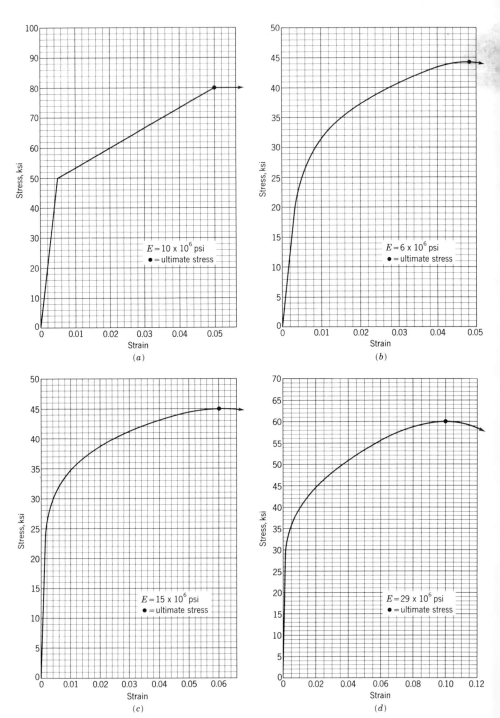

Figure A.1. Hypothetical stress-strain diagrams. (Figure A.1a to d is included for use in conjunction with assigned problems. Figures A.2 to A.5 may be put to similar use.)

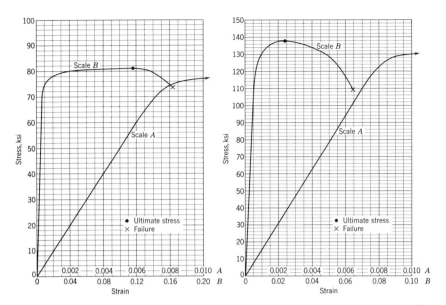

Figure A.2. Typical stress-strain curve for 7075-T6 aluminum alloy at room temperature. (Strain measured over a 2 in. gauge length. Strain rate 0.002 min⁻¹.)

Figure A.3. Typical stress-strain curve for annealed 5AL-2.5Sn titanium alloy at room temperature. (Strain measured over a 2 in. gauge length. Strain rate 0.002 min⁻¹.)

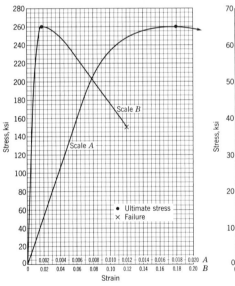

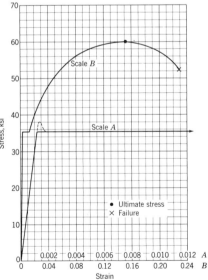

Figure A.4. Typical stress-strain curve for 18 percent nickel maraging steel at room temperature (other similar alloys have $\sigma_u > 350,000$ psi). (Strain measured over a 2 in. gauge length. Strain rate 0.002 min⁻¹.)

Figure A.5. Typical stress-strain curve for ASTM A36 structural steel. (Strain measured over a 2 in. gauge length. Strain rate 0.002 min⁻¹.)

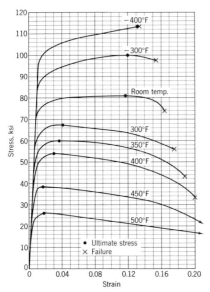

Figure A.6. Typical stress-strain curves for 7075-T6 aluminum alloy at various temperatures. (Strain measured over 2 in. gauge length: $\frac{1}{2}$ hour exposure at temperature.)

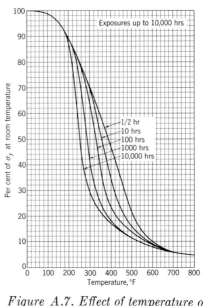

Figure A.7. Effect of temperature on the tensile yield strength of 7076-T6 aluminum alloy (Ref. 39). (Curves are drawn no higher than 5 percent above the minimum data obtained at a given temperature.)

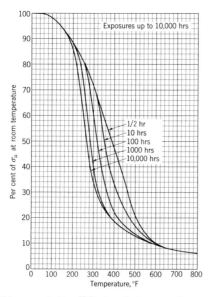

Figure A.8. Effect of temperature on the ultimate tensile strength of 7075-T6 aluminum alloy (Ref. 39). (Curves are drawn no higher than 5 percent above the minimum data obtained at a given temperature.)

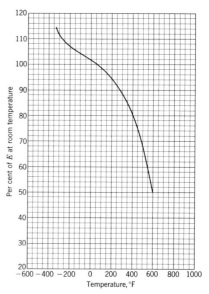

Figure A.9. Effect of temperature on the modulus of elasticity of 7075-T6 aluminum alloy (Ref. 39). (Curve is drawn no higher than 5 percent above the minimum data obtained at a given temperature.)

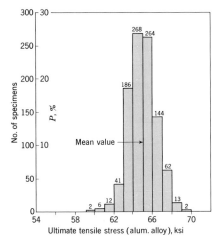

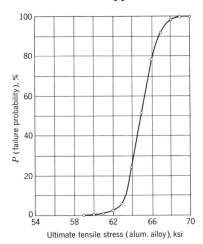

Figure A.10. Histogram for observed ultimate tensile stresses for 1,000 specimens of aluminum alloy.

Figure A.11. Distribution function (cumulative) for data of Fig. A.10.

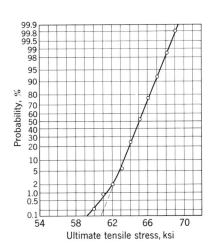

Figure A.12. Data of Fig. A.11 plotted on normal probability graph paper.

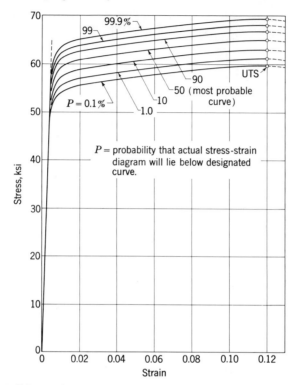

Figure A.13. Schematic stress-strain-probability diagrams for an aluminum alloy (based on statistical data for ultimate tensile stress).

Geometrical Properties of Plane Areas

TABLE B.1

Formulas for common elements of area

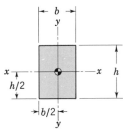

Rectangle:

$$A = bh$$
$$I_x = \tfrac{1}{12}bh^3 \qquad I_y = \tfrac{1}{12}b^3h$$
$$\rho_x = \frac{h}{\sqrt{12}} = 0.289h$$
$$\rho_y = \frac{b}{\sqrt{12}} = 0.289b$$

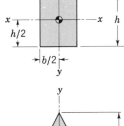

Isosceles triangle:

$$A = \tfrac{1}{2}bh$$
$$I_x = \tfrac{1}{36}bh^3 \qquad I_y = \tfrac{1}{48}b^3h$$
$$\rho_x = \frac{h}{\sqrt{18}} = 0.236h$$
$$\rho_y = \frac{b}{\sqrt{24}} = 0.204b$$

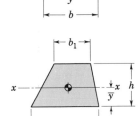

Trapezoid:

$$A = \tfrac{1}{2}(b_1 + b_2)h$$
$$\bar{y} = \frac{1}{3}\frac{(2b_1 + b_2)h}{b_1 + b_2}$$
$$I_x = \frac{h^3}{36}\frac{b_1{}^2 + 4b_1b_2 + b_2{}^2}{b_1 + b_2}$$
$$\rho_x = \frac{h}{6}\frac{\sqrt{2(b_1{}^2 + 4b_1b_2 + b_2{}^2)}}{b_1 + b_2}$$

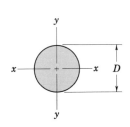

Solid circle:

$$A = \frac{\pi}{4}D^2 = 0.7854D^2$$
$$I_x = I_y = \frac{\pi}{64}D^4 = 0.0491D^4$$
$$\rho_x = \rho_y = \frac{D}{4} = 0.250D$$

TABLE B.1 (*Continued*)

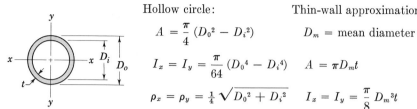

Hollow circle:

$$A = \frac{\pi}{4}(D_o{}^2 - D_i{}^2)$$

$$I_x = I_y = \frac{\pi}{64}(D_o{}^4 - D_i{}^4)$$

$$\rho_x = \rho_y = \tfrac{1}{4}\sqrt{D_o{}^2 + D_i{}^2}$$

Thin-wall approximation:

$$D_m = \text{mean diameter}$$

$$A = \pi D_m t$$

$$I_x = I_y = \frac{\pi}{8} D_m{}^3 t$$

$$\rho_x = \rho_y = \sqrt{\tfrac{1}{8}}\, D_m$$
$$= 0.353 D_m$$

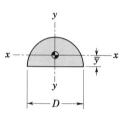

Solid semicircle:

$$A = \frac{\pi D^2}{8}$$

$$\bar{y} = \frac{2D}{3\pi}$$

$$I_x = \frac{D^4(9\pi^2 - 64)}{1{,}152\pi} = 0.00686 D^4$$

$$I_y = \frac{\pi D^4}{128} = 0.0245 D^4$$

Hollow semicircle:

$$A = \frac{\pi}{8}(D_o{}^2 - D_i{}^2)$$

$$\bar{y} = \frac{2}{3\pi}\frac{D_o{}^3 - D_i{}^3}{D_o{}^2 - D_i{}^2}$$

$$I_x = \frac{\pi}{128}(D_o{}^4 - D_i{}^4)$$
$$- \frac{(D_o{}^3 - D_i{}^3)^2}{18\pi(D_o{}^2 - D_i{}^2)}$$

$$I_y = \frac{\pi}{128}(D_o{}^4 - D_i{}^4)$$

Thin-wall approximation:

$$D_m = \text{mean diameter}$$

$$A = \frac{\pi}{2} D_m t$$

$$\bar{y} = \frac{D_m}{\pi}$$

$$I_x = \left(\frac{\pi}{16} - \frac{1}{2\pi}\right) D_m{}^3 t$$

$$I_y = \frac{\pi}{16} D_m{}^3 t$$

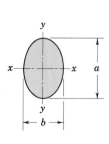

Solid ellipse:

$$A = \frac{\pi}{4} ab$$

$$I_x = \frac{\pi}{64} a^3 b$$

$$I_y = \frac{\pi}{64} b^3 a$$

$$\rho_x = \frac{a}{4}$$

$$\rho_y = \frac{b}{4}$$

TABLE B.2

Section properties of solid round bars

OD,* in.	A, in.^{2}	ρ, in.	I, in.^{4}	Z,† in.^{3}	A_s,‡ in.^{2}
$\frac{1}{8}$	0.01227	0.03125	0.000012	0.000192	0.00920
$\frac{1}{4}$	0.04909	0.06250	0.000192	0.001534	0.03682
$\frac{3}{8}$	0.1104	0.09375	0.000971	0.005177	0.08280
$\frac{1}{2}$	0.1963	0.1250	0.003068	0.01227	0.1472
$\frac{5}{8}$	0.3068	0.1562	0.007490	0.02397	0.2301
$\frac{3}{4}$	0.4418	0.1875	0.01553	0.04142	0.3314
$\frac{7}{8}$	0.6013	0.2188	0.02877	0.06577	0.4510
1	0.7854	0.2500	0.04909	0.09817	0.5891
$1\frac{1}{4}$	1.227	0.3125	0.1198	0.1917	0.9203
$1\frac{1}{2}$	1.767	0.3750	0.2485	0.3313	1.3253
$1\frac{3}{4}$	2.405	0.4375	0.4604	0.5262	1.8038
2	3.142	0.5000	0.7854	0.7854	2.3565
$2\frac{1}{4}$	3.976	0.5625	1.258	1.118	2.982
$2\frac{1}{2}$	4.909	0.6250	1.917	1.534	3.6818
$2\frac{3}{4}$	5.940	0.6875	2.807	2.042	4.4550
3	7.069	0.7500	3.976	2.651	5.3018
$3\frac{1}{2}$	9.621	0.8750	7.366	4.209	7.2158
4	12.57	1.000	12.57	6.283	9.4275
$4\frac{1}{2}$	15.90	1.125	20.13	8.946	11.9250
5	19.63	1.250	30.68	12.27	14.7225

* OD refers to outside diameter.
† Z is section modulus.
‡ A_s is equivalent shear area (divide transverse shear load by A_s to obtain maximum shear stress at neutral axis).

TABLE B.3

Section properties of round tubes

OD*	t,† in.	A, in.²	ρ, in.	I, in.⁴	Z,‡ in.³	D/t	A_s,¶ in.²
$\frac{3}{16}$	0.028	0.01403	0.05726	0.000046	0.000491	6.70	0.007169
	0.035	0.01677	0.05531	0.000051	0.000547	5.36	0.008680
$\frac{1}{4}$	0.022	0.01576	0.08100	0.000103	0.000825	11.38	0.007932
	0.028	0.01953	0.07911	0.000122	0.000978	8.93	0.009869
	0.035	0.02364	0.07701	0.000140	0.001122	7.14	0.01202
	0.049	0.03094	0.07314	0.000166	0.001324	5.10	0.01609
	0.058	0.03498	0.07091	0.000176	0.001407	4.31	0.01855
	0.065	0.03778	0.06933	0.000182	0.001453	3.85	0.02040
$\frac{5}{16}$	0.022	0.02008	0.1030	0.000213	0.001363	14.20	0.01008
	0.028	0.02503	0.1011	0.000256	0.001636	11.16	0.01260
	0.035	0.03051	0.09889	0.000298	0.001910	8.93	0.01542
	0.049	0.04056	0.09476	0.000364	0.002331	6.38	0.02078
	0.058	0.04637	0.09228	0.000395	0.002527	5.39	0.02399
	0.065	0.05054	0.09048	0.000414	0.002648	4.81	0.02643
	0.095	0.06491	0.08392	0.000457	0.002925	3.29	0.03632
$\frac{3}{8}$	0.028	0.03053	0.1231	0.000462	0.002466	13.39	0.01533
	0.035	0.03738	0.1208	0.000546	0.002912	10.72	0.01882
	0.049	0.05018	0.1166	0.000682	0.003636	7.65	0.02551
	0.058	0.05776	0.1139	0.000750	0.003999	6.47	0.02956
	0.065	0.06330	0.1120	0.000794	0.004234	5.77	0.03260
	0.083	0.07614	0.1073	0.000877	0.004678	4.52	0.04014
	0.095	0.08357	0.1045	0.000913	0.004870	3.95	0.04481
$\frac{7}{16}$	0.028	0.03602	0.1451	0.000759	0.003468	15.63	0.01807
	0.035	0.04426	0.1428	0.000903	0.004128	12.50	0.02224
	0.049	0.05981	0.1384	0.001146	0.005240	8.93	0.03022
	0.058	0.06915	0.1357	0.001274	0.005824	7.54	0.03519
	0.065	0.07607	0.1337	0.001360	0.006215	6.73	0.03887
	0.083	0.09244	0.1287	0.001532	0.007002	5.27	0.04790
	0.095	0.1022	0.1257	0.001614	0.007379	4.61	0.05373
$\frac{1}{2}$	0.022	0.03304	0.1692	0.000946	0.003782	22.73	0.01654
	0.028	0.04152	0.1672	0.001160	0.004641	17.86	0.02081
	0.035	0.05113	0.1649	0.001390	0.005559	14.28	0.02566
$\frac{1}{2}$	0.049	0.06943	0.1576	0.001786	0.007144	10.20	0.03499
	0.058	0.08054	0.1576	0.002001	0.008002	8.62	0.04082
	0.065	0.08883	0.1555	0.002148	0.008592	7.69	0.04516
	0.083	0.1087	0.1503	0.002457	0.009828	6.02	0.05577
	0.095	0.1209	0.1471	0.002615	0.01046	5.26	0.06264
	0.120	0.1433	0.1409	0.002844	0.01137	4.17	0.07635
$\frac{9}{16}$	0.028	0.04702	0.1892	0.001684	0.005986	20.09	0.02356
	0.035	0.05800	0.1869	0.002026	0.007205	16.07	0.02909
	0.049	0.07905	0.1824	0.002629	0.009348	11.48	0.03976

TABLE B.3 (*Continued*)

OD*	t,† in.	A, in.²	ρ, in.	I, in.⁴	Z,‡ in.³	D/t	A_s,¶ in.²
$\frac{9}{16}$	0.058	0.09193	0.1795	0.002963	0.01054	9.70	0.04638
	0.120	0.1668	0.1621	0.004383	0.01558	4.69	0.08747
$\frac{5}{8}$	0.028	0.05252	0.2113	0.002345	0.007503	22.32	0.02630
	0.035	0.06487	0.2090	0.002833	0.009065	17.85	0.03252
	0.049	0.08867	0.2044	0.003704	0.01185	12.77	0.04456
	0.058	0.1033	0.2016	0.004195	0.01342	10.79	0.05201
	0.065	0.1144	0.1993	0.004543	0.01454	9.62	0.05787
	0.083	0.1413	0.1939	0.005311	0.01700	7.53	0.07202
	0.095	0.1582	0.1904	0.005732	0.01834	6.58	0.08092
	0.120	0.1904	0.1835	0.006412	0.02052	5.21	0.09876
$\frac{11}{16}$	0.028	0.05801	0.2334	0.003160	0.009192	24.55	0.02904
	0.035	0.07175	0.2310	0.003829	0.01114	19.64	0.03595
	0.049	0.09829	0.2264	0.005038	0.01466	14.03	0.04934
	0.058	0.1147	0.2235	0.005730	0.01667	11.85	0.05265
$\frac{3}{4}$	0.028	0.06351	0.2555	0.004145	0.01105	26.80	0.03179
	0.035	0.07862	0.2531	0.005036	0.01343	21.42	0.03938
	0.049	0.1079	0.2485	0.006661	0.01776	15.30	0.05413
	0.058	0.1261	0.2455	0.007601	0.02027	12.94	0.06334
	0.065	0.1399	0.2433	0.008278	0.02208	11.53	0.07037
	0.083	0.1739	0.2376	0.009820	0.02619	9.04	0.08805
	0.095	0.1955	0.2340	0.01070	0.02854	7.89	0.09934
	0.120	0.2375	0.2267	0.01221	0.03256	6.25	0.12179
	0.156	0.2911	0.2171	0.01372	0.03660	4.81	0.15225
$\frac{7}{8}$	0.028	0.07451	0.2996	0.006689	0.01529	31.23	0.03728
	0.035	0.09236	0.2973	0.008161	0.01865	25.00	0.04624
	0.049	0.1272	0.2925	0.01088	0.02487	17.85	0.06376
	0.058	0.1489	0.2896	0.01248	0.02853	15.10	0.07471
	0.065	0.1654	0.2865	0.01365	0.03121	13.47	0.08306
	0.083	0.2065	0.2815	0.01637	0.03742	10.54	0.10403
	0.095	0.2328	0.2778	0.01797	0.04107	9.21	0.11781
	0.120	0.2846	0.2703	0.02079	0.04753	7.29	0.14491
	0.156	0.3524	0.2601	0.02384	0.05450	5.61	0.18184
1	0.028	0.08550	0.3438	0.01011	0.02021	35.71	0.04277
	0.035	0.1061	0.3414	0.01237	0.02474	28.56	0.05310
	0.049	0.1464	0.3367	0.01659	0.03319	20.40	0.07335
	0.058	0.1716	0.3337	0.01911	0.03822	17.25	0.08604
	0.065	0.1909	0.3314	0.02097	0.04193	15.38	0.09576
	0.083	0.2391	0.3255	0.02534	0.05068	12.05	0.12021
	0.095	0.2701	0.3217	0.02796	0.05591	10.53	0.13607
	0.120	0.3318	0.3140	0.03271	0.06542	8.33	0.16826
	0.156	0.4142	0.3034	0.03809	0.07618	6.41	0.21208
	0.187	0.4776	0.2949	0.04155	0.08310	5.35	0.24720

TABLE B.3 (Continued)

OD*	t,† in.	A, in.²	ρ, in.	I, in.⁴	Z,‡ in.³	D/t	A_s,¶ in.²
$1\frac{1}{8}$	0.028	0.09640	0.3880	0.01453	0.02582	40.18	0.04822
	0.035	0.1198	0.3856	0.01782	0.03168	32.10	0.05994
	0.049	0.1656	0.3808	0.02402	0.04270	22.95	0.08292
	0.058	0.1944	0.3780	0.02775	0.04933	19.40	0.09742
	0.065	0.2165	0.3755	0.03052	0.05425	17.30	0.10855
	0.083	0.2717	0.3696	0.03711	0.06597	13.55	0.13644
	0.095	0.3074	0.3657	0.04111	0.07309	11.84	0.15460
	0.120	0.3789	0.3578	0.04852	0.08625	9.38	0.19165
$1\frac{1}{4}$	0.028	0.1075	0.4321	0.02007	0.03212	44.64	0.05377
	0.035	0.1336	0.4297	0.02467	0.03948	35.70	0.06683
	0.049	0.1849	0.4250	0.03339	0.05342	25.50	0.09255
	0.058	0.2172	0.4219	0.03867	0.06187	21.55	0.10879
	0.065	0.2420	0.4196	0.04260	0.06816	19.22	0.12128
	0.083	0.3043	0.4136	0.05206	0.08330	15.06	0.15267
	0.095	0.3447	0.4097	0.05787	0.09259	13.16	0.17314
	0.120	0.4260	0.4018	0.06876	0.1100	10.42	0.21466
	0.156	0.5362	0.3907	0.08184	0.1310	8.01	0.27177
$1\frac{3}{8}$	0.028	0.1185	0.4764	0.02689	0.03911	49.11	0.05927
	0.035	0.1473	0.4739	0.03309	0.04814	39.25	0.07368
	0.049	0.2041	0.4691	0.04492	0.06534	28.05	0.10215
	0.058	0.2400	0.4661	0.05213	0.07583	23.70	0.12018
	0.065	0.2675	0.4638	0.05753	0.08367	21.15	0.13400
	0.083	0.3369	0.4577	0.07059	0.1027	16.57	0.16896
	0.095	0.3820	0.4538	0.07867	0.1144	14.47	0.19172
	0.120	0.4731	0.4457	0.09400	0.1367	11.46	0.23804
	0.156	0.5974	0.4345	0.1129	0.1642	8.81	0.3025
	0.187	0.6979	0.4252	0.1262	0.1835	7.35	0.3553
$1\frac{1}{2}$	0.028	0.1295	0.5205	0.03508	0.04678	53.57	0.06477
	0.035	0.1611	0.5181	0.04324	0.05765	42.80	0.08058
	0.049	0.2234	0.5132	0.05885	0.07847	30.60	0.1118
	0.058	0.2628	0.5102	0.06841	0.09121	25.85	0.1315
	0.065	0.2930	0.5079	0.07558	0.1008	23.05	0.1467
	0.083	0.3695	0.5018	0.09305	0.1241	18.08	0.1852
	0.095	0.4193	0.4979	0.1039	0.1386	15.79	0.2103
	0.120	0.5202	0.4897	0.1248	0.1664	12.50	0.2614
	0.156	0.6587	0.4784	0.1507	0.2010	9.62	0.3332
	0.187	0.7714	0.4689	0.1696	0.2261	8.02	0.3910
$1\frac{5}{8}$	0.028	0.1405	0.5647	0.04480	0.05514	58.04	0.07026
	0.035	0.1748	0.5622	0.05528	0.06803	46.40	0.08743
	0.049	0.2426	0.5575	0.07540	0.09279	33.15	0.1214
	0.058	0.2855	0.5544	0.08776	0.1080	28.00	0.1429
	0.065	0.3186	0.5520	0.09707	0.1195	25.00	0.1595

TABLE B.3 (Continued)

OD*	t,† in.	A, in.²	ρ, in.	I, in.⁴	Z,‡ in.³	D/t	A_s,¶ in.²
$1\frac{5}{8}$	0.083	0.4021	0.5459	0.1198	0.1475	19.58	0.2015
	0.095	0.4566	0.5420	0.1341	0.1651	17.11	0.2289
	0.120	0.5674	0.5338	0.1617	0.1990	13.54	0.2849
$1\frac{3}{4}$	0.028	0.1515	0.6089	0.05616	0.06418	62.50	0.07577
	0.035	0.1885	0.6065	0.06936	0.07927	50.00	0.09428
	0.049	0.2618	0.6017	0.09478	0.1083	35.70	0.1310
	0.058	0.3083	0.5986	0.1105	0.1262	30.20	0.1543
	0.065	0.3441	0.5962	0.1223	0.1398	26.90	0.1722
	0.083	0.4347	0.5901	0.1514	0.1730	21.10	0.2178
	0.095	0.4939	0.5861	0.1697	0.1939	18.42	0.2476
	0.120	0.6145	0.5778	0.2052	0.2345	14.58	0.3084
$1\frac{7}{8}$	0.028	0.1625	0.6531	0.06930	0.07392	66.96	0.08126
	0.035	0.2023	0.6507	0.08565	0.09136	53.60	0.1012
	0.049	0.2811	0.6458	0.1172	0.1250	38.25	0.1406
	0.058	0.3311	0.6427	0.1368	0.1459	32.30	0.1657
	0.065	0.3696	0.6404	0.1516	0.1617	28.80	0.1850
	0.083	0.4673	0.6342	0.1880	0.2005	22.60	0.2340
	0.095	0.5312	0.6302	0.2110	0.2251	19.74	0.2662
	0.120	0.6616	0.6219	0.2559	0.2730	15.63	0.3319
2	0.028	0.1735	0.6973	0.08434	0.08434	71.43	0.08676
	0.035	0.2161	0.6948	0.1043	0.1043	57.14	0.1081
	0.049	0.3003	0.6900	0.1430	0.1430	40.80	0.1502
	0.058	0.3539	0.6869	0.1670	0.1670	34.45	0.1770
	0.065	0.3951	0.6845	0.1851	0.1851	30.75	0.1977
	0.083	0.4999	0.6783	0.2300	0.2301	24.10	0.2503
	0.095	0.5685	0.6744	0.2586	0.2586	21.05	0.2848
	0.109	0.6476	0.6697	0.2904	0.2904	18.35	0.3246
	0.120	0.7087	0.6660	0.3144	0.3144	16.67	0.3554
	0.156	0.9037	0.6543	0.3869	0.3869	12.82	0.4541
	0.188	1.070	0.6441	0.4440	0.4440	10.64	0.5390
	0.250	1.374	0.6250	0.5369	0.5369	8.00	0.6963
$2\frac{1}{8}$	0.035	0.2298	0.7390	0.1255	0.1181	60.71	0.1149
	0.049	0.3196	0.7342	0.1723	0.1621	43.37	0.1599
	0.058	0.3766	0.7311	0.2013	0.1895	36.64	0.1884
	0.065	0.4207	0.7287	0.2234	0.2102	32.69	0.2105
	0.083	0.5325	0.7226	0.2780	0.2616	25.60	0.2665
	0.095	0.6059	0.7185	0.3128	0.2944	22.37	0.3034
	0.120	0.7559	0.7101	0.3812	0.3588	17.71	0.3789
	0.156	0.9650	0.6983	0.4706	0.4429	13.62	0.4846
$2\frac{1}{4}$	0.035	0.2436	0.7832	0.1494	0.1328	64.29	0.1218
	0.049	0.3388	0.7783	0.2052	0.1824	45.90	0.1695
	0.058	0.3994	0.7753	0.2401	0.2134	38.80	0.1998

TABLE B.3 (Continued)

OD*	t,† in.	A, in.^{2}	ρ, in.	I, in.^{4}	Z,‡ in.^{3}	D/t	A_s,¶ in.^{2}
$2\frac{1}{4}$	0.065	0.4462	0.7728	0.2665	0.2369	34.60	0.2232
	0.083	0.5651	0.7667	0.3322	0.2953	27.15	0.2828
	0.095	0.6432	0.7626	0.3741	0.3325	23.70	0.3221
	0.120	0.8030	0.7543	0.4568	0.4061	18.75	0.4025
	0.156	1.026	0.7424	0.5656	0.5028	14.42	0.5149
	0.188	1.218	0.7320	0.6526	0.5801	11.97	0.6124
	0.250	1.571	0.7126	0.7977	0.7090	9.00	0.7936
$2\frac{5}{16}$	0.250	1.620	0.7345	0.8740	0.7559	9.25	0.8103
$2\frac{3}{8}$	0.049	0.3581	0.8225	0.2423	0.2040	48.47	0.1791
	0.058	0.4222	0.8194	0.2835	0.2387	40.95	0.2112
	0.065	0.4717	0.8170	0.3149	0.2651	36.54	0.2360
	0.083	0.5976	0.8109	0.3930	0.3309	28.61	0.2991
	0.095	0.6805	0.8068	0.4429	0.3730	25.00	0.3406
	0.120	0.8501	0.7984	0.5419	0.4563	19.79	0.4259
	0.156	1.088	0.7865	0.6727	0.5664	15.22	0.5459
	0.188	1.292	0.7761	0.7780	0.6551	12.63	0.6492
	0.250	1.669	0.7565	0.9551	0.8043	9.50	0.8429
	0.375	2.356	0.7194	1.220	1.027	6.33	1.2070
$2\frac{1}{2}$	0.049	0.3773	0.8667	0.2834	0.2267	51.00	0.1887
	0.058	0.4450	0.8635	0.3318	0.2655	43.10	0.2226
	0.065	0.4972	0.8613	0.3688	0.2950	38.45	0.2487
	0.083	0.6302	0.8550	0.4607	0.3686	30.10	0.3154
	0.095	0.7178	0.8509	0.5197	0.4158	26.30	0.3593
	0.120	0.8972	0.8425	0.6369	0.5095	20.83	0.4495
	0.156	1.149	0.8306	0.7925	0.6340	16.03	0.5762
	0.188	1.366	0.8201	0.9184	0.7347	13.30	0.6860
	0.250	1.767	0.8004	1.132	0.9057	10.00	0.8908
$2\frac{3}{4}$	0.049	0.4158	0.9551	0.3793	0.2759	56.10	0.2080
	0.058	0.4905	0.9521	0.4446	0.3233	47.40	0.2453
	0.065	0.5483	0.9496	0.4944	0.3596	42.30	0.2743
	0.083	0.6954	0.9434	0.6189	0.4501	33.15	0.3479
	0.095	0.7924	0.9393	0.6991	0.5084	28.95	0.3966
	0.120	0.9915	0.9308	0.8590	0.6247	22.92	0.4965
	0.156	1.271	0.9188	1.073	0.7805	17.63	0.6372
	0.188	1.513	0.9082	1.248	0.9078	14.63	0.7592
	0.250	1.964	0.8883	1.549	1.127	11.00	0.9885
3	0.049	0.4543	1.044	0.4946	0.3298	61.22	0.2272
	0.058	0.5361	1.040	0.5802	0.3868	51.70	0.2681
	0.065	0.5993	1.038	0.6457	0.4305	46.20	0.2998
	0.083	0.7606	1.032	0.8097	0.5398	36.15	0.3805
	0.095	0.8670	1.028	0.9156	0.6104	31.58	0.4338
	0.120	1.086	1.019	1.128	0.7518	25.00	0.5436

TABLE B.3 (*Continued*)

OD*	t,† in.	A, in.²	ρ, in.	I, in.⁴	Z,‡ in.³	D/t	A_s,¶ in.²
3	0.156	1.394	1.007	1.413	0.9423	19.23	0.6986
	0.188	1.661	0.9964	1.649	1.099	15.96	0.8330
	0.250	2.160	0.9763	2.059	1.372	12.00	1.0859
	0.375	3.093	0.9375	2.718	1.812	8.00	1.5674
$3\frac{1}{4}$	0.049	0.4928	1.132	0.6313	0.3885	66.33	0.2464
	0.058	0.5816	1.129	0.7410	0.4560	56.10	0.2909
	0.065	0.6504	1.126	0.8251	0.5077	50.00	0.3253
	0.083	0.8258	1.120	1.036	0.6376	39.15	0.4131
	0.095	0.9416	1.116	1.173	0.7217	34.20	0.4711
	0.120	1.180	1.107	1.447	0.8906	27.10	0.5906
	0.156	1.516	1.095	1.819	1.119	20.83	0.7594
	0.188	1.808	1.085	2.127	1.309	17.29	0.9065
	0.250	2.356	1.064	2.669	1.643	13.00	1.1834
$3\frac{1}{2}$	0.065	0.7014	1.215	1.035	0.5914	53.80	0.3508
	0.083	0.8910	1.208	1.301	0.7435	42.20	0.4457
	0.095	1.016	1.204	1.474	0.8422	36.85	0.5083
	0.120	1.274	1.196	1.822	1.041	29.15	0.6376
	0.156	1.639	1.184	2.296	1.312	22.44	0.8208
	0.188	1.956	1.173	2.691	1.538	18.62	0.9804
	0.250	2.553	1.152	3.390	1.937	14.00	1.2815
$3\frac{3}{4}$	0.065	0.7525	1.303	1.278	0.6814	57.60	0.3763
	0.083	0.9562	1.297	1.608	0.8576	45.20	0.4783
	0.095	1.091	1.293	1.823	0.9722	39.50	0.5457
	0.120	1.368	1.284	2.256	1.204	31.25	0.6845
	0.156	1.761	1.272	2.849	1.520	24.04	0.8817
	0.188	2.104	1.261	3.346	1.784	19.95	1.0541
	0.219	2.429	1.251	3.801	2.027	17.12	1.2180
	0.250	2.749	1.241	4.231	2.256	15.00	1.3792
4	0.065	0.8035	1.392	1.556	0.7779	61.50	0.4018
	0.083	1.021	1.385	1.960	0.9799	48.20	0.5107
	0.095	1.166	1.381	2.223	1.111	42.10	0.5833
	0.120	1.463	1.372	2.755	1.378	33.33	0.7320
	0.156	1.884	1.360	3.485	1.743	25.64	0.9430
	0.188	2.251	1.349	4.099	2.050	21.28	1.1276
	0.219	2.601	1.339	4.664	2.332	18.26	1.3038
	0.250	2.945	1.329	5.200	2.600	16.00	1.4770
	0.313	3.626	1.308	6.205	3.102	6.39	1.8576
$4\frac{1}{4}$	0.065	0.8546	1.480	1.871	0.8806	65.38	0.4274
	0.083	1.087	1.474	2.359	1.110	51.20	0.5437
	0.095	1.240	1.469	2.677	1.260	44.74	0.6202
	0.120	1.557	1.461	3.322	1.564	35.42	0.7789
	0.134	1.733	1.456	3.673	1.741	31.75	0.8672

TABLE B.3 (*Continued*)

OD*	t,† in.	A, in.²	ρ, in.	I, in.⁴	Z,‡ in.³	D/t	A_s,¶ in.²
$4\frac{1}{4}$	0.156	2.006	1.448	4.210	1.981	27.24	1.0040
	0.188	2.399	1.438	4.959	2.334	22.60	1.2014
	0.219	2.773	1.427	5.650	2.659	19.40	1.3896
	0.250	3.142	1.417	6.308	2.968	17.00	1.5753
	0.313	3.871	1.396	7.548	3.552	13.58	1.9439
$4\frac{1}{2}$	0.065	0.9056	1.568	2.227	0.9898	69.23	0.4529
	0.083	1.152	1.562	2.810	1.249	54.22	0.5761
	0.095	1.315	1.558	3.190	1.418	47.37	0.6577
	0.120	1.651	1.549	3.963	1.761	37.50	0.8259
	0.156	2.129	1.537	5.028	2.235	28.80	1.0654
	0.188	2.547	1.526	5.930	2.636	23.94	1.2753
	0.219	2.945	1.516	6.765	3.007	20.55	1.4755
	0.250	3.338	1.505	7.562	3.361	18.00	1.6732
	0.313	4.117	1.484	9.073	4.032	14.38	2.0662
	0.375	4.860	1.464	10.42	4.632	12.00	2.4433
$4\frac{3}{4}$	0.065	0.9567	1.657	2.625	1.105	73.08	0.4784
	0.083	1.217	1.650	3.314	1.396	57.23	0.6087
	0.095	1.389	1.646	3.765	1.585	50.00	0.6947
	0.120	1.745	1.638	4.680	1.971	39.58	0.8729
	0.156	2.251	1.625	5.946	2.504	30.45	1.1264
	0.188	2.694	1.614	7.021	2.956	25.25	1.3486
	0.219	3.117	1.604	8.019	3.376	21.69	1.5612
	0.250	3.534	1.593	8.974	3.778	19.00	1.7711
	0.313	4.363	1.573	10.79	4.543	15.18	2.1889
	0.375	5.154	1.552	12.42	5.230	12.66	2.5897
5	0.083	1.282	1.739	3.876	1.550	60.24	0.6411
	0.095	1.464	1.734	4.404	1.762	52.63	0.7322
	0.120	1.840	1.726	5.480	2.192	41.67	0.9204
	0.156	2.374	1.714	6.970	2.788	32.05	1.1879
	0.188	2.842	1.703	8.239	3.295	26.60	1.4226
	0.219	3.289	1.692	9.418	3.767	22.83	1.6470
	0.250	3.731	1.682	10.55	4.220	20.00	1.8692
	0.313	4.609	1.661	12.71	5.085	15.97	2.3114
	0.375	5.449	1.640	14.66	5.866	13.33	2.7364

* OD refers to outside diameter.
† t is wall thickness.
‡ Z is section modulus.
¶ A_s is equivalent shear area (divide transverse shear load by A_s to obtain maximum shear stress at neutral axis).

TABLE B.4

Section properties of wide-flange beams

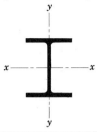

Nominal size, in.	Weight per ft, lb	Area of section, in.²	Depth of section, in.	Flange Width, in.	Flange Thickness, in.	Web thickness, in.	I_x, in.⁴	Z_x, in.³	ρ_x, in.	I_y, in.⁴	Z_y, in.³	ρ_y, in.
14 × 16	193	56.73	15.50	15.71	1.438	0.890	2,402	310.0	6.51	930	118.4	4.05
	184	54.07	15.38	15.66	1.378	0.840	2,274	295.8	6.49	882	112.7	4.04
	176	51.73	15.25	15.64	1.313	0.820	2,149	281.9	6.45	837	107.1	4.02
	167	49.09	15.12	15.60	1.248	0.780	2,020	267.3	6.42	790	101.3	4.01
	158	46.47	15.00	15.55	1.188	0.730	1,900	253.4	6.40	745	95.8	4.00
	150	44.08	14.88	15.51	1.128	0.695	1,786	240.2	6.37	702	90.6	3.99
	142	41.85	14.75	15.50	1.063	0.680	1,672	226.7	6.32	660	85.2	3.97
14 × 14½	136	39.98	14.75	14.74	1.063	0.660	1,593	216.0	6.31	567	77.0	3.77
	127	37.33	14.62	14.69	0.998	0.610	1,476	202.0	6.29	527	71.8	3.76
	119	34.99	14.50	14.65	0.938	0.570	1,373	189.4	6.26	491	67.1	3.75
	111	32.65	14.37	14.62	0.873	0.540	1,266	176.3	6.23	454	62.2	3.73
	103	30.26	14.25	14.57	0.813	0.495	1,165	163.6	6.21	419	57.6	3.72
	95	27.94	14.12	14.54	0.748	0.465	1,063	150.6	6.17	383	52.8	3.71
	87	25.56	14.00	14.50	0.688	0.420	966	138.1	6.15	349	48.2	3.70
14 × 12	84	24.71	14.18	12.02	0.778	0.451	928	130.9	6.13	225.5	37.5	3.02
	78	22.94	14.06	12.00	0.718	0.428	851	121.1	6.09	206.9	34.5	3.00
14 × 10	74	21.76	14.19	10.07	0.783	0.450	796	112.3	6.05	133.5	26.5	2.48
	68	20.00	14.06	10.04	0.718	0.418	724	103.0	6.02	121.2	24.1	2.46
	61	17.94	13.91	10.00	0.643	0.378	641	92.2	5.98	107.3	21.5	2.45
14 × 8	53	15.59	13.94	8.06	0.658	0.370	542	77.8	5.90	57.5	14.3	1.92
	48	14.11	13.81	8.03	0.593	0.339	484	70.2	5.86	51.3	12.8	1.91
	43	12.65	13.68	8.00	0.528	0.308	429	62.7	5.82	45.1	11.3	1.89
14 × 6¾	38	11.17	14.12	6.77	0.513	0.313	385	54.6	5.87	24.6	7.3	1.49
	34	10.00	14.00	6.75	0.453	0.287	339	48.5	5.83	21.3	6.3	1.46
	30	8.81	13.86	6.73	0.383	0.270	289	41.8	5.73	17.5	5.2	1.41
12 × 12	190	55.86	14.38	12.67	1.736	1.060	1,892	263.2	5.82	589.7	93.1	3.25
	161	47.38	13.88	12.51	1.486	0.905	1,541	222.2	5.70	486.2	77.7	3.20
	133	39.11	13.38	12.36	1.236	0.755	1,221	182.5	5.59	389.9	63.1	3.16
	120	35.31	13.12	12.32	1.106	0.710	1,071	163.4	5.51	345.1	56.0	3.13
	106	31.19	12.88	12.23	0.986	0.620	930	144.5	5.46	300.9	49.2	3.11
	99	29.09	12.75	12.19	0.921	0.580	858	134.7	5.43	278.2	45.7	3.09
	92	27.06	12.62	12.15	0.856	0.545	788	125.0	5.40	256.4	42.2	3.08
	85	24.98	12.50	12.10	0.796	0.495	723	115.7	5.38	235.5	38.9	3.07
	79	23.22	12.38	12.08	0.736	0.470	663	107.1	5.34	216.4	35.8	3.05
	72	21.16	12.25	12.04	0.671	0.430	597	97.5	5.31	195.3	32.4	3.04
	65	19.11	12.12	12.00	0.606	0.390	533	88.0	5.28	174.6	29.1	3.02
12 × 10	58	17.06	12.19	10.01	0.641	0.359	476	78.1	5.28	107.4	21.4	2.51
	53	15.59	12.06	10.00	0.576	0.345	426	70.7	5.23	96.1	19.2	2.48

TABLE B.4 (Continued)

Nominal size, in.	Weight per ft, lb	Area of section, in.²	Depth of section, in.	Flange Width, in.	Flange Thickness, in.	Web thickness, in.	Axis xx I_x, in.⁴	Z_x, in.³	ρ_x, in.	Axis yy I_y, in.⁴	Z_y, in.³	ρ_y, in.
12 × 8	50	14.71	12.19	8.07	0.641	0.371	394.0	64.7	5.18	56.4	14.0	1.96
	45	13.24	12.06	8.04	0.576	0.336	350.0	58.2	5.15	50.0	12.4	1.94
	40	11.77	11.94	8.00	0.516	0.294	310.0	51.9	5.13	44.1	11.0	1.94
12 × 6½	36	10.59	12.24	6.56	0.540	0.305	280.0	45.9	5.15	23.7	7.2	1.50
	31	9.12	12.09	6.52	0.465	0.265	238.0	39.4	5.11	19.8	6.1	1.47
	27	7.97	11.95	6.50	0.400	0.240	204.0	34.1	5.06	16.6	5.1	1.44
10 × 10	112	32.92	11.38	10.41	1.248	0.755	718.7	126.3	4.67	235.4	45.2	2.67
	100	29.43	11.12	10.34	1.118	0.685	625.0	112.4	4.61	206.6	39.9	2.65
	89	26.19	10.88	10.27	0.998	0.615	542.4	99.7	4.55	180.6	35.2	2.63
	77	22.67	10.62	10.19	0.868	0.535	457.2	86.1	4.49	153.4	30.1	2.60
	72	21.18	10.50	10.17	0.808	0.510	420.7	80.1	4.46	141.8	27.9	2.59
	66	19.41	10.38	10.11	0.748	0.457	382.5	73.7	4.44	129.2	25.5	2.58
	60	17.66	10.25	10.07	0.683	0.415	343.7	67.1	4.41	116.3	23.1	2.57
	54	15.88	10.12	10.02	0.618	0.368	305.7	60.4	4.39	103.9	20.7	2.56
	49	14.40	10.00	10.00	0.558	0.340	272.9	54.6	4.35	93.0	18.6	2.54
10 × 8	45	13.24	10.12	8.02	0.618	0.350	248.6	49.1	4.35	53.2	13.3	2.00
	39	11.48	9.94	7.99	0.528	0.318	209.7	42.2	4.27	44.9	11.2	1.98
	33	9.71	9.75	7.96	0.433	0.292	170.9	35.0	4.20	36.5	9.2	1.94
10 × 5¾	29	8.53	10.22	5.79	0.500	0.289	157.3	30.8	4.29	15.2	5.2	1.34
	25	7.35	10.08	5.76	0.430	0.252	133.2	26.4	4.26	12.7	4.4	1.31
	21	6.19	9.90	5.75	0.340	0.240	106.3	21.5	4.14	9.7	3.4	1.25
8 × 8	67	19.70	9.00	8.28	0.933	0.575	271.8	60.4	3.71	88.6	21.4	2.12
	58	17.06	8.75	8.22	0.808	0.510	227.3	52.0	3.65	74.9	18.2	2.10
	48	14.11	8.50	8.11	0.683	0.405	183.7	43.2	3.61	60.9	15.0	2.08
	40	11.76	8.25	8.07	0.558	0.365	146.3	35.5	3.53	49.0	12.1	2.04
	35	10.30	8.12	8.02	0.493	0.315	126.5	31.1	3.50	42.5	10.6	2.03
	31	9.12	8.00	8.00	0.433	0.228	109.7	27.4	3.47	37.0	9.2	2.01
8 × 6½	28	8.23	8.06	6.54	0.463	0.285	97.8	24.3	3.45	21.6	6.6	1.62
	24	7.06	7.93	6.50	0.398	0.245	82.5	20.8	3.42	18.2	5.6	1.61
8 × 5¼	20	5.88	8.14	5.27	0.378	0.248	69.2	17.0	3.43	8.5	3.2	1.20
	17	5.00	8.00	5.25	0.308	0.230	56.4	14.1	3.36	6.7	2.6	1.16

Notes: Flanges of wide-flange beams and columns are not tapered, have constant thickness. Light-weight beams for each nominal size, and beams with depth in even inches, are most usually stocked. Designation of wide-flange beams is made by giving nominal depth and weight, thus, 8-WF-40.

TABLE B.5

Section properties of standard I beams

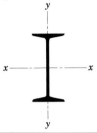

Depth of beam, in.	Weight per ft, lb	Area of section, in.^{2}	Width of flange in.	Thickness of web, in.	Axis xx			Axis yy		
					I_x, in.^{4}	Z_x, in.^{3}	ρ_x, in.	I_y, in.^{4}	Z_y, in.^{3}	ρ_y, in.
24	120.0	35.13	8.048	0.798	3010.8	250.9	9.26	84.9	21.1	1.56
	105.9	30.98	7.875	0.625	2811.5	234.3	9.53	78.9	20.0	1.60
	100.0	29.25	7.247	0.747	2371.8	197.6	9.05	48.4	13.4	1.29
	90.0	26.30	7.124	0.624	2230.1	185.8	9.21	45.5	12.8	1.32
	79.9	23.33	7.000	0.500	2087.2	173.9	9.46	42.9	12.2	1.36
20	95.0	27.74	7.200	0.800	1599.7	160.0	7.59	50.5	14.0	1.35
	85.0	24.80	7.053	0.653	1501.7	150.2	7.78	47.0	13.3	1.38
	75.0	21.90	6.391	0.641	1263.5	126.3	7.60	30.1	9.4	1.17
	65.4	19.08	6.250	0.500	1169.5	116.9	7.83	27.9	8.9	1.21
18	70.0	20.46	6.251	0.711	917.5	101.9	6.70	24.5	7.8	1.09
	54.7	15.94	6.000	0.460	795.5	88.4	7.07	21.2	7.1	1.15
15	50.0	14.59	5.640	0.550	481.1	64.2	5.74	16.0	5.7	1.05
	42.9	12.49	5.500	0.410	441.8	58.9	5.95	14.6	5.3	1.08
12	50.0	14.57	5.477	0.687	301.6	50.3	4.55	16.0	5.8	1.05
	40.8	11.84	5.250	0.460	268.9	44.8	4.77	13.8	5.3	1.08
	35.0	10.20	5.078	0.428	227.0	37.8	4.72	10.0	3.9	0.99
	31.8	9.26	5.000	0.350	215.8	36.0	4.83	9.5	3.8	1.01
10	35.0	10.22	4.944	0.594	145.8	29.2	3.78	8.5	3.4	0.91
	25.4	7.38	4.660	0.310	122.1	24.4	4.07	6.9	3.0	0.97
8	23.0	6.71	4.171	0.441	64.2	16.0	3.09	4.4	2.1	0.81
	18.4	5.34	4.000	0.270	56.9	14.2	3.26	3.8	1.9	0.84
7	20.0	5.83	3.860	0.450	41.9	12.0	2.68	3.1	1.6	0.74
	15.3	4.43	3.660	0.250	36.2	10.4	2.86	2.7	1.5	0.78
6	17.25	5.02	3.565	0.465	26.0	8.7	2.28	2.3	1.3	0.68
	12.5	3.61	3.330	0.230	21.8	7.3	2.46	1.8	1.1	0.72
5	14.75	4.29	3.284	0.494	15.0	6.0	1.87	1.7	1.0	0.63
	10.0	2.87	3.000	0.210	12.1	4.8	2.05	1.2	0.82	0.65
4	9.5	2.76	2.796	0.326	6.7	3.3	1.56	0.91	0.65	0.58
	7.7	2.21	2.660	0.190	6.0	3.0	1.64	0.77	0.58	0.59
3	7.5	2.17	2.509	0.349	2.9	1.9	1.15	0.59	0.47	0.52
	5.7	1.64	2.330	0.170	2.5	1.7	1.23	0.46	0.40	0.53

TABLE B.6

Section properties of standard channels

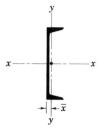

Depth of channel, in.	Weight per ft, lb	Area of section, in.^{2}	Width of flange, in.	Thickness of web, in.	Axis xx			Axis yy	$\bar{x}$, in.
					I, in.^{4}	Z, in.^{3}	ρ_x, in.	ρ_y, in.	
15	50.0	14.64	3.716	0.716	401.4	53.6	5.24	0.87	0.80
	40.0	11.70	3.520	0.520	346.3	46.2	5.44	0.89	0.78
	33.9	9.90	3.400	0.400	312.6	41.7	5.62	0.91	0.79
12	30.0	8.79	3.170	0.510	161.2	26.9	4.28	0.77	0.68
	25.0	7.32	3.047	0.387	143.5	23.9	4.43	0.79	0.68
	20.7	6.03	2.940	0.280	128.1	21.4	4.61	0.81	0.70
10	30.0	8.80	3.033	0.673	103.0	20.6	3.42	0.67	0.65
	25.0	7.33	2.886	0.526	90.7	18.1	3.52	0.68	0.62
	20.0	5.86	2.739	0.379	78.5	15.7	3.66	0.70	0.61
	15.3	4.47	2.600	0.240	66.9	13.4	3.87	0.72	0.64
9	20.0	5.86	2.648	0.448	60.6	13.5	3.22	0.65	0.59
	15.0	4.39	2.485	0.285	50.7	11.3	3.40	0.67	0.59
	13.4	3.89	2.430	0.230	47.3	10.5	3.49	0.67	0.61
8	18.75	5.49	2.527	0.487	43.7	10.9	2.82	0.60	0.57
	13.75	4.02	2.343	0.303	35.8	9.0	2.99	0.62	0.56
	11.5	3.36	2.260	0.220	32.3	8.1	3.10	0.63	0.58
7	14.75	4.32	2.299	0.419	27.1	7.7	2.51	0.57	0.53
	12.25	3.58	2.194	0.314	24.1	6.9	2.59	0.58	0.53
	9.8	2.85	2.090	0.210	21.1	6.0	2.72	0.59	0.55
6	13.0	3.81	2.157	0.437	17.3	5.8	2.13	0.53	0.52
	10.5	3.07	2.034	0.314	15.1	5.0	2.22	0.53	0.50
	8.2	2.39	1.920	0.200	13.0	4.3	2.34	0.54	0.52
5	9.0	2.63	1.885	0.325	8.8	3.5	1.83	0.49	0.48
	6.7	1.95	1.750	0.190	7.4	3.0	1.95	0.50	0.49
4	7.25	2.12	1.720	0.320	4.5	2.3	1.47	0.46	0.46
	5.4	1.56	1.580	0.180	3.8	1.9	1.56	0.45	0.46
3	6.0	1.75	1.596	0.356	2.1	1.4	1.08	0.42	0.46
	5.0	1.46	1.498	0.258	1.8	1.2	1.12	0.41	0.44
	4.1	1.19	1.410	0.170	1.6	1.1	1.17	0.41	0.44

TABLE B.7

Section properties of standard equal angles

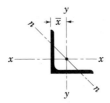

Size, in.	Thickness, in.	Weight per ft, lb	Area of section, in.^{2}	Axis xx and axis yy				Axis nn
				I, in.^{4}	Z, in.^{3}	ρ, in.	$\bar{x}$, in.	ρ_{min}, in.
8 × 8	$1\frac{1}{8}$	56.9	16.73	98.0	17.5	2.42	2.41	1.56
	1	51.0	15.00	89.0	15.8	2.44	2.37	1.56
	$\frac{7}{8}$	45.0	13.23	79.6	14.0	2.45	2.32	1.57
	$\frac{3}{4}$	38.9	11.44	69.7	12.2	2.47	2.28	1.57
	$\frac{5}{8}$	32.7	9.61	59.4	10.3	2.49	2.23	1.58
	$\frac{1}{2}$	26.4	7.75	48.6	8.4	2.50	2.19	1.59
6 × 6	1	37.4	11.00	35.5	8.6	1.80	1.86	1.17
	$\frac{7}{8}$	33.1	9.73	31.9	7.6	1.81	1.82	1.17
	$\frac{3}{4}$	28.7	8.44	28.2	6.7	1.83	1.78	1.17
	$\frac{5}{8}$	24.2	7.11	24.2	5.7	1.84	1.73	1.18
	$\frac{1}{2}$	19.6	5.75	19.9	4.6	1.86	1.68	1.18
	$\frac{3}{8}$	14.9	4.36	15.4	3.5	1.88	1.64	1.19
5 × 5	$\frac{7}{8}$	27.2	7.98	17.8	5.2	1.49	1.57	0.97
	$\frac{3}{4}$	23.6	6.94	15.7	4.5	1.51	1.52	0.97
	$\frac{5}{8}$	20.0	5.86	13.6	3.9	1.52	1.48	0.98
	$\frac{1}{2}$	16.2	4.75	11.3	3.2	1.54	1.43	0.98
	$\frac{3}{8}$	12.3	3.61	8.7	2.4	1.56	1.39	0.99
4 × 4	$\frac{3}{4}$	18.5	5.44	7.7	2.8	1.19	1.27	0.78
	$\frac{5}{8}$	15.7	4.61	6.7	2.4	1.20	1.23	0.78
	$\frac{1}{2}$	12.8	3.75	5.6	2.0	1.22	1.18	0.78
	$\frac{3}{8}$	9.8	2.86	4.4	1.5	1.23	1.14	0.79
	$\frac{1}{4}$	6.6	1.94	3.0	1.1	1.25	1.09	0.80
$3\frac{1}{2} \times 3\frac{1}{2}$	$\frac{1}{2}$	11.1	3.25	3.6	1.5	1.06	1.06	0.68
	$\frac{3}{8}$	8.5	2.48	2.9	1.2	1.07	1.01	0.69
	$\frac{1}{4}$	5.8	1.69	2.0	0.79	1.09	0.97	0.69
3 × 3	$\frac{1}{2}$	9.4	2.75	2.2	1.1	0.90	0.93	0.58
	$\frac{3}{8}$	7.2	2.11	1.8	0.83	0.91	0.89	0.58
	$\frac{1}{4}$	4.9	1.44	1.2	0.58	0.93	0.84	0.59
$2\frac{1}{2} \times 2\frac{1}{2}$	$\frac{1}{2}$	7.7	2.25	1.2	0.74	0.74	0.81	0.49
	$\frac{3}{8}$	5.9	1.73	0.98	0.57	0.75	0.76	0.49
	$\frac{1}{4}$	4.1	1.19	0.70	0.39	0.77	0.72	0.49
2 × 2	$\frac{3}{8}$	4.7	1.36	0.48	0.35	0.59	0.64	0.39
	$\frac{1}{4}$	3.19	0.94	0.35	0.25	0.61	0.59	0.39
	$\frac{1}{8}$	1.65	0.48	0.19	0.13	0.63	0.55	0.40

TABLE B.7 (*Continued*)

Size, in.	Thick-ness, in.	Weight per ft, lb	Area of section, in.^{2}	Axis xx and axis yy				Axis nn ρ_{min}, in.
				I, in.^{4}	Z, in.^{3}	ρ, in.	$\bar{x}$, in.	
$1\frac{3}{4} \times 1\frac{3}{4}$	$\frac{1}{4}$	2.77	0.81	0.23	0.19	0.53	0.53	0.34
	$\frac{1}{8}$	1.44	0.42	0.13	0.10	0.55	0.48	0.35
$1\frac{1}{2} \times 1\frac{1}{2}$	$\frac{1}{4}$	2.34	0.69	0.14	0.13	0.45	0.47	0.29
	$\frac{1}{8}$	1.23	0.36	0.08	0.07	0.47	0.42	0.30
$1\frac{1}{4} \times 1\frac{1}{4}$	$\frac{1}{4}$	1.92	0.56	0.08	0.09	0.37	0.40	0.24
	$\frac{1}{8}$	1.01	0.30	0.04	0.05	0.38	0.36	0.25
1×1	$\frac{1}{4}$	1.49	0.44	0.04	0.06	0.29	0.34	0.20
	$\frac{1}{8}$	0.80	0.23	0.02	0.03	0.31	0.30	0.20

TABLE B.8

Section properties of standard unequal angles

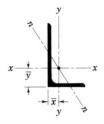

Size, in.	Thickness, in.	Weight per ft, lb	Area of section, in.²	Axis xx				Axis yy				Axis nn
				I_x, in.⁴	Z_x, in.³	ρ_x, in.	$\bar{y}$, in.	I_y, in.⁴	Z_y, in.³	ρ_y, in.	$\bar{x}$, in.	ρ_{min}, in.
8 × 6	1	44.2	13.00	80.8	15.1	2.49	2.65	38.8	8.9	1.73	1.65	1.28
	¾	33.8	9.94	63.4	11.7	2.53	2.56	30.7	6.9	1.76	1.56	1.29
	½	23.0	6.75	44.3	8.0	2.56	2.47	21.7	4.8	1.79	1.47	1.30
	7/16	20.2	5.93	39.2	7.1	2.57	2.45	19.3	4.2	1.80	1.45	1.31
8 × 4	1	37.4	11.00	69.6	14.1	2.52	3.05	11.6	3.9	1.03	1.05	0.85
	¾	28.7	8.44	54.9	10.9	2.55	2.95	9.4	3.1	1.05	0.95	0.85
	½	19.6	5.75	38.5	7.5	2.59	2.86	6.7	2.2	1.08	0.86	0.86
	7/16	17.2	5.06	34.1	6.6	2.60	2.83	6.0	1.9	1.09	0.83	0.87
7 × 4	⅞	30.2	8.86	42.9	9.7	2.20	2.55	10.2	3.5	1.07	1.05	0.86
	¾	26.2	7.69	37.8	8.4	2.22	2.51	9.1	3.0	1.09	1.01	0.86
	½	17.9	5.25	26.7	5.8	2.25	2.42	6.5	2.1	1.11	0.92	0.87
	⅜	13.6	3.98	20.6	4.4	2.27	2.37	5.1	1.6	1.13	0.87	0.88
6 × 4	⅞	27.2	7.98	27.7	7.2	1.86	2.12	9.8	3.4	1.11	1.12	0.86
	¾	23.6	6.94	24.5	6.3	1.88	2.08	8.7	3.0	1.12	1.08	0.86
	½	16.2	4.75	17.4	4.3	1.91	1.99	6.3	2.1	1.15	0.99	0.87
	⅜	12.3	3.61	13.5	3.3	1.93	1.94	4.9	1.6	1.17	0.94	0.88
	5/16	10.3	3.03	11.4	2.8	1.94	1.92	4.2	1.4	1.17	0.92	0.88
6 × 3½	½	15.3	4.50	16.6	4.2	1.92	2.08	4.3	1.6	0.97	0.83	0.76
	⅜	11.7	3.42	12.9	3.3	1.94	2.04	3.3	1.2	0.99	0.79	0.77
	¼	7.9	2.31	8.9	2.2	1.96	1.99	2.3	0.85	1.01	0.74	0.78
5 × 3½	¾	19.8	4.81	13.9	4.3	1.55	1.75	5.6	2.2	0.98	1.00	0.75
	½	13.6	4.00	10.0	3.0	1.58	1.66	4.1	1.6	1.01	0.91	0.75
	¼	7.0	2.06	5.4	1.6	1.61	1.56	2.2	0.83	1.04	0.81	0.76
5 × 3	½	12.8	3.75	9.5	2.9	1.59	1.75	2.6	1.1	0.83	0.75	0.65
	⅜	9.8	2.86	7.4	2.2	1.61	1.70	2.0	0.89	0.84	0.70	0.65
	¼	6.6	1.94	5.1	1.5	1.62	1.66	1.4	0.61	0.86	0.66	0.66
4 × 3½	⅝	14.7	4.30	6.4	2.4	1.22	1.29	4.5	1.8	1.03	1.04	0.72
	½	11.9	3.50	5.3	1.9	1.23	1.25	3.8	1.5	1.04	1.00	0.72
	⅜	9.1	2.67	4.2	1.5	1.25	1.21	3.0	1.2	1.06	0.96	0.73
	¼	6.2	1.81	2.9	1.0	1.27	1.16	2.1	0.81	1.07	0.91	0.73
4 × 3	⅝	13.6	3.98	6.0	2.3	1.23	1.37	2.9	1.4	0.85	0.87	0.64
	½	11.1	3.25	5.1	1.9	1.25	1.33	2.4	1.1	0.86	0.83	0.64
	¼	5.8	1.69	2.8	1.0	1.28	1.24	1.4	0.60	0.90	0.74	0.65

TABLE B.8 (Continued)

Size, in.	Thickness, in.	Weight per ft, lb	Area of section, in.²	Axis xx				Axis yy				Axis nn
				$I_x,$ in.⁴	$Z_x,$ in.³	$\rho_x,$ in.	$\bar{y},$ in.	$I_y,$ in.⁴	$Z_y,$ in.³	$\rho_y,$ in.	$\bar{x},$ in.	$\rho_{min},$ in.
$3\frac{1}{2} \times 3$	$\frac{1}{2}$	10.2	3.00	3.5	1.5	1.07	1.13	2.3	1.1	0.88	0.88	0.62
	$\frac{1}{4}$	5.4	1.56	1.9	0.78	1.11	1.04	1.3	0.59	0.91	0.79	0.63
$3\frac{1}{2} \times 2\frac{1}{2}$	$\frac{1}{2}$	9.4	2.75	3.2	1.4	1.09	1.20	1.4	0.76	0.70	0.70	0.53
	$\frac{1}{4}$	4.9	1.44	1.8	0.75	1.12	1.11	0.78	0.41	0.74	0.61	0.54
$3 \times 2\frac{1}{2}$	$\frac{1}{2}$	8.5	2.50	2.1	1.0	0.91	1.00	1.3	0.74	0.72	0.75	0.52
	$\frac{3}{8}$	6.6	1.92	1.7	0.81	0.93	0.96	1.0	0.58	0.74	0.71	0.52
	$\frac{1}{4}$	4.5	1.31	1.2	0.56	0.95	0.91	0.74	0.40	0.75	0.66	0.53
3×2	$\frac{1}{2}$	7.7	2.25	1.9	1.0	0.92	1.08	0.67	0.47	0.55	0.58	0.43
	$\frac{3}{16}$	3.07	0.90	0.84	0.41	0.97	0.97	0.31	0.20	0.58	0.47	0.44
$2\frac{1}{2} \times 2$	$\frac{3}{8}$	5.3	1.55	0.91	0.55	0.77	0.83	0.51	0.36	0.58	0.58	0.42
	$\frac{3}{16}$	2.75	0.81	0.51	0.29	0.79	0.76	0.29	0.20	0.60	0.51	0.43
$2 \times 1\frac{1}{2}$	$\frac{1}{4}$	2.77	0.81	0.32	0.24	0.62	0.66	0.15	0.14	0.43	0.41	0.32
	$\frac{1}{8}$	1.44	0.42	0.17	0.13	0.64	0.62	0.09	0.08	0.45	0.37	0.33
$1\frac{3}{4} \times 1\frac{1}{4}$	$\frac{1}{4}$	2.34	0.69	0.20	0.18	0.54	0.60	0.09	0.10	0.35	0.35	0.27
	$\frac{1}{8}$	1.23	0.36	0.11	0.09	0.56	0.56	0.05	0.05	0.37	0.31	0.27

References

1. Timoshenko, Stephen: "History of Strength of Materials," McGraw-Hill Book Company, New York, 1953.

2. Timoshenko, Stephen, and J. N. Goodier: "Theory of Elasticity," 2d ed., McGraw-Hill Book Company, New York, 1951.

3. Timoshenko, Stephen: "Strength of Materials," 3d ed., vol. 2, D. Van Nostrand Company, Inc., Princeton, N.J., 1956.

4. Hetenyi, M.: "Handbook of Experimental Stress Analysis," John Wiley & Sons, Inc., New York, 1950.

5. Bridgman, P. W.: "Studies in Large Plastic Flow and Fracture," McGraw-Hill Book Company, New York, 1952.

6. Crandall, S. H., and N. C. Dahl: "An Introduction to the Mechanics of Solids," McGraw-Hill Book Company, New York, 1959.

7. Galileo, G.: "Two New Sciences," Dover Publications, Inc., New York. (Copyright 1914, The Macmillan Company.)

8. Durelli, A. J., E. A. Phillips, and C. H. Tsao: "Introduction to the Theoretical and Experimental Analysis of Stress and Strain," McGraw-Hill Book Company, New York, 1958.

9. Nádai, A.: "Theory of Flow and Fracture of Solids," 2d ed., McGraw-Hill Book Company, New York, 1950.

10. Hill, R.: "The Mathematical Theory of Plasticity," Oxford University Press, Fair Lawn, N.J., 1950.

11. Frocht, Max M.: "Photoelasticity," vol. 1, John Wiley & Sons, Inc., New York, 1941.

12. Pipes, Louis A.: "Applied Mathematics for Engineers and Physicists," McGraw-Hill Book Company, New York, 1958.

13. Shanley, F. R.: "Weight-Strength Analysis of Aircraft Structures," Dover Publications, Inc., New York, 1960.

14. Libove, Charles: Creep Buckling of Columns, *J. Aeron. Sci.*, vol. 19, no. 7, p. 459, July, 1952.

15. Dorn, J. E.: Some Fundamental Experiments on High Temperature Creep, *J. Mech. Phys. Solids*, vol. 3, no. 2, January, 1955.

16. Shanley, F. R.: Tensile Instability (Necking) of Ductile Materials, *Aerospace Eng.*, vol. 20, no. 12, pp. 30–61, 1961.

17. Ramberg, W., and W. R. Osgood: Description of Stress-Strain Curves by Three Parameters, *NACA TN* 902, July, 1943.

18. Hoel, Paul G.: "Introduction to Mathematical Statistics," 2d ed., John Wiley & Sons, Inc., New York, 1954.

19. Shanley, F. R.: "Strength of Materials," McGraw-Hill Book Company, New York, 1957.

20. Timoshenko, Stephen, and James M. Gere: "Theory of Elastic Stability," McGraw-Hill Book Company, New York, 1961.

21. Bleich, F.: "Buckling Strength of Metal Structures," McGraw-Hill Book Company, New York, 1952. (See also Ref. 22, pp. 90–207.)

22. Von Kármán, Theodore: "Collected Works," vol. 1, pp. 24–35, Butterworth & Co. (Publishers), Ltd., London, 1956.

23. Shanley, F. R.: The Column Paradox, *J. Aeron. Sci.*, vol. 13, no. 12, December, 1946.

24. Shanley, F. R.: Inelastic Column Theory, *J. Aeron. Sci.*, vol. 14, no. 5, May, 1947.

25. Cozzone, F. P., and M. A. Melcon: Non-dimensional Buckling Curves— Their Development and Application, *J. Aeron. Sci.*, vol. 13, no. 10, p. 511, October, 1946.

26. Shanley, F. R.: Strength Analysis of Eccentrically Loaded Columns, *Univ. Calif. Dept. Eng.*, *Rept* 54–57, Los Angeles, May, 1954.

27. Southwell, R. V.: "Theory of Elasticity," pp. 428, 429, Oxford University Press, Fair Lawn, N.J., 1941.

28. Van den Broek, J. A.: Column Formula for Materials of Variable Modulus, *Eng. J. (Canada)*, vol. 28, no. 12, p. 772, December, 1945.

29. De Vries, Karl: Strength of Beams as Determined by Lateral Buckling, *Trans. ASCE*, vol. 112, pp. 1245–1271, 1947.

30. Winter, G.: Discussion of Ref. 29, *Trans. ASCE*, vol. 112, pp. 1272–1276, 1947.

31. Gerard, George: Compressive and Torsional Buckling of Thin-wall Cylinders in Yield Region, *NACA TN* 3726, August, 1956.

32. Batdorf, S. B.: A Simplified Method of Elastic-stability Analysis for Thin Cylindrical Shells: I, Donnell's Equation, *NACA TN* 1341, 1947.

33. Shanley, F. R., and E. I. Ryder: Stress Ratios, *Aviation*, vol. 36, no. 6, p. 28, June, 1937.

34 Bridget, F. J., C. C. Jerome, and A. B. Vosseller: Some New Experiments on Buckling of Thin-walled Construction, *Trans. ASME*, vol. 56, p. 569, 1934.

35. Stowell, E. Z.: A Unified Theory of Plastic Buckling of Columns and Plates, *NACA Rept* 898, 1948.

36. Bijlaard, P. P.: Theory of Tests on the Plastic Stability of Plates and Shells, *J. Aeron. Sci.*, vol. 16, no. 9, pp. 529–541, September, 1949.

37. Von Kármán, Theodore, E. E. Sechler, and L. H. Donnell: The Strength of Thin Plates in Compression, *Trans. ASME*, vol. 54, no. 2, June 30, 1932.

38. Goland, M., and E. Reissner: The Stresses in Cemented Joints, *J. Appl. Mech.*, vol. 11, no. 1, p. A-17, March, 1944.

39. "Metallic Materials and Elements for Flight Vehicle Structures," *MIL-HDBK* 5, U.S. Government Printing Office, 1962.

40. Peterson, R. E.: "Stress Concentration Design Factors," John Wiley & Sons, Inc., New York, 1953.

41. Duffy, J., and T. C. Lee: Measurement of Surface Strain by Means of Bonded Birefringent Strips, *Exptl Mech.*, vol. 1, no. 9, pp. 109–112, 1961.

42. Neuber, H.: "Theory of Notch Stresses" (Kerbspannungslehre), J. W. Edwards, Publisher, Incorporated, Ann Arbor, Mich., 1946.

43. Hardrath, H. F., and L. Ohman: A Study of Elastic and Plastic Stress Concentration Factors due to Notches and Fillets in Flat Plates, *NACA TN* 2566, December, 1951.

44. Dana, A. W., E. L. Aul, and G. Sachs: Tensile Properties of Aluminum Alloys in the Presence of Stress Raisers: I and II, *NACA TN* 1830 and 1831, March, 1939.

45. Gough, H. J.: "The Fatigue of Metals," Ernest Benn, Ltd., London, 1926.

46. Murray, W. M. (ed.): "Fatigue and Fracture of Metals," John Wiley & Sons, Inc., New York, 1952.

47. Sines, George, and J. L. Waisman: "Metal Fatigue," McGraw-Hill Book Company, New York, 1959.

48. Hardrath, H. F., and E. C. Utley, Jr.: An Experimental Investigation of the Behavior of 24S-T4 Aluminum Alloy Subjected to Repeated Stresses of Constant and Varying Amplitudes, *NACA TN* 2798, October, 1952.

49. Grover, H. J., S. M. Bishop, and L. R. Jackson: Axial Load Fatigue Tests of Notched Sheet Specimens of 24S-T3 and 75S-T6 Aluminum Alloys and of SAE 4130 Steel with Stress Concentration Factors of 2, 4, and 5, *NACA TN* 2389 and 2390, June, 1951.

50. Battelle Memorial Institute: "Prevention of the Failure of Metals under Repeated Stress," John Wiley & Sons, Inc., New York, 1941.

51. Palmgren, A.: Die Lebensdauer von Kugellagern, *Z. Ver. deut. Ing.*, vol. 68, no. 14, pp. 339–341, April, 1924.

52. Langer, B. F.: Fatigue Failure from Stress Cycles of Varying Amplitudes, *J. Appl. Mech.*, vol. 4, no. 4, December, 1937.

53. Miner, M. A.: Cumulative Damage in Fatigue, *J. Appl. Mech.*, vol. 12, no. 1, September, 1945.

54. Parker, Earl R.: "Brittle Behavior of Engineering Structures," John Wiley & Sons, Inc., New York, 1957.

55. Griffith, A. A.: The Phenomena of Rupture and Flow in Solids, *Trans. Roy. Soc. (London)*, A, vol. 221, p. 163, 1920.

56. Orowan, E.: "Fatigue and Fracture of Metals," p. 154, John Wiley & Sons, Inc., New York, 1952.

57. Drucker, D. C., and J. J. Gilman (eds.): "Fracture of Solids," Interscience Publishers, Inc., New York, 1963.

58. Wahl, A. M.: "Mechanical Springs," Penton Publishing Company, Cleveland, 1944.

59. Wagner, H., Remarks on Airplane Struts and Girders under Compressive and Bending Stresses; Index Values, *NACA TM* 500, February, 1929.

60. Holman, J. P.: "Experimental Methods for Engineers," McGraw-Hill Book Company, New York, 1966.

61. Schenck, Hilbert: "Theories of Engineering Experimentation," McGraw-Hill Book Company, New York, 1961.

62. Durelli, A. J., and W. F. Riley: "Introduction to Photomechanics," Prentice-Hall, Inc., Englewood Cliffs, N.J., 1965.

63. Moore, R. L.: Torsional Strength of Aluminum Alloy Round Tubing, *NACA TN* 879, January, 1943.

64. Weibull, W.: A New Method for the Statistical Treatment of Fatigue Data, *SAAB TN* 30, SAAB Aircraft Company, Sweden, May, 1954.

65. Mains, R. M.: Measurement of the Distribution of Tensile and Bond Stresses along Reinforcing Bars, Title 48-17, American Iron and Steel Institute, Committee on Reinforced Concrete Research, New York, 1951.

66. Dorn, John E. (ed.), "Mechanical Behavior of Materials at Elevated Temperatures," McGraw-Hill Book Company, New York, 1961.

67. Dalley, James W., and William F. Riley: "Experimental Stress Analysis," McGraw-Hill Book Company, New York, 1965.

68. "Manual of Steel Construction," American Institute of Steel Construction, Inc., New York, 1965.

69. FAR, Part 25: Airworthiness Standards, Transport Category Airplanes, U.S. Government Printing Office, 1965.

70. Wood, K. D.: "Aerospace Vehicle Design, Vol. II of Spacecraft Design," Johnson Publishing Co., Boulder, Colorado, 1964.

71. Hoff, N. J.: "The Analysis of Structures," John Wiley & Sons, Inc., New York, 1956.

72. Borg, S. F.: "Matrix-Tensor Methods in Continuum Mechanics," D. Van Nostrand Company, Inc., Princeton, N.J., 1963.

73. Tuckerman, L. B.: Aircraft: Materials and Testing, Edgar Marburg Lecture, *Proc. ASTM*, vol. 35, part II, 1935.

74. Schmit, Lucien A., Jr., and Robert H. Mallet: Structural Synthesis and Design Parameter Hierarchy, *Journ. Struct. Div., Proc. ASCE*, vol. 89, no. ST4, August, 1963.

75. Shanley, F. R.: Optimum Design of Eccentrically Loaded Columns, Conference Preprint no. 322, American Society of Civil Engineers, 1966.

76. Cox, H. L.: "The Design of Structures of Least Weight," Pergamon Press, New York, 1965.

77. Shanley, F. R.: Design Notebook, *Univ. Calif. (Los Angeles) Dept. Eng., Rept.* EDP-1-62, 1962.

78. Shanley, F. R.: Historical Note on the 1.5 Factor of Safety for Aircraft Structures, *J. Aeron. Sci.*, vol. 29, no. 2, p. 243, February, 1962.

79. Lin, T. Y.: "Design of Prestressed Concrete Structures," John Wiley & Sons, Inc., New York, 1963.

80. Massonnet, C. E., and M. A. Save: "Plastic Analysis and Design," vol. 1, "Beams and Frames," Blaisdell Publishing Company, New York, 1965.

Answers to Selected Problems

Chapter 1

1.1. $M_x'' = -9,678$ in.-lb, $M_y'' = 763$ in.-lb, $M_z'' = 117,000$ in.-lb

1.4. (a) 0.428 in.; (b) 1.193 in.

1.6. (Column 1.) $\delta = 0.0185$ in., $U = 277$ in.-lb

1.7. (a) 4.2 in.; (b) 14,700 in.-lb; (c) 115,500 in.-lb; (d) 100,800 in.-lb; (e) 116.64 in.

1.8. (a) 30,000 lb; (b) 30,600 lb, 0.806 in.

1.9. (Column 4.) (a) 0.173 in.; (b) 4,850 in.-lb; (c) 5,420 in.-lb; (d) 576 in.-lb; (e) 11.977 in.

1.13. 42,100 psi (steel)

1.14. $\sigma = -4,250$ psi (steel), $\sigma = 8,550$ psi (titanium), $\delta = 0.228$ in.

1.16. 2,000 psi

1.17. $\sigma = 31,200$ psi, $\Delta D = 0.0215$ in.

1.18. $F = 6,275$ lb, $A = 0.21$ in.^{2}, $\delta = 0.026$ in.

Chapter 2

2.1. $\theta = 30°$: $\sigma = 3,750$ psi, $\tau = 2,165$ psi

2.2. (Column 1.) $\sigma_1 = 23,070$ psi, $\sigma_2 = 8,930$ psi, $\sigma_3 = 0$, $\tau_{max} = 11,540$ psi

2.3. (Column 1.) (a) $\sigma_1 = \sigma_2 = 10,000$ psi, $\tau_{max} = 5,000$ psi; (b) $\sigma_1 = \sigma_2 = 24,700$ psi, $\tau_{max} = 12,350$ psi

2.4. (Column 1.) (a) $\sigma_1 = 30,000$ psi, $\sigma_2 = 15,000$ psi, $\sigma_3 = 0$; (b) $\sigma_x' = 26,250$ psi, $\sigma_y' = 18,750$ psi, $\tau_{xy}' = 6,490$ psi

2.6. $q_n = 4,650$ lb/in., $q_s = 582$ lb/in.

2.7. $q_1 = 1,433$ lb/in., $q_2 = 267$ lb/in., $\tau_{max} = 5,732$ psi

2.8. (a) $\sigma_1 = 9,600$ psi, $\sigma_2 = 2,400$ psi, $\sigma_3 = -4,000$ psi, $\tau_{max} = 6,800$ psi

Chapter 3

3.1. $\gamma = 0.000667$
3.2. (Column 1.) (a) $\epsilon_1 = 191.5 \times 10^{-6}$, $\epsilon_2 = 14.5 \times 10^{-6}$, $\theta = 39.5°$; (b) $\epsilon'_x = 186.5 \times 10^{-6}$, $\epsilon'_y = 18.5 \times 10^{-6}$, $\gamma'_{xy} = 57.9 \times 10^{-6}$
3.3. (Column 1.) $\epsilon_1 = 0.00741$, $\epsilon_2 = -0.00407$, $\theta = 48.4°$
3.5. $\theta = 60°$, $\theta = 54.7°$

Chapter 4

4.1. (Column 1.) (a) $\epsilon_1 = 0.000863$, $\epsilon_2 = 0.0001726$, $\epsilon_3 = -0.000518$; (b) 0.0104 in.; (c) $\epsilon'_x = 0.00069$, $\epsilon'_y = 0.000345$, $\gamma'_{xy} = 0.000598$; (d) 14.25 in.-lb/in.^{3}; (e) 0.00155
4.2. (a) 0.0625 in.; (b) 0.00667 in.
4.3. (Column 1.) $\sigma_1 = 132{,}000$ psi, $\sigma_2 = 12{,}000$ psi
4.4. (a) $\epsilon_1 = 0.0208$, $\epsilon_2 = -0.0108$, $\theta = 9.21°$; (b) $\sigma_1 = 193{,}500$ psi, $\sigma_2 = -43{,}600$ psi
4.5. 1.667
4.7. 0.00667
4.10. (a) 8.89×10^5 psi; (b) 0.005; (c) 0.0333 in.; (d) 11.3×10^6 in.-lb
4.11. (a) $-11{,}310$ psi; (b) $-16{,}960$ psi

Chapter 5

5.1. (a) $E_{app} = \frac{9}{7}E$; (b) $E_{app} = \frac{9}{11}E$; (c) $E_{app} = 3E$
5.7. (b) 33,000 psi $(K = 1.0)$, 38,100 psi $(K = \frac{1}{2})$, 25,000 psi $(K = -\frac{1}{2})$, 19,050 psi $(K = -1.0)$
5.8. (a) 27.5 ksi
5.10. (a) 1,185 hr; (b) 2,070 psi

Chapter 6

6.7. 163.3 k-ft
6.10. $M_{max} = 6{,}090$ in.-lb

Chapter 7

7.1. (Rectangular section.) (a) 556 psi; (b) 1,110 psi; (c) 1,178 psi
7.3. (Column 1.) (b) $I_{max} = 0.997$ in.^{4}, $I_{min} = 0.089$ in.^{4}; (c) $1/R = 1.70 \times 10^{-3}$ in.$^{-1}$; (d) $\epsilon_{max} = -0.52 \times 10^{-3}$; (f) 5.07 in.-lb/in.
7.4. (Column a; rectangular section.) $B = 1.22$ in., $D = 2.44$ in.
7.5. (Column 1.) $\sigma_{max} = 6{,}200$ psi
7.7. (b) 41.4%; (c) 27%
7.8. (a) $D = 2.0$ in., $A = 3.14$ in.^{2}; (b) $R_0 = 1.192$ in., $A = 0.161$ in.^{2}
7.9. (Column 1.) 159,200 in.-lb
7.12. (Column 1.) 28,500 psi

7.14. (*a*) 7,500 in.-lb
7.15. (*a*) 15,000 psi
7.17. $E/(1 - \nu^2)$

Chapter 8

8.2. (Column 1.) (*a*) $\tau_1 = 805$ psi, $\tau_2 = 1,187$ psi; (*b*) 3,560 lb
8.4. (Column 1.) 59.3 psi
8.6. (Column 1.) (*a*) $\bar{x} = 1.92$ in.; (*b*) $q_1 = 640$ lb/in., $q_2 = 721$ lb/in.
8.8. $q_{1,2} = q_{2,3} = 0$, $q_{1,3} = V/h$
8.10. (Column 1.) (*a*) $q_1 = 300$ psi, $q_2 = 769$ psi, $q_3 = 1,268$ psi; (*b*) $t_1 = 0.020$ in., $t_2 = 0.0513$ in., $t_3 = 0.0845$ in.; (*c*) 0.0896 in.; (*d*) 640 in.-lb

Chapter 9

9.8. $y_{\max} = -\sqrt{3}\, M_A L^2 / 27EI$
9.9. $M_B = -\frac{1}{2}M_A$, $\phi_A = -M_A L/4EI$
9.10. $M_B = q_0 L^2/8$, $\phi_A = q_0 L^3/48EI$

Chapter 10

10.1. (Column 1.) (*a*) 15,750 psi; (*b*) 4.92° (steel); (*c*) 859 in.-lb (steel)
10.2. (Column 1.) (*a*) 0.799 in.
10.5. (Column 1.) (*a*) 0.73 in.; (*b*) 283 lb; (*c*) 142 in.-lb
10.8. 50,300 in.-lb
10.11. 563 in.-lb (Oct. theory)

Chapter 11

11.1. $P_{\mathrm{cr}} = KL/4$
11.5. (*a*) $B = 3.98$ in.; (*b*) $B = 3.35$ in.
11.9. 54,700 lb
11.13. 29.1 ft
11.14. $\sigma = 7,920$ psi, $\delta = 0.188$ in.
11.21. (*a*) 53.9; (*b*) 89.1; (*c*) $k = 1/\sqrt{6}$; (*d*) $b = 3.3$ in., $t = 0.0612$ in., $q = 2,210$ lb/in.
11.22. $\tau_{\mathrm{cr}} = 13,900$ psi, $V = 8,900$ lb
11.23. $\sigma_{\mathrm{cr}} = 38,700$ psi, $M = 21,900$ in.-lb
11.24. 168,500 in.-lb
11.25. (*a*) 40.9 lb/in.; (*b*) 2,640 lb
11.27. $P = 16,800$ lb, $M = 3,590$ in.-lb

Chapter 12

12.1. $\theta = 30°$: $P = 1,540$ lb
12.2. (*a*) 20 rivets

12.3. (Column 1.) 1,932 lb
12.5. (Column 1.) $q = 1,290$ lb/in., $\eta = 41.3\%$
12.6. (Column 1.) $q = 2,350$ lb/in., $\eta = 75\%$
12.7. (Column 1.) $q = 2,850$ lb/in., $\eta = 82.5\%$
12.8. (Column 1.) $D = 0.41$ in., $p = 1.15$ in.
12.9. (Column 1.) $D = 0.41$ in., $p = 1.88$ in.
12.10. (Column 1.) $t = 0.206$ in., $D = 0.675$ in., $p = 3.1$ in.
12.11. $P_1 = 810$ lb, $P_2 = 983$ lb, $P_3 = 810$ lb
12.12. $P_1 = 480$ lb, $P_2 = 719$ lb, $P_3 = 480$ lb, $P_4 = 719$ lb
12.13. 436 lb
12.14. (*a*) 1.7 in.
12.16. 2.43 in.
12.17. $a = 2.57$ in., $b = 6.77$ in.

Chapter 13

13.1. $P = 1,250$ lb, $M = 157$ in.-lb $(K_t = 3.0)$
13.2. (*c*) $M = 39,300$ in.-lb; (*d*) $M = 16,600$ in.-lb; (*e*) $M = 7,200$ in.-lb
13.3. 0.97 in.
13.4. 13,000 psi

Chapter 14

14.1. (*a*) $D = 1.25$ in.; (*b*) $D = 1.8$ in.
14.3. (*a*) 1.56 in.; (*b*) 1.62 in.
14.4. 0.053 in.
14.5. 1.28
14.7. 1.70

Chapter 15

15.1. (Column 1.) $\delta_2 = 0.0347$ in., $\delta_3 = 0.0333$ in.
15.3. 1.0 in.
15.5. (*a*) $\alpha = \beta = 45°$
15.8. (Column 1.) $d = 37$ in., $A_{st} = 3.1$ in.^{2}
15.10. (Column 1.) (*a*) $D = 2.55$ in.; (*c*) $D = 6.19$ in., $t = 0.0843$ in.

Index